THE RETAIL
FLORIST BUSINESS

Second Edition

THE RETAIL
FLORIST BUSINESS

PETER B. PFAHL, B.S., M.S., PH.D.

Associate Professor of Floriculture,
The Pennsylvania State University

THE INTERSTATE
Printers & Publishers, Inc.
Danville, Illinois

To my wife, Edythe

PREFACE

The retail florist industry in the United States is a complex structure of many retail establishments, most of which are classified as small shops employing from one to ten employees. Each retail florist is an individual and no two of them operate their shops in the same manner. We often speak of an "average" florist or a "typical" florist, but there really is no such person.

In this book the author has tried to present material of benefit to several groups of people. Primarily, the volume is a textbook to be used by college, high school, and vocational students who expect to become retail florists or work in the retail florist industry. It was also planned to aid retail florists who are already in the business, by presenting new ideas on the management and operation phase of the retail florist industry.

Many florists have different ways of doing things in their shops and this book does not try to present all of the ideas. It essentially summarizes activities and provides several ideas and ways of doing each of the many jobs involved in operating and managing a retail florist shop.

The reader should keep in mind that not all of the ideas presented in this book will be applicable to all florists. Each florist must try out the ideas, adopt the ones which he finds beneficial, and discard the ones which do not seem pertinent to his business.

The author does not profess to know everything about the retail florist industry. He is presenting ideas from his 24 years of teaching Retail Flower Store Management to future florists and from his personal experiences and observations gained from his close association for over 20 years with many retail florists. Prior to his teaching experience he worked in a retail florist shop for several years in the Pittsburgh area.

There is very little published material in this field so it is the author's hope that this will be of value to young people who are training to become retail florists as well as those who are already in the retail florist business.

PETER B. PFAHL

ACKNOWLEDGMENTS

The author gratefully acknowledges the assistance and advice given him by William Curtis, Dr. Elwood Kalin, Prof. Paul Krone, Herbert Mitchell, FTDA, TELEFLORA, Florafax and the many others whose names appear as references in the book. Appreciation is also given to the *Florists' Review, The Exchange,* and the *Southern Florist and Nurseryman* for the articles used as a reference to this book. Pictures are acknowledged by the name of the shop. Pictures not marked are courtesy of Agricultural Photographic Department, The Pennsylvania State University.

TABLE OF CONTENTS

DESIGN IN FLOWER ARRANGING

SPECIAL USES

BUSINESS MANAGEMENT

Chapter 1

INTRODUCTION

Everybody loves flowers and enjoys having them in their homes. Flowers seem to speak a language of their own. The following fable written by Dr. M. E. John, The Pennsylvania State University, will illustrate the point: "Something was different. I sensed it as I entered the living room. No one else was there. Everything seemed to be in its place. Yet I knew something had been added. Soon my eyes turned to the coffee table where someone had placed a bouquet of flowers. At once I recognized that this was the cause of the change. As I sat down in my chair I could feel their effect. My spirits were lifted. I felt cheerful and everything seemed right with the world. All of this caused me to stop and ponder as to why these flowers have such power. They cannot speak as we speak. They cannot move. Yet somehow they have a great influence over our moods. . . . Somehow they touch us when we are unaware. At times when one is depressed they pull man out of himself and broaden his outlook. Yes, flowers really speak: not English, or Spanish, or Chinese, but their own language —a language without words, but one with the universal meaning of love, beauty and cheer. This is what gives them power." The retail florist business is based on the love of flowers.

The retail florist industry is comprised of many small businesses, in contrast to the trend towards consolidation in other retail industries. Figures from the U.S. Department of Agriculture and the Society of American Florists indicate that in 1970 there were 22.451 retail florists in the United States, whose total gross sales were $1.8 billion annually. Compare this with three shops in the United States in 1800. Two out of every three florists have businesses with annual gross sales of less than $60.000. accounting for less than one-third the total sales of the industry. In the United States the average retail florist with a payroll in 1967 had $66.600 in sales—quite an increase over $52.200 reported in 1963. The average shop without a payroll had $49.087 in

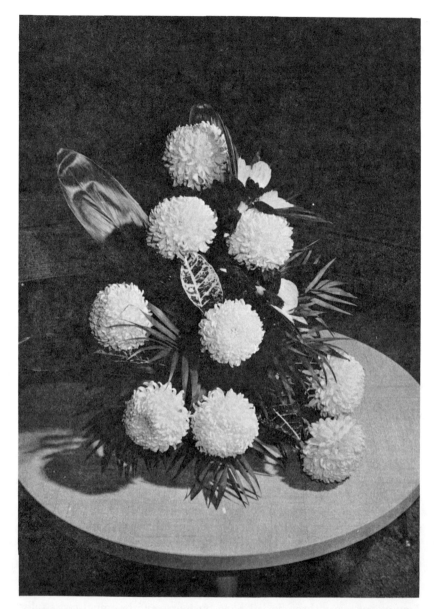

Figure 1-1. A flower arrangement says "Welcome" in a customer's home.

1967. In 1970 the total average sales per single unit shop in the United States was $85.219. One-fourth of the businesses are medium in size with sales of $60,000 to $125.000, and only one in nine florists has annual sales over $125,000 and is considered a "large" florist.

In 1968 in the United States there were just seven retail florists who grossed a million dollars. The total number of retail florists has increased from 1948 to 1968 and is now beginning to level off.

Only one out of every 11 flower shops has a paid manager. Most of the retail florist shops are family shops with the owner as the manager, plus his wife and maybe a son or daughter working in the store.

The florist business has changed considerably since the end of World War II. The business is not just one of raising and selling flowers with particular emphasis on funeral flowers. The retail florist business today is one of designing and service. The majority of flowers going out of many shops are arranged rather than being sent out as just loose cut flowers in a box. They are designed, delivered, and charged.

Retail florists are merchants, fundamentally occupied in buying and selling. They sell services as well as merchandise, and the words "sentiment," "service," "emotion," and "artistry" are all important in this specialized business. The florist business is really like no other business because the florists do specialize in many operations of design, service, and selling. The service is just as important as the artistry that goes with it. The florist must also consider sentiment in his business and take into consideration the feelings of others. When a hostess requests that a florist "do" the flowers, the florist has a golden opportunity to show off his special talents. The creative possibilities are limitless, and here is his chance to demonstrate once again his flower shop's services in a professional manner.

Retail florists are important to the economy of the United States. Retail florists should be acquainted with modern merchandising methods that will sell their merchandise most efficiently and most profitably. Successful retail florists are those who are competent to carry on a large-scale promotion to compete for the consumer's dollar. The success of any business is measured by its profits. The profits in the retail florist shop are due to the successful management of the business by the manager or owner.

As flowers play an important role for the retail florist, we expect him to be a good designer. But that is not enough. Today's retail florist must also be a salesman, a merchandiser, and, particularly, a good businessman.

The retail florists of the United States conduct about 75 per cent of their business by telephone and many of their customers are only names and voices. To serve these customers, florists provide considerable extra service to them. For example, 84 per cent offer some form of flowers-by-wire service, 95 per cent offer credit to their customers, and 97 per cent offer free delivery. They also offer advice on appropriate flowers for weddings and funerals, as well as helping customers make decisions on these occasions. All of these services cost money and must be figured in the overall costs of operation which will be discussed in detail in Chapter 6. Most florists have a tradition of services. These include delivery, gift wrapping, reminder service for anniversaries and birthdays, cashing checks, charge accounts, and civic services.

The retail florist business is considered an easy entry industry. It is easy to get into with a moderate investment, and it is easy to get out. Although there are approximately 22,000 retail florists in the country today, the country as a whole is uncrowded in some areas. Competition is keen in the large cities, but there are hun-

Figure 1-2. The interior of a modern retail flower shop. (Courtesy, Geralis Florist, Washington, D.C.)

dreds of cities in the United States that could support flower shops and where competition does not exist. Past experience has shown that it takes approximately 10,000 people to adequately support a retail flower shop. In many communities, however, this ratio is considerably lower. The total area to be served and the purchasing power of the people are important points. Many other factors must be considered, so that the ratio of 1 to 10,000 is only a tentative figure.

There is much to attract people into the retail flower business. The average flower shop is an attractive place in which to work, and, in general, is a business that requires relatively little capital to get started. It is a business in which several members of the family can work at regular or irregular intervals without too much extensive training. It is also a business where the owner can be his own boss.

There are unattractive features as well. The sale of flowers is irregular from day to day and there is seasonal variation to the supply of flowers. The flowers are perishable and as such constitute a certain amount of risk. Probably the two greatest disadvantages to the retail florist business are the long working hours and the relatively low wages. However, these may be offset by the enjoyment of working with flowers and being one's own boss.

Flower arrangement and design are important to a retail florist. Although he must know how to design, he must be a good salesman and businessman as well. The floral designs which go out of the retail florist shop will contribute greatly to his reputation as will the service which he gives. In this book we will first discuss the elements of being a florist and how to manage a retail florist shop, and conclude with the fundamentals of flower arrangement and good design which are so important to the success of any retail florist.

There are no two identical flower shops in the country today, so that suggestions made in this book will not apply to all florists.

References

1. *Census of Business.* U.S. Department of Commerce, Washington, D.C., 1964.
2. Hall, R. and S. M. Raleigh, Jr. *Commercial Floriculture and Related Products.* U.S. Department of Agriculture Marketing Research Report #855, 1969.
3. John, M. E. *The Language of Flowers.* The Pennsylvania State University, 2 pp.

4. Valencia, Sylvia. "Retailing from A to Z," *Florists' Review*, Vol. 135, No. 3500 (December 24, 1964), pp. 15-16, 38-41.

Chapter 2

QUALIFICATIONS OF
A RETAIL FLORIST

What are the qualifications of a retail florist? *What is a retail florist?* We all know that a retail florist is one who sells flowers, and who designs flower arrangements. But there is more to being a florist than just this. A retail florist must be an artist or designer, a businessman, a buyer, a salesman, a provider of services, and an advisor. Sylvia Valencia once said that if she were asked for a definition of a florist, she would have to say: "a florist is a composite of the doctor, the lawyer, and the minister because each day he is truthfully required to act in the capacity of advisor to many." A florist should have at his fingertips the knowledge of the correct protocol for formal dining and for weddings. He should be aware of the basic differences of the various religions: what is permitted by the churches in the way of flowers for altar decorations and for formal services. Information should be readily available for customers on all matters pertaining strictly to flowers, their care, and how they should be used. In other words, a retail florist should be a knowledgeable person who is ready to give information and service when it is requested.

There are, however, certain qualifications which every retail florist should possess if he wishes to be successful. Every florist will not have all of these, but he should be able to satisfy at least three-fourths of the requirements for being a retail florist. Here are 12 such qualifications for a successful retail florist:

1. The first qualification of being a successful retail florist is to be a good businessman. The florist should know how to run his business and make a profit. Every retailer, whether florist or not, is in the business to make money and not just for the fun of it.

2. A good retail florist should be an artist and have the ability to design. It is the design work going out to the customer which

9

forms the foundation for the florist's reputation. There are many florists in the country, and it is usually the ones who have flower arrangements which are above average that are the most successful. In a large shop where all the designers are hired, an owner may feel he himself does not need to know how to design. This is a fallacy and sooner or later the customer will want to see the owner's work or ask for specific suggestions and ideas. He may ask the florist to start the design and describe it. So, the ability to design is as paramount to a successful florist as is being a good businessman.

3. The retail florist should have enough capital to get started and to keep going for two years without profit. During the first six to nine months in the florist business he will just make enough to cover his expenses and maybe pay himself a small salary. The profits will not be realized until the second or third year. He must have enough cash on hand to pay for his supplies and merchandise and establish a good credit rating for himself, besides paying for his own living.

4. Another qualification of a successful retail florist is that he be a good buyer. Careful buying is necessary in order to achieve a fair profit from the business.

5. The retail florist should be really interested in his business. He should have the love for, and the appreciation of, flowers. It is not enough just to want to make money. He must like working with flowers and also like working with people. He must know how to cater to the general public, and like it.

6. The retail florist should have the ability to meet people and to talk to them. He should be a good salesman if he wants to be above average as a florist, and not be simply an order taker.

7. He should know how to advertise. A florist must know how much to spend on advertising, when to advertise, what to say, and which media to use. He should also know how to arrange his store attractively and be able to set up good window displays to attract customers into his shop. These are all a part of advertising.

8. The retail florist must know how to train and handle employees. He must keep them satisfied with their jobs and with one another. He must know how to train them so they will be an asset to the business and he must know how to handle them properly so that he will get the maximum amount of work from each one. Satisfied employees will stay with the florist and reduce the trouble and expense of finding and training new employees. Employee turnover should be kept to a minimum.

Figure 2-1. Future retail florists learning the art of flower arranging and the mechanics of retail design.

9. Experience is another very important attribute for a retail florist. The best advice anyone can give a young man or woman who wants to become a florist is to tell him to *get some experience and work for another florist for at least a year* before going into business for himself. We say at least a year so that he will have the experience of going through all of the florists' holidays. There are seven main ones and each is different. It would be preferable to work several years with another florist, but one year's experience should be the absolute minimum. This type of training will enable a person to gain knowledge of the types of flowers and materials handled throughout the year in the retail flower shop and the sort of flowers that customers prefer and why they prefer them. Knowledge of both wholesale and retail prices and how they fluctuate throughout the year can be obtained. Other knowledge gained will be on sales methods, buying procedures, record keeping, customer relations, and stock control. If the person keeps his eyes open and is observant he can learn a lot in a year's time. Many new businesses fail the first year because of the inexperience of the owner. (See Voigt's report from Dun and Bradstreet, Chapter 11.)

10. Another qualification of a retail florist is to be a merchandiser. In today's economy, if a florist wants to get his fair share of the consumer's dollar, he must know how to merchandise his product. There is more to it than just *selling* flowers and this will be discussed later in detail.

11. A retail florist should have a thorough knowledge of the plants and flowers that he handles. He should know how to take care of them and make them last longer in his own shop as well as in the customer's home. Many people will bring all sorts of questions on horticulture to their local florist and expect him to be able to answer them. A retail florist may not know all the answers, but he should know the answers concerning the specific materials he sells, and he should know how to care for plants and flowers in the home.

12. The final, but not the least important, qualification of a retail florist is that he should be active in civic affairs. He should take an interest and an active part in community life. He isn't expected to join all civic organizations and drives, but he should be active in some of them. He should also join his own trade associations so he will know what is going on within the florist industry, and help support it.

All of these qualifications are important and most of them will be discussed in detail in other chapters in this book.

Training

Most retail florists of today were trained for the business by working in a flower shop for many years. This was the way they gained experience and it is part of the training needed now. The small retail florist is not a specialist in one thing only. He must train himself in many more operations than just floral designing.

A formal college education is not essential for the successful operation of a retail floral shop, *but it is highly desirable*. A major in floriculture will give the student a background of fundamental knowledge in botany, chemistry, and physiology; as well as in the growing, caring, and keeping quality of cut flowers and pot plants; besides learning the rudiments of floral design and the management of a retail florist shop. If he augments his program with courses in accounting, bookkeeping, salesmanship, psychology, business ethics, marketing, and merchandising he will have a good foundation for the retail florist business. In addition to this, a session at one of the design schools throughout the country would be very beneficial. These design schools are also a *must* for high school students who do not go to college but want to become retail florists.

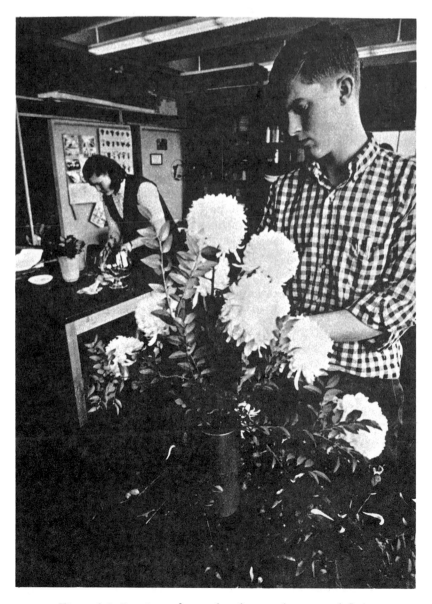

Figure 2-2. Practice makes perfect for two future retail florists.

A good basic education is essential for success as a retail florist, but upon completion of any kind of academic training, whether it be a college degree in floriculture or business management, or a high school diploma, the student must obtain specialized training and experience by working in a retail florist shop.

These, then, are some of the main qualifications that one should have or develop to become a successful retail florist. With these go the prerequisite of any successful business—*hard work*. The retail florist works long hours and must work hard if he wishes to show a profit at the end of the year.

When a person is planning to go into business for himself there is a check list which he may obtain from the Small Business Administration, Washington, D.C. 20008. He should go over this in detail and fill in all the questions honestly so that he can properly analyze his chances for success. There are about 100 questions under the following headings: "(1) Are you the type? (2) What are your chances of success? (3) How much capital will you need? (4) Should you share ownership with others? (5) Where should you locate? (6) Should you buy a going business? (7) Are you qualified to supervise buying and selling? (8) How will you price your products and services? (9) What selling methods will you use? (10) How will you manage personnel? (11) What records will you keep? (12) What laws will affect you? (13) What other problems will you face? (14) Will you keep up-to-date?" Just thinking about each of these questions will help in planning a future in the retail florist business.

The life of a retail florist is a good one and a rewarding one financially and personally. The product is one of the best liked products in the world, and most of a florist's efforts will result in bringing cheer and happiness to others, as well as providing a good living for him and his family. The opportunities for women in this field are excellent.

References

1. Valencia, Sylvia. "How to Succeed by Trying," *Florists' Review*, Vol. 135, No. 3501 (December 31, 1964), pp. 17-18, 58-59.
2. Voigt, A. O., "What Causes Business Failures?" *Florists' and Nursery Exchange*, Vol. 145, No. 21 (May 21, 1966), pp. 16, 18.

Chapter 3

TYPES OF RETAIL FLOWER SHOPS

The retail flower shop as we know it today has only been in existence about 80 years. Flowers were sold originally from the greenhouse to the people who came to buy them. As designing of flowers became necessary, one end of the greenhouse or the head-house was set apart for the designing and sale of floral pieces.

At about the same time, some greenhouse producers of flowers began to market the flowers through local grocery stores. The retail sale of flowers was simply an adjunct of the local general store. It was not long before separate retail flower shops began to spring up all over the country, leading to the retail florist industry of today.

Most of the 22,451 retail florist shops in the United States today would fall into one of 12 catagories or types. Many of them are what we call "average shop" florists, but some of them are more specialized. However, even the so-called average florists differ from one another.

The percentage of retail florists who are retail-only (shops which buy everything they sell) compared to the retail florists who are also growers is about 50 per cent. A survey by *The Exchange*, in 1963, showed that 53.5 per cent of the florists were retail-only and 46.5 per cent were retail-growers. The survey also showed that of the retail-only shops, 35.2 per cent were downtown, 56.0 per cent were suburban, and 8.8 per cent were rural; whereas of the retail-grower shops, only 5.1 per cent were downtown, 72.1 per cent were suburban, and 22.8 per cent were rural. This indicates that the location of the shop will play a large part in the type of shop chosen by the prospective retail florist. The survey showed that over 50 per cent of all the retail florist shops were in suburban areas, and that less than 50 per cent of them were downtown. There seems to be a concentration of shops, both retail-only and retail-grower, in the suburban areas and this may account for the remarks heard from time to time that there are too many retail florists in the business today. Many areas, however, still are not adequately served by the retail florist industry.

Which type of shop should you choose? Let's look at a few of the details concerning 12 different types of retail flower shops in existence today.

1. **Average shop.** This is the category in which the majority of shops belong, and the one which is the hardest to describe and typify. The shop is small to medium in size as far as gross volume of business and number of employees are concerned. It will have moderate prices and average-to-good designs. It has a large clientele with at least half of these as telephone customers. These shops are found in small towns, suburban areas, and some downtown in our cities. The hours of staying open are long and often irregular. The supply of flowers on hand is usually just enough to make a nice display, but not large. The quality must be medium to good. In a small town, the florist will be acquainted with all of his customers, and there will be very few strangers. He will extend credit to almost anyone who' requests it. The average shop is often a family shop with husband, wife, son, and maybe one other employee. The owner is usually the manager, buyer, and often the designer because the average retail flower shop in the United States today is a small shop with few employees, not a large shop with a manager and a dozen employees. As the census figures show, the majority of retail florists in the United States are under $60,000 in gross volume of sales (Chapter 1). Over 50 per cent of the customers will charge their flowers. The business includes many services including packing, designing, delivery, charging, and advice on the best and most appropriate flowers for all occasions. Even in the "average shop" category no two florists are exactly alike.

2. **High class shop.** This shop is often found in the suburban areas' catering to people who have more than an average income and are willing to spend money on flowers. The prices will be high, and so will the quality of the merchandise. Only merchandise of the highest quality would be permitted to leave this type of shop. This is closely controlled at all times. The artistry in design must be the highest in the industry because that is what the customers will expect for their money. Most of the customers will be regular customers, who will charge their flowers and often telephone most of their orders. It has been estimated that at least 80 per cent of them will have a charge account at the retail florist shop. The

Figure 3-1. A modern retail-grower florist. (Courtesy, Frederick's Flowers, Souderton, Pa.)

shop hours will be definite and more regular than in some shops, and not so long as in certain other types of shops. The customers are willing to spend money, but they will be more exacting in their likes and dislikes. There must be no duplicating of designs for funerals, parties, hospitals, weddings, or other occasions. This type of business will also include many services such as credit, delivery, and advice, as well as outstanding work in design. In selling, patience is required because many of the customers will be "fussy" about their orders and may take quite a while to make up their minds as to what they want. Others will be very precise and definite about their orders. The owner must have originality and a good imagination to be able to suggest unusual designs to the customer. Extra services will be required, such as keeping the customer's personal name cards on hand to send with funeral and other orders, as well as keeping an up-to-date reminder card file system of each customer's birthday and anniversary. These services are eventually paid for by the customers. The shop will be attractive and kept up-to-date, and the rental will be high.

3. **Cash-and-carry shop.** A cash-and-carry shop is usually a small downtown shop utilizing a small area for its operation. One example would be a subway shop, or small shop in an office building, but there are many others in small shops on the main and side streets. The majority of the business will be from transient trade with few regular customers. The business will be mostly cash-and-carry with a minimum of charge accounts and delivery. Requests for design or make-up work will be at a minimum, so that only a small workroom will be necessary. The prices on the merchandise will be low and the quality medium to good. The success of the business depends on volume, so window streamers and displays for catching the eye of the passerby are essential. Cash-and-carry specials will bring in more customers. As experience has shown that a retail florist cannot exist on cash-and-carry sales alone, some regular customers must be cultivated. The hours are usually quite regular and determined by the other merchants in the area. The shop must be located downtown where plenty of foot traffic passes the store.

4. **Retail-grown combination florist.** Surveys have shown that 46.5 per cent of our florists are retail-growers. (See Figure 3-1.) These include many florists who have just one small greenhouse as well as florists with many greenhouses. Their operations are quite different depending upon their size. However, they all have several things in common. One of the greatest advantages of a retail-grower florist is the fact that he can advertise that he grows his own flowers. The implication is that everything in his shop is fresh. Actually he may only raise 2 per cent of his merchandise, or he may raise as much as 80 per cent of it. None of them are able to raise 100 per cent of the flowers they sell. In fact it doesn't pay to raise roses on a small scale. Research workers tell us that a rose grower must have at least 10,000 plants in his greenhouse to make the operation pay. Other advantages to being a retail-grower are that he can raise novelty items for his retail shop which may be hard to get on the market, and that he can often get a few extra flowers very quickly for the flower arrangement that he is making. A primary advantage to a greenhouse is that the florist is able to buy a larger quantity of plants at one time. He can make up his own planters and dish gardens and can increase his profits in the spring through the use of bedding plants grown in his own greenhouse. The use of one or more greenhouses or conservatories is excellent for an open house before Christmas and Easter. If there is space, the florist can build good will by staging a flower show. The green-

house also offers an excellent opportunity for growing and storing foliage plants for weddings and other decorating jobs. There are, of course, some disadvantages to a retail-grower florist. The florist must be a grower as well as a designer, and know how to take care of plants in the greenhouse as well as in the home. More investment is necessary for this type of business, since greenhouse construction is expensive. Usually one part of the business carries the other financially, and most of these florists do not keep adequate records to tell which is making the money. If the retail shop gets the attention, the greenhouse will suffer or vice versa. Theoretically, the retail shop should pay (on paper) for the flowers used from the greenhouse at the regular market price. However, often the paper work and bookkeeping are not worth the time and effort unless the business is a large operation, and most of our shops in the florist industry are small to medium in size. Another disadvantage is that a retail-grower florist usually must be located out of the cities and business districts because of zoning laws, rents, and taxes. The hours are usually irregular and long, because many people feel they can call a greenhouse anytime at night or on Sundays and they will find someone there. This type of shop can be very successful in a small town. Prices are usually average and quality will be good. Some retail florists have a garden center in connection with the shop and would fit into this category.

5. **College town shop.** A retail florist shop in a college town is usually an average shop with certain special functions. The prices are usually moderate and the design work is average to good. The moderate prices are necessitated by the salaries of the faculty, and the spending money of the students. The shop should correlate its advertising, promotion, and sales to the activities of the school. Window displays should tie in with college functions. Corsages should be cultivated for the dances and centerpieces for sorority and fraternity parties. A good rapport should be established between the florists and the students. A majority of the design work will be corsages and decorations. The hours will usually be fairly regular. Customers will be about half and half between charge accounts and cash customers. Many college town florists have encouraged "will calls" for the corsages, to cut down on the enormous expense of delivery and the time spent trying to deliver flowers to the girls in the residence halls. The extent of holiday work will depend on whether the students are in school or have gone home for the vacation. The time table of the college must be studied ahead of time so that plans can be made for the holidays. There will usually be plenty of telephone or wire orders both incoming and outgoing

Figure 3-2. A flower shop with an all glass front and a conservatory greenhouse.
(Courtesy, Penny Hill Flowers, Wilmington, Del.)

for Mother's Day and other holidays depending upon the activities
of the student population.

6. **Hotel shop.** A hotel flower shop is a very specialized type
of retail flower shop. Sometimes it is a branch store of another
shop, or it may be a complete shop in itself. The rent is usually
quite high and the shop is small with limited space for a design
area and for storage. The refrigerator and store must be well
stocked at all times, because much of the work will be rush work.
The majority of the customers will pay cash and often will take
the merchandise with them. Thus, there must be plenty of cut
flowers on hand as well as several made-up gift pieces in attractive containers. The designer must be able to design a piece quickly
while the customer waits. Many customers in a hotel shop will be
men, so a large supply of red roses must be kept on hand. This
is the most common flower purchased by them. Although many
regular male customers are learning about flowers, the majority of
men who enter a flower shop always ask for red roses. They don't
seem to know that any other flowers exist. Many also know that
red roses signify "love," and that is what they wish to say with the

flowers. Prices will be high due to the high rental, and the quality of the flowers should be excellent. Most shops do not open early in the morning, but often stay open at night. Many are open on Sunday. The funeral work in a hotel shop will be at a minimum unless the store is an old established firm with many regular, charge account customers. The operation of the hotel flower shop will be determined by the type of hotel: that is, whether it is a resident hotel with permanent guests, or a downtown hotel with mostly transient guests.

Figure 3-3. A hotel flower shop. (Courtesy, Buning The Florist, Fort Lauderdale, Fla.)

7. **Hospital shop.** A hospital flower shop is usually a small flower shop located in the lobby of a hospital. Sometimes a hospital shop is a florist shop in the vicinity of the hospital specializing in hospital arrangements. It is sometimes a branch of a regular shop or else a part-time shop operated by a person who has another income or business. The space will be limited for the shop, and the orders will be mainly for small hospital arrangements in con-

tainers. There will be very little funeral or decoration business. There should be gift novelties, novelty flower arrangements, baby novelties, and small vase arrangements on hand at all times. Merchandise must be well displayed for the customer to see because there will be plenty of spontaneous or impulse buying by people coming to visit someone in the hospital. The business will be mostly cash-and-carry. Most hospitals today require flowers to be in containers, so there will not be many loose flowers sold. Most containers should be inexpensive and the prices for the merchandise will be moderate. People will spend more money on hospital flowers if they see them already arranged and on display. Bright flowers should be used for men and pastels for women. Do not stock many flowers with pollen or strong fragrance or odors which may cause discomfort to the patient. A good many pot plants are sold for hospital orders. Comic books, crayons, toys, puzzles, books, and other items which will delight youngsters who are hospitalized should be kept in stock and used in arrangements. Small arrangements, novelties, and pot plants in the range of $5 to $15 will be the best sellers in most hospital flower shops.

8. **Apartment house flower shop.** The retail florist shop located in an apartment house is another specialized type of shop. It is usually small to medium in size with a small workroom with quite a high rental involved. It must be kept attractive at all times with made-up arrangements in the display refrigerator. It is comparable to a high class suburban shop, except for size, with high prices and high quality merchandise. The majority of customers will be regular ones who charge their flowers. There will be very little transient trade and very little cash-and-carry business. A large part of the business will be funeral, wedding, gift, and decoration work for private parties. The apartment will probably be in a fairly large city and advertising will be very important to this florist. People may not even know there is a florist shop in the apartment building, unless it is well advertised. Space may be a problem and the florist will have to make arrangements to find ample storage areas or rooms somewhere in the basement. Getting to the delivery truck entrance to load his deliveries may also be a problem. He should cultivate the tenants in his and neighboring apartment buildings to try to encourage them to become regular customers of his shop. He must build a good word-of-mouth reputation for his shop. He should build up a good centerpiece and party decoration business. High prices will be charged for the flowers, designs, and services rendered. Quality merchandise must be used at all

times to build a good reputation for the florist. Regular hours, which are not too long, will usually prevail in an apartment flower shop.

9. **Shopping center flower shop.** This is one of the newest types of retail florist shops to develop in the past 20 years. The operation of it is quite different from most shops. The rental is usually very high and in the contract a percentage of the gross sales may be paid to the management as well as contributing to a share of the advertising. The florist should be sure to read the contract very carefully. The space is usually limited and the florist may have to rent another area for storage. This type of business will depend mainly on volume sales from the foot traffic of the shopping center. Attractive displays, prices on merchandise, and cash-and-carry sales will help to bring in customers. The florist will not have many telephone or charge customers at first, nor much funeral work until he has been there several years and become established. Specials are very good according to some florists who have been successful in opening a branch store in a shopping center. Specials help to promote extra sales when other merchandise and impulse items are attractively displayed. Browsing should be encouraged in these shops. One of the drawbacks would be the hours which usually must conform to the shopping center. This often means staying open until 9:00 or 10:00 p.m. several nights a week. However, the shop may not open until 10:00 a.m. or noon. One of the biggest assets is ample, and usually free, parking. There will be different merchandise in a shop of this type and more group promotions and advertising. There is much more leisure shopping and the florist should not try to hurry the sale. Usually with the small space involved, the make-up work must be done in the rear of the sales area. Many shopping center shops carry as large a gift line as space permits. There are many problems to this type of business, such as a fair rental, extra costs, types of merchandise to handle, credit policies, salary schedules because of odd hours, and other factors. Many of these are still unsolved because florist shops in shopping centers are relatively new. It is best not to expect to make any money the first three years until the shop is established. Before choosing a particular center, the developer's market analysis should be consulted to be sure that the center attracts the sort of customers desired by the florist.

There are basically three types of shopping centers: neighborhood, community, and regional; and the florist must choose the one best suited to his shop. The International Council of Shopping Centers may help him in his final decision.

10. **Department store retail florist.** Another new type of retail florist shop will be found in some of our larger department stores. Although the sales area may be large, the workroom may be small. The merchandise must be good quality at moderate prices, and volume sales are needed. There will be plenty of foot traffic in the store and the florist must persuade a good share of the people to buy his flowers. There will be many impulse sales. Mass displays and cash-and-carry specials are useful. Made-up pieces should be kept in the display refrigerator at all times. Browsing should be encouraged and everything should be priced. There are advantages and disadvantages to the department store flower shop. Read the contract carefully so that all of the profits do not go to the store. The hours must conform to those of the store and the florist will have to get special permission to work in the store after hours on special occasions or at holiday times. The shop will never be open on Sundays. This can be a problem with Sunday weddings and funerals. The florist will have to give discounts to all store personnel, but the increase in volume will offset this. A big advantage is that he will have no costs for billing the customers nor any bad debts, since the store pays for all charges and assumes the responsibility of collecting all accounts. Often the store will supply paper and bags for wrapping and carrying the merchandise. The store will usually keep the windows clean, carry out the trash, and keep the place painted. The florist can tie in the flower shop with the bridal salon and may attract a great deal of wedding work. There will be more gift items and cash-and-carry sales than funeral work until the florist has established a reputation with some of the regular customers in the store. There will be very few telephone customers at first. There are problems in being a department store retail florist, but if he knows what is in his contract and knows how to *merchandise* flowers, he will succeed. Problems will be: the competition with the gift and artificial flower departments of the store, working after hours on funeral or wedding work, buying carefully but in quantity, not giving all the profits to the store, supplying too many flowers to other departments without getting a proper markup, and other problems which might arise. The shop owner or manager must have a complete understanding with the store about deliveries, whether he uses his own delivery trucks or not.

11. **Bachman's European flower market.** Bachman's of Minneapolis is introducing the European type of flower markets called "Bouquet

Boutiques" (Figure 3-4) into 700 to 800 supermarkets by 1973. This is a new innovation in cut flower merchandising that keeps flowers fresh by using a uniform blanket of cool air. Open on all sides, it allows the customers complete accessibility to the flowers for their cash-and-carry purchases. This type of selling takes the flowers to the people to get more people to buy flowers more often.

Figure 3-4. A Bouquet Boutique. (Courtesy, Bachman's European Flower Markets, Bloomington, Minn.)

12. **Mini-shops.** These shops are just 10′ x 20′ and are pre-built by a company with headquarters in Seattle, Washington. They are built for convenience, speed, and economy to serve the customer instantly. They are successful in high density areas, such as shopping centers, where they sell cameras and films as well as fresh and permanent flowers and pot plants. Costs are cut down because there is no delivery, no charging, and little design work.

Leasing

Large department stores, to provide better customer services and conveniences, are leasing more and more departments, especially those requiring a high degree of specialization. Retail florists are a natural for this new leasing venture, but must carefully weigh all the factors before starting into this type of a business. The following factors should be considered: (1) Pick a store that has a place in the community and does a good job of filling community needs. (2) Is the store a prestige store or one concerned with price? (3) Aim for the downtown base store, not one with many small branches. (4) Only consider a large suburban branch if the main store has just one or two, but be alert to long hours of 10 to 12 hours every day. (5) Make sure the store's position is clearly defined. Be sure the florist knows what it will cost him. The advantages and disadvantages to leasing a store in a department store are similar to those already discussed.

The retail florist has certain advantages to offer the department store, and these should be presented and discussed when coming to any business agreement with the store: (1) The leased flower shop can add prestige to the store. (2) It gives the store additional customer convenience. (3) It adds to the store's fashion leadership. (4) Flower buyers are consistent customers and will help to build overall store traffic. (5) Flower departments are a natural source for display material. (6) Flowers-by-wire or telephone will give the department store a unique service not open to other competing stores.

We have discussed some of the features of the various types of retail flower shops in the United States. However, there are many shops which are combinations of two or more of these. Also, when asked to describe a typical florist shop it is impossible, because there is really no such thing as a typical retail florist. Each florist is different, even those which we call "average" florists.

Sole Owner or Partnership

There are three general types of businesses for the retail florist. The most common form is that of individual ownership or proprietorship. The second one, in which quite a few businesses fall, is that of a partnership. The third category is that of a corporation and not too many retail florist shops are large enough to be in this category.

There are advantages and disadvantages to both proprietorships and partnerships. These should be considered before a person decides definitely on one type or another.

The advantages of a proprietorship are as follows: (1) Everything is in the hands of the owner. (2) The owner is his own boss. (3) There is full freedom of operation in this type of business. (4) No profits are shared.

The disadvantages to a proprietorship are as follows: (1) The business is usually discontinued when the owner dies, unless the family is capable of carrying on. (2) The owner is personally liable for all debts. (3) The owner usually has limited personal assets to encourage lenders. (4) The owner does not usually possess all the talents for selling, bookkeeping, and management as well as designing.

The advantages of a partnership are as follows: (1) Two viewpoints will tend to counter rash actions. (2) Two people might be a great success together if each has a specific responsibility and/or talent not possessed by the other, where singly they might fail. (3) This type provides a broader base than the proprietorship for obtaining capital.

The disadvantages of a partnership are as follows: (1) Each partner is individually responsible for all business debts. (2) The death of a partner automatically dissolves the business. (3) Working together closely can result in disagreements with friction between the partners. (4) Each partner is responsible for the business commitments of the other. Before going into a partnership, the florist should think it over carefully and be sure he knows the habits, honesty, and management abilities of his partner. He might be better off on his own. Each individual case is different and must be studied by all parties concerned.

A corporation is formed only when the business is large enough that it is economically advantageous to the owner to incorporate. The laws are so complicated that this must be accomplished only with the help of an attorney, and will not be discussed here.

A prospective retail florist must decide on the type of a retail florist shop he wishes to operate and also on the type of business which will be most advantageous to him.

Shop Name

Selecting the name of a retail florist shop is one other important consideration. Many florists use their own name because they feel it is a real advantage to keep their name constantly in the public eye, and have people associate their name with that of a good reliable retail florist shop. Others will take the name of the street, section of town, name of the city, hotel, or shopping center. Select the name which you feel will give you the best publicity and result in establishing a profitable business.

Planning ahead on the type of retail florist shop, type of business, and name of the shop is essential, and will reduce the number of headaches later on in the business.

References

1. Baker, Rolinda B. "Mini-Shops Sell Flowers and Film," *Southern Florist and Nurseryman* (December 25, 1970), pp. 8, 9.
2. Golden, William P. "Selling Flowers in the European Manner," *Florist* (May 1971), pp. 54-57.

Chapter 4

SITE AND LOCATION

One of the most important aspects to consider in establishing a retail florist shop is the location. This single factor can often make the difference that spells success or failure for the florist. Many failures in the flower business occur because the owner didn't investigate thoroughly enough to determine the need for a florist shop in the community chosen. Location does not entail the mere physical site of the shop, but includes the city or community, the people, their incomes, their habits, the competition, the availability of suppliers, and other factors. The location should be decided on a practical businesslike basis. All too often a person's home town may already have enough or even too many retail florists. Although the figure of one florist per 10,000 people is often quoted, there are many other considerations and variables to take into account to really use this figure except as a general guide. Other considerations would be the earning power or average income of the people, growth of the community, type of industries, nationalities of the people, per-capita retail sales, and just how flower minded the people seem to be. Will they spend money for flowers? This is the ultimate goal.

A good location is the major ingredient necessary to insure the success of the retail flower shop. The factors to be considered in selecting a location for the retail florist shop can be divided into two main categories: (1) selection of the city and (2) the location within the city. These will both be discussed in detail.

Selection of the City

The selection of the city or community should be made very carefully by studying and analyzing the community, its business, and its people. Much of the information can be obtained from the local government, chamber of commerce, sales tax figures, and census figures.

First to consider are the people in the community and surrounding areas who are to be potential customers. The population of the area is important since it should be correlated with the number of existing retail florist shops. The nationality of the people should be considered because some are better flower buyers than others. A breakdown of the population by religion will also be a guide to their flower purchases. The people's attitude towards flowers is very important and will greatly determine the success or failure of the business.

Next to consider are the businesses and industries in the community. How many are there? If there is only one, and that business or industry slumps, it will affect the retail florist business almost immediately. Several businesses and industries in a community lead to a more stable economy. The types of businesses are important because they indicate the type of people in the area. Of course, if a florist locates in a strictly residential area, then there will not be any business to consider. The progressiveness of the community is important whether there are businesses there or not.

The income of the people in the community is another factor. Figures are usually available to give the average income or median income level of the people in the community. It should also be determined if most of the people are in the same income bracket or if there is a wide range between the high and low income levels. People in all income brackets like and buy flowers so that in some areas a florist might have more potential sales in a particular low income area than in some other high income area. This is tied in with people's nationalities and attitudes towards flowers.

A study of the existing flower shops is essential. Are they well managed and operated? Are they successful and making money? What is the reputation of each shop and its owner? What is the appearance of these shops? What is the quality of the merchandise and the quality of their designs? How many shops are there that will be competitors? Are the present florists an integral part of the community life? All of these things should be considered to see if a new florist can successfully compete with the existing retail flower shops in the area. The chances of his success may depend upon these factors.

Another factor that will help to decide on the city is the per capita sales of the area. A person may not be able to get the florist figures, but he can get either the per capita sales figure or the total sales figures from the local business bureau or from local governmental records. Although per capita sales for flowers will vary considerably from one city to another, it is usually found that, on the average, 1/2 of 1 per cent of all retail sales in a community will be for flowers. So, anyone can figure the amount spent on flowers in the area and, with the number of retail florists, have some idea of the gross for each shop. Another way to evaluate the existing florists' shops as to their gross return is to figure that each employee accounts for from $16,000 to $20,000 gross sales. The average is $18,000, but the better shops aim for $20,000 gross volume of sales per full-time employee.

Transportation facilities are also important to the retail florist because he handles such a perishable product. It is important for a retail florist to be near the flower market or production areas, or else to have good transportation of flowers to the city and to his shop. If the community is isolated from good transportation facilities, then it may not be the correct one to select for a florist shop. However, if wholesale florist trucks come into town daily or several times a week, then a florist can operate a successful business with a little advance planning. Transportation of flowers and supplies is important to the retail florist industry and should be considered before making the final decision on the exact location of the shop.

The last factor is to determine if a florist thinks he can make money in this community or not. A complete analysis of all of these factors is necessary to determine if he thinks his business will be successful.

Location Within the City

After the city has been decided upon for the location of the shop then it is necessary to decide on the specific location within the city.

The first factor to determine is to find the progressive part of the town. Check on the area where the establishments are modernizing and seem to be the most progressive. Don't locate in an area which is going downhill.

The retail florist shop should preferably be located in or near a business district. Even in a highly residential suburb, there will usually be a few stores, and it is wise to locate with them. The other alternative is to locate on a large piece of property on a well travelled street where the florist is by himself and can offer ample free parking. Whether the location is in the business district or not may be determined by the type of shop the florist expects to operate.

Parking is another factor to consider unless the florist is in a shopping center where plenty will be provided. It will not be his responsibility or concern if he locates in a hospital, hotel, or department store. But, for most of our regular retail florists, parking is a problem and must be considered. If he can provide several spaces on his property this will be ideal, or he may have a good half acre for parking. But, this is found in only a few locations. In the city, he may want to consider being near the local city public parking, or on a street with plenty of parking meters. In a small town, parking may not be as much of a problem as in a larger community. If the shop is by itself in a residential area, be sure

Figure 4-1. A flower shop with parking facilities provided. (Courtesy, Royer's Flowers, Lebanon, Pa.)

there is some convenient parking nearby even though the majority of the orders will be by phone. A certain number of customers will drive to the shop and want to see the store, the displays, and the merchandise. Since most of a florist's customers are women, be sure the parking is simple and easy for them.

If a florist decides to build a retail flower shop on a drive-in site, the following points may be helpful: (1) Fast traffic or congested areas do not produce drop-in traffic for the drive-in retailer —traffic averaging 35 to 45 miles per hour is preferable. (2) A stop sign slows traffic. (3) A street where cross-over is possible increases the number of directions from which a site may be approached. (4) Sites at intersections of two streets are classified as far corner, near corner, or inside location which means between the corners; far corner site is preferred as it provides greater visibility. (5) The quicker the customer recognizes a site as a drive-in retailer, the better. A drive-in site should have adequate frontage of at least 100 feet for a park-and-shop drive-in; on a highway, 300 feet is preferred. (6) The site should be deep enough to allow adequate parking at peak periods. (7) The site should be easy to enter and leave. (8) Parking spaces should be sufficient to allow ease of parking, turning around, and backing. (9) Zoning regulations should be such as to permit the sign to be seen. (10) Avoid fast traffic and congested areas. (11) Avoid areas that have a great deal of competition for customers from the same flow of traffic. (12) Do not locate on a hillside or on the inside of a curve on a highway. (13) Do not locate too close to the road as it may be widened later.

Other factors to be considered in selecting the site within the city are the taxes and zoning laws. The taxes may be higher than a retail florist can afford. The zoning laws may prohibit certain sized signs or types or placement of signs. They may prohibit greenhouses which a florist may want to incorporate with the shop. Also the zoning laws may not allow anything to be set or displayed on the sidewalk which could limit or hinder his holiday and impulse sales.

A survey of the foot traffic passing the location is important for most types of shops. In a downtown area try to locate on the side of the street where most people walk. Figures indicate that the following number of persons will pass a downtown shop in cities of various sizes: for a city of 2,500 to 25,000, 372 per hour or up to 4,464 per day can be expected; for a city of 50,000 to 250,000, 1,791 per hour or up to 21,492 per day; and for a city of above 250,000 population, 3,500 per hour, or as many as 42,000 per day.

Try to locate on the side of the street away from the sun. The sun streaming in the display window will wilt the flowers very quickly. An awning may help part of the day, but is not the best idea as it reduces the effectiveness of the window display.

Another factor to consider is the rent, or the mortgage payments if a florist is buying or constructing 'his own building. Make sure the rent is comparable to others in the area. As a rule of thumb, most retail florists do not allow more than 3 to 4 per cent of their gross volume of sales to be spent for rent. This is a good reason it is important to try to estimate the expected gross sales before going into business. The utilities should not exceed 2 per cent of the gross volume of sales.

Delivery is an important part of the business so be sure that there is adequate space, preferably in the rear of the store, for the delivery truck to be loaded and unloaded. A lot of time can be lost, and much inconvenience found, if the truck must be loaded through the front door. Both arrival of material and delivery of merchandise can be enhanced and quickened by having a good delivery area at the rear or side of the shop. Check on the laws concerning delivery trucks, and parking, if the store opens on an alley, parking lot, or side street.

One final factor in selecting the site within the city is to check the condition of nearby buildings. Be sure they are in good repair, and neat and attractive, because this will influence the reputation of the florist's shop. The type of design will also influence the front of the store (Chapter 7).

Buying a Business

If a potential florist decides to buy a business, he should consider many of the previously mentioned factors even though the actual site and location are already established. Many of those factors should be studied before investing money in the business. A thumbnail guide to buying a business would be the following: (1) Don't be too anxious to buy. (2) Find out why the business is for sale. (3) Seek advice from a lawyer and have an accountant go over the books. (4) Be sure to examine the gross volume sales figures, net returns, and net profit after taxes, and ask to see the income tax report for the past two years. (5) Beware of hidden liens, mortgages, and back taxes. (6) Find out if the employees are staying with the business or going to a competitor.

Purchasing an existing business has certain advantages which should not be overlooked. These advantages are as follows: (1) The volume of business and the potential can be measured. (2) The store and fixtures are already set up. (3) There are already customers patronizing the store. (4) Competition can be measured. (5) The inventory of stock is definite. (6) There may be the benefits of obtaining a long-term, low-cost lease. There are also disadvantages to buying a business, including the following: (1) The business may be going downhill through mismanagement or other reasons. (2) The neighborhood may be changing. (3) The business may have certain agreements with employees involving heavy fixed operating expenses. (4) There may be too much trade tied up with the personality of the former owner. (5) The good will may be overpriced resulting in too high a purchase price. (6) The net profit may not be enough for the gross volume of sales.

Buying a Second Shop

When a florist buys another flower shop for his business operations, the following factors should be considered: (1) Is there any merchandise listed in the inventory which is on a consignment basis? (2) How well have the fixed assets been maintained and repaired? (3) What are the conditions of the mortgage on the property? (4) Are there any contingent liabilities not listed by the seller? (5) What are the employment contracts with the employees and what about vacations and employee benefits? (6) What are the legislative laws and restrictions on the physical aspects of the property? (7) What future changes are planned for the area? (8) Study the inventory carefully to see what percentage is really saleable. (9) Is there a competent manager for the second shop? (10) Will this second shop compete unprofitably with the mother shop? (11) How much capital will be needed to modernize the shop? (12) What is the present reputation of the shop? If it is unsatisfactory, how much will it cost to change?

Adherence to the right answers to the foregoing factors will provide greater assurance that the purchase of another flower shop has the best possible chance of being a good business move.

Whether one starts a new business or purchases an existing florist shop, the consideration of the site and location is one of the most important factors to the success of a retail florist.

The florist should also consider whether his present customers will follow him to his new location if he decides to relocate his business.

References

1. Anonymous. "What to Look for When You Buy Another Shop," *Florists'
   and Nursery Exchange,* Vol. 145, No. 10 (March 5, 1966), pp. 20, 22.
2. Anonymous. "Where to Locate and Why," *The Exchange,* Vol. 141, No.
   8 (February 22, 1964), pp. 32-33.
3. Mertes, J. E. "Site Opportunities for the Small Retailer," *Florists' Review,*
   Vol. 135, No. 3478 (July 23, 1964), pp. 15-16, 35-39.

Chapter 5

COST OF STARTING IN BUSINESS

The retail florist business is an easy-entry business. It is a freely competitive industry and it does not take much capital to get started. A person can spend as little or as much as he wishes so long as he has a certain minimum, plus some reserve to carry him through the first two years. The minimum today should be $25,000 and should be unencumbered. Twenty-eight thousand dollars would be better, in order to pay a decent living until the profits start coming into the business.

Before going into the retail florist business it is essential to have a thorough knowledge of the trade and all its branches, sufficient capital, and the incentive to work hard and long hours. Many people prefer to work for themselves rather than for someone else, even if it means sacrifices such as longer hours, possibly lower pay, harder work, and the worries of ownership.

There are two ways to open a business: (1) buy an existing retail florist shop or (2) build or rent a shop and start the florist shop from scratch.

Buying a Going Business

The advantages and disadvantages of buying an existing business were discussed in Chapter 4. However, we have not discussed the worth of the shop, nor the price to pay for one.

Worth of a Shop

In determining the worth of a shop, many important questions must be considered as follows: (1) What is the asset valuation? Assets are significant only as they enable a flower shop to sell its merchandise profitably. (2) What is the book value? This is the net worth and considered a good evaluation, but it doesn't always hold up in the market place. (3) What is the reproductive value? This is the current cost of reproducing the assets of the flower shop. Owners who use this evaluation reason as follows: cost of duplicating the business may be higher than the balance sheet shows and inflation might have affected the price. The disadvantage is that the reproduction value has a tendency to be too high a price for the business. A new flower shop can be started for less. (4) What is the liquidation value? This is the amount that would be available to the owner if the store were liquidated. (5) What is the capitalization rate? This depends on the risks involved, and the higher the risk of generating projected earnings, the lower the capitalization rate. (6) What is the store's earning history? By studying net earnings one gets an indication of what he can reasonably expect in the future. This history is recorded in income statements dating back for five years or more. (7) What are the external influences? These include the national and local economy, location of the flower shop, competition, financial condition, and management of the store.

Determining the price to pay for an existing business is something like old-fashioned horse trading. It is hard to find a formula for automatically setting a fair price on a going business. Fundamentally, a price is set on the worth of the stock and fixtures plus the value of the future earnings to the seller. Price is also influenced by supply and demand, as well as the negotiating abilities of the buyer and the seller. A three-year survey conducted at The Pennsylvania State University of retail florist shops in the United States which were offered for sale in the trade papers, resulted in the following rule of thumb: The base figure to use is 25 to 30 per cent of the annual gross volume of the sales depending on the florist's evaluation of the worth of the shop and good will of the shop. He may start with either the 25 per cent figure or the 30 per cent. (A figure of five times the average annual earnings or net profit is cited by some florists as a reasonable figure for good will. This comes out to about the same amount.) To the 25 to 30 per cent figure is added the value of inventory and fixed equipment. If there is a building or greenhouse involved, the present market value of these structures is added. Thus, a $60,000 annual gross volume business with $3,000 in inventory and $7,000 in equipment (such as two refrigerators, truck, cash register, etc.) might be sold for from $25,000 to $28,000. (The accounts receivable are included in the 25 to 30 per cent base.) This is a general method to use to get some idea of a base from which to start in pricing a business. However, location, type of customers, age of business, reputation, management, type of business, number of excessive accounts receivable, and the factor of supply and demand will all help to influence this figure either up or down. All of these factors must be considered.

Starting into Business

Before signing any agreement to buy a business, a future florist should ask himself how long it will take him before a similar business, started by him, would yield the same income. Opening a business at a new location offers a different set of circumstances than does buying an existing shop. It is an untried proposition and will require careful planning, management, and effective advertising to build up the business. We have already discussed the location and site of the shop, as well as the various types of flower shops.

If a florist rents a property he may pay from 4 to 18 per cent of his gross volume of sales for rent. The value of a lease at a given location is in direct proportion to the dollar volume of sales transacted at that location. Various studies have shown that the average florist pays from 4 to 5 per cent of his annual gross volume of sales for rent including utilities. It would be better for a new business to spend no more than 4 per cent of expected gross sales, if possible, and thus have more money to put into advertising which must necessarily be higher for a new business than for one already established.

Leasing a business property today is more complicated than it may have been some years ago. To protect himself, the retail florist should be sure he knows all the provisions of the lease and has an attorney go over it for him. He should be sure to read the *fine print*. Be sure also that the lease covers at least the following points: (1) the basis or amount of rent—either flat dollar amount or percentage of sales, or a combination of the two; (2) the date that payments are due; (3) the duration of the lease; (4) definite provisions and terms for renewal of the lease; (5) whether signs for advertising are allowed or not; (6) what improvements can be made, and. who pays for them; (7) the responsibility for injuries to third parties on the premises; (8) what guarantee the owner makes; and (9) whether or not either party can cancel on short notice. These are the important points a florist should consider before signing a lease.

Financing a Business

Financing a business takes thought, planning, and capital. A healthy financial structure means having enough capital available at the proper time so that the business will run smoothly. A business needs capital for two main reasons: (1) to purchase necessary fixed assets and (2) as working capital. Necessary fixed assets mean only those which are absolutely essential to the business. Do not throw money down the drain on unnecessary items. Working capital is the money an operation needs for wages, supplies, inventory, overhead, and the financing of accounts receivable.

There are essentially three ways to obtain capital for a new business: (1) by investing one's own money in the business, (2) by borrowing from banks or other sources, or (3) by retaining the profits from the business and reinvesting them in the business. The worst way is to borrow so much that every cent made must go into paying off the loan. A loan is the easiest way to obtain capital, but also the most expensive. It is essential that a retail florist have some capital of his own to start a business. He should have enough capital of his own to purchase the fixed assets plus at least 50 per cent of the working capital needed by the business. Thus, he will have to borrow only a minimum amount of money. Too much borrowing can eat up most of the profits. To obtain a loan from a bank, the following are necessary: (1) a certified balance sheet and profit-and-loss statement; (2) comparative balance sheets and profit-and-loss statements for the past five years; (3) an operating budget covering an entire year's operation; (4) a cash flow forecast for the period covered in the operating budget.

How Much?

We said earlier in this chapter that it would take a minimum of $25,000 to start in business. How is this figured? Let us assume a florist is starting a small business and expects to gross around $40,000 a year. The sales will take care of the cost of merchandise, and probably pay the rent. These will be about 54 per cent of the gross volume. The retail florist should not expect to make any profit the first two years. He will need money to pay salaries, taxes, advertising, and other overhead expenses for the first year. This could amount to approximately $14,000 (36 per cent—not including rent

Figure 5-1. Good display of inventory items. (Courtesy, Lazy Susan Flower Shop, Venice, Fla.)

and wire service membership). A delivery car or truck may cost $3,000 or more, depending upon the type and age. Two refrigerators will cost about $4,500 depending upon size and whether they are new or not. A cash register will cost from $200 up. Baskets, ribbon, wire, and other supplies will cost $600, and pottery and refrigerator vases will cost another $600. The total of these expenses comes to $22,900 plus his own expenses which brings it up to the $25,000 quoted previously. The owner's own salary is included in the overhead, but it will be low at first (10 to 12 per cent per Chapter 6), or $4,000. The extra $2,100 which is left from the $25,000 will give him a total of $6,100 for his living. These expenses can be higher or lower depending on the scale of the business he wishes to establish and whether the equipment is new or used. These are minimum figures, and will increase as time goes on. A large amount of money can be invested if the florist expects to have a larger gross volume of business. This is one reason it is important to plan the business carefully and try to determine the expected gross volume of sales. The $25,000 should be in cash and unencumbered since he won't have any profit the first two years. To determine if he can afford some gadget or piece of equipment, he will need to find out by a time study if the improved method will save time and how long it will take to pay it off.

Operating expenses and overhead compared to cost of merchandise and gross sales will be discussed in Chapter 6.

Alternatives

Before investing his money in a retail florist shop, a person might wish to consider the alternatives in the industry. With the increased specialization in our society, the young florist has alternative opportunities for developing his skills and investing his capital. He can specialize in flower production, wholesale florist activities, retail flower store management, or he may combine production and retailing activities. In deciding upon his type of business, personal preference is one factor, previous experience another, and availability of capital another. A florist shop with a greenhouse has many advantages, but it is much more costly to establish. A greenhouse may cost from $5 to $10 a square foot. Thus a 100' x 20' greenhouse could cost $20,000 on top of the cost of the retail shop.

Floriculture is a very specialized business and unless the student is really interested in it, perhaps he or she should consider some other field. However, if he is really interested in flowers and plants, there is no better field. The opportunities for women are particularly good in the retail florist business.

Reference

1. Anonymous. "Where to Locate and Why," *The Exchange*, Vol. 141, No. 8 (February 22, 1964), pp. 32-33.

Chapter 6

OPERATING EXPENSES; OVERHEAD

Operating Expenses

The costs of operation for the retail florist business are high, and will fluctuate depending upon the gross volume of business. The total *operating expenses* will *increase* as the gross volume of sales *increases*. However, the *cost of merchandise* usually will *decrease* as the gross *increases*. The *net profit* percentage may *decrease* as the gross volume *increases*. Merchandise and labor are the two factors which change the most as the gross volume of business changes. These two figures when compared with gross sales will show the net profit for the business. All of these are tied together in the successful management of the shop.

The cost of merchandise is hard to check in many florist shop operations because many retail florists do not have separate figures for the perishable items and the inventory items such as containers, fillers, ribbon, and other materials which usually amount to from 3.5 to 6.5 per cent of the sale. The cost of merchandise is a major item of expense in the retail florist shop and offers a tremendous possibility for cutting costs. Another large item of expense is labor. The percentage of gross volume of sales utilized in labor (including the manager's or owner's salary) will vary from 15 to 30 per cent depending upon the gross dollar volume of business. A third large item of expense is that of overhead which includes rent, utilities, advertising, office expense, delivery, telephone, taxes, and depreciation. All of these items of operating expense, plus the cost of merchandise, must of course be less than 100 per cent of the gross sales if a profit is to be realized from the business. The net profit will vary from one to 10 per cent after taxes. A 10 per cent profit is the theoretical profit which most florists aim for, but few attain. Many retail florists who own their own shops do not include their own salaries in labor, but simply make periodic withdrawals

43

and take the profit from the shops. Many do not pay their wives any wages. Both of these practices lead to a false profit picture, which shows their net profit to be higher than it is in reality. The owner should take out a regular salary each week and should pay his wife if she works full time. Thus, the net profit at the end of the year will give a truer picture of the business and the return on his investment.

Most figures published in recent years are *averages* and as such do not show the true picture of the florist industry. The only important figures are the ones from a retail florist's own business which show how profitably he is operating. If the profit for a particular business is low, then he should compare the percentage figures for his various operating expenses and cost of merchandise, with the average given for shops in the same gross dollar volume category as his own, to see where the discrepancies occur. Then he will know where to try to change his business management practices to obtain a larger profit. It may be in his cost of merchandise, payroll, advertising budget, bad debts, rent, or any other items of expense.

Let's look at some figures to see how operating expenses affect the profit picture. These are from a 1965 FTD survey, and are shown in Table 6-1.

The survey showed that for the shops in this study, the net profit averaged approximately 7.6 per cent before federal and state income taxes. Operating expenses ranged from 45.1 per cent of total sales for the smaller shops to 53.2 per cent for the largest volume group. Principal items of expense for all groups were salaries and wages (ranging from 16.9 to 30.5 per cent), and overhead (ranging from 8.1 to 10.6 per cent).

The figures show very clearly that in retail florist shops, the cost of merchandise decreased as the gross volume of sales increased. This is due to better buying practices where a florist can get a better price by purchasing in larger quantities and also is able to take advantage of discounts on inventory items. Expenses, on the other hand, increased as gross sales increased due mainly to the need for more employees, which resulted in a higher percentage of the gross going towards labor.

Keep in mind that the owner or owner-manager does take a salary which is part of the percentage allotted to salaries and wages, besides receiving the net profit from the business. Also remember these figures are just *averages* of shops from all over the United States, and are useful for comparative purposes only. Many of our most

Table 6-1. Operating Expense Analysis by Shops Grouped as to Annual Dollar Volume, 1965.

	Under $30,000	$30,000 to $70,000	$70,000 to $125,000	Over $125,000
TOTAL SALES AND OTHER INCOME	100.0%	100.0%	100.0%	100.0%
COST OF MERCHANDISE	47.6	44.3	45.4	41.9
GROSS PROFIT	52.4	55.7	54.6	58.1
EXPENSES:				
Salaries and wages (including owner's salary and withdrawals)	16.9	22.5	24.9	30.5
Rent, utilities, and repairs (depreciation on buildings only)	7.1	6.1	4.9	4.7
Advertising and promotion	1.5	2.1	2.4	2.4
Commissions, FTD, and clearing house charges	3.1	2.3	2.2	2.0
Delivery (not wages)	5.9	6.1	4.3	5.4
OVERHEAD:				
Office expenses (not wages)	1.5	1.0	.8	.9
Telephone and telegraph	2.2	2.1	1.7	1.4
Professional fees	.2	.3	.6	.4
Dues and subscriptions	.3	.3	.2	.2
Donations	.3	.2	.1	.1
Insurance	1.2	1.1	.9	1.1
Interest	.5	.6	.4	.2
Payroll taxes	.5	.5	.7	.9
Other taxes and licenses	1.7	.9	.8	1.0
Depreciation	.7	.7	.7	.5
Bad debts	.3	.3	.3	.5
Cash over and shortages	—	—	.1	.3
Miscellaneous	1.2	.8	.8	.7
TOTAL EXPENSES	45.1	47.9	46.8	53.2
Net profit (loss) before income taxes but after deducting officer-owner salaries and withdrawals	7.3	7.8	7.8	4.9

successful shops are netting from 6 to 10 per cent of the gross sales as profit. Unfortunately, many retail florists are only realizing a net profit of from 1 to 3 per cent of the gross which is less than they could get by investing their money.

Employees' wages vary considerably in various parts of the country, different cities, and in different gross volume shops. The previous FTD survey showed that salaries for designers ranged from $1.10 an hour in shops under $30,000 gross up to $2.50 an

hour in shops grossing over $125,000. Sales employee wages ranged
from 85¢ an hour up to $1.60. Delivery men's wages ranged from
$1.10 an hour up to $1.75. Office employees' wages ranged from
$1.25 an hour up to $1.90. Other help ranged from $1.10 to $1.50
an hour. These wages are from 1964, and have risen only slightly
in the past five years. The Federal Minimum Wage and Hours
Law affects this now. Volume is the key to determining whether your
shop comes under the Fair Labor Standards Act or is exempt. Total
annual sales of $250,000 mark the dividing line, but there are other
factors which must be considered, so it is best to consult legal counsel
on this.

Overhead

A retail florist shop can fail if the overhead costs get out of
line. There are many items listed as overhead as seen in Table 6-1.
Many retail florists also include rent, salaries, advertising, and delivery
as overhead, while others count those as expenses. Some of these costs
are fixed and cannot be controlled. However, others can be controlled, may be improved, and should be watched carefully. It is
very easy for expenses to get out of line. Overhead costs should be
watched by a suitably long term overhead accounting system. Such
items as dumpage, overbuying, and bad debts should be kept to
a minimum. These are very important and often will result in a
loss in profits. Excess buying with poor sales will result in too much
dumpage of flowers. This must be watched very carefully at all
times by the manager or owner. Bad debts will also reduce the
profits. The advertising budget should be figured carefully so that
the florist gets the expected return from his expenditure. One of the
most critical areas is in depreciation. It can give him a false profit
picture if not figured realistically. This means figuring the loss in
value of an item annually, due to wear and tear, based on the
number of years he expects the item to last. There are three
methods for depreciating items of equipment, and the florist must
use the one best suited to his type of operation and expected
profits. Check with an accountant as to which one to use for each item.
It is important to depreciate the items carefully and truthfully so that
they are exactly correct. If a 10-year depreciation is set up on an
item that must be replaced in six years, a false picture is developed,
and the florist is actually losing money, and may have trouble
financing the new item.

Figure 6-1. Unusual features and displays will add to the cost of overhead but are well worth it. (Courtesy, Geralis Florist, Washington, D.C.)

The following message delivered by a successful retail florist, Charles Hum, while he was President of Florists Transworld Delivery Association is something for all florists and potential florists to think about. "While this past year (1965) has been a very good year for our industry, with business never better and sales at an all time high, we should not ignore the corresponding increases in wholesale prices, labor costs, delivery costs and in overhead.

"I am deeply concerned with keeping our industry's small retailers healthy, as our Association is only as vital as the retailers who comprise the membership. I am afraid that many retail florists have been so busy coping with sales, that they have not taken time to keep abreast of, and take acccount of, the rising costs that, if ignored, could turn these boom years into a period of serious financial difficulty for small businesses.

"Take time out during the summer months to look over the financial hard facts of your businesses. *Make sure you're getting paid properly for your flowers, your costs, and your service.* By being alert to costs as well as sales, you'll avoid the pitfalls that all too many small businessmen encounter."

Bad Debts

Bad debts occur in any business, and will not be a problem if kept to a minimum. In the retail florist business it is considered best to keep them at less than ½ of 1 per cent of the annual gross volume of sales. These can be easily checked from the records and if they exceed ½ of 1 per cent of the gross, then something should be done to correct it.

When a debt becomes bad or uncollectable, the deduction on the income tax form must be taken in the year in which it occurs. Many florists let their bad debts go much too long. The retail florist has actually loaned the customer the money, and if it is not paid, it is the florist's money that is tied up. He cannot recover all of it, but he can get part of it by deducting it on his income tax return.

A bad debt is one which is uncollectable now and seems so in the future. This is after the businessman has made every effort to collect it. Worthlessness is the test. It is not necessary for the entire debt to be uncollectable. A businessman is permitted to claim a deduction for a partially worthless debt where it can be shown that the debt is recoverable only in part. A reserve for bad debts can be set up in the accounting procedure and this is usually based on past experience. For a new florist, it will be based on a *good guess* the first year.

If a bad debt is paid later after it has been deducted, the florist must report the payment on his income tax return as income, but only to the extent that the earlier charge-off helped reduce his taxes. The amount of tax saved has nothing to do with it. It is the amount of the bad debt that he was able to use advantageously as a deduction that is considered here. It is best to check with an accountant on this.

Personal Withdrawals

The amount of money a florist withdraws from his business for personal needs can have a tremendous effect on his shop, for good or evil. He can restrict his personal withdrawals and assure himself of a solvent business, or he can withdraw more than is wise and lose the business. Determining the amount of cash one can take out of a business isn't as simple as it seems. Obviously a florist should not withdraw more than is represented by his net earnings. He must also hold back enough of the net earnings for expected repairs, new equipment, and other items.

Business survival dictates that a person consistently withdraws less cash than his business earns. How much less will depend on his basic personal needs and his business needs.

Every year the business gets older and eventually the florist will need to modernize. New equipment is needed periodically and even though he depreciates these items yearly, the total depreciation charges won't begin to pay for the replacements. He will be short, which means he is not staying even with today's higher prices.

To determine basic withdrawals consult the previous year's income tax returns and estimate the net earnings. From this deduct the estimated income tax. Then determine the extra amount that will be needed for necessary replacements and set this aside. Figure the extra amount needed to increase the inventory and equity and deduct this. The resulting figure (which may be only 1/2 to 2/3 of the originally estimated earnings) is now divided by 12 to give some idea of the monthly withdrawal. The florist must stick to this and not be tempted to spend more on personal needs or he will be in financial trouble at the end of the year.

In a partnership it is no less important that there should be restraints and controls on personal withdrawals to keep the partnership from being strained.

Expenses and the costs of operation of a retail florist shop must be checked constantly so that the business will show a proper profit at the end of the year. Many florists check their income and expenses daily or weekly while others do it monthly. Current figures should be compared with last year's figures and thus there will not be any trouble at the end of the year. A successful retail florist should realize the expected profit, after taxes, if he has managed the business properly.

References

1. Anonymous. "New Survey Reveals Average Profits, Expenses," *FTD News* (April 1966), pp. 24-25.
2. Hum, C. R. "President's Message," *FTD News* (August 1966), p. 29.
3. Ritter, B. "Overhead Shouldn't Be Over Your Head," *The Exchange*, Vol. 143, No. 6 (February 6, 1965), pp. 28, 46.

Chapter 7

STORE EXTERIOR; WINDOW DISPLAY

Store Exterior

The exterior of the retail florist shop accounts for approximately 35 per cent of all sales according to several surveys. This figure is a little lower if most of the business is by phone, although many customers will still drive by and see the window displays. This figure of 35 per cent includes the appearance of the store as well as the display window. A customer's first impression of the store is very important, so the exterior must not be neglected. The design of the store should be in keeping with the rest of the shops in the neighborhood. There is no reason, however, that a shop in an older section of town cannot be modernized if it is not done to extremes. Don't make it too different!

There are essentially five things that make a store stand out, even at a distance: (1) The paint or building material of the front which gives the first, and best, impression of the store. (2) Lighting at night helps to make the store stand out. Good lighting will include not only lighting in the store but the window display and spotlights both in the window and outside of the shop. People usually walk on the side of the street with the most lights, so this is a good means of advertising the shop. (3) The window is the most important part of the exterior of the shop and will be discussed in detail later in this chapter. (4) The sign should be prominently displayed so that people can not only read the name of the shop, but also know the type of store. The sign should show up both day and night. (5) Plants and flowers always attract attention. If there is space in front of the store, and if the city ordinances will permit them, the use of window boxes and tubbed plants will more than pay for themselves.

To find out how the store looks to others and if the owner is satisfied with the front of it, he should try this simple test. He

Figure 7-1. Exterior stone carries into interior of the shop. (Courtesy, Penny Hill Flowers, Wilmington, Del.)

can drive around aimlessly for awhile in his car and then turn around and drive slowly towards the shop. He can use his imagination and pretend that he is an average citizen, not a florist. How good is the location? Are the parking facilities adequate? What is the first impression of the shop? How does the shop stack up with others in the neighborhood? Are the windows clean? Does the window display catch the eye and make one stop and look at it? How effective is the sign? Is it neat, clean, and freshly painted? If these impressions are good, and he likes it, great! If not, then some changes must be made.

Display Windows

The window display is one of the most powerful media of advertising in the world today. It is often referred to as point-of-sale advertising or visual merchandising. It leads all other forms of advertising in sales return for dollar expended. Window display as an art has reached its present high state of development as a direct result of competition. The primary purpose of a window display is to stimulate sales. The greatest advantage of window displays over other forms of advertising is its low cost. Just ½ to 1 per cent of gross sales may be enough. The cost of flowers used in the display, which must be charged to advertising, will probably raise this by another ½ per cent.

Some florists say that "display is half the sale." A good window display will involve the creative imagination of the individual florist. The window is the biggest factor in accounting for up to 35 per cent of the sales in many shops. There are numerous types of windows from small, waist-high windows to those that stretch from sidewalk to roof and encompass the whole front of the store. The shop may have from one to 10 windows across the front. The majority of florists' shops in this country have from one to three windows of varying sizes. The modern trend in shops today is to have the windows from floor to ceiling with most of the front of the store in glass. These lend themselves better to tall decorations, large displays, and help to open up the whole store to the customer on the street. They also provide more light inside the shop. Raised windows may be cheaper to decorate but they are not as effective, nor do they give as much display area.

Figure 7-2. Window display is attractive from both outside and inside the shop. (Courtesy, Fries Florists, Lancaster, Pa.)

Fresh Material

Flowers and plants should be used in florist shop windows since they are the best form of advertising for a retail florist. Many other industries use flowers and plants to help sell their products, so why not the florist? Some pottery and novelties can be used, but there should always be some fresh plant material in the window. The windows should be changed quite often—at least every week—except when there is some very spectacular display for a holiday like Christmas or Easter. Then it can remain two weeks. The display should never be permitted to get dirty. A few large florists in the larger cities change their displays several times a week and one even changes them every day. The theme of the display should be appropriate for a holiday, local event, special occasion, or other idea. Simple designs are usually best, with just one main center of interest or focal point in each window. The window displays should not be crowded. Originality in display is necessary if the display is to be successful.

Eleven Seconds

A window display is a flashing picture to the average pedestrian. He or she approaches it, observes it, and responds to it, all in less than *11 seconds*. This picture must be attractive and interesting to bring customers into the store. Since the average pedestrian spends less than 11 seconds considering a window, the display has to "talk fast."

Every display window should do four things:

1. **Attract attention.** The window display should attract the attention of people passing by. One way this can be accomplished is by motion in the window. Anything that moves will attract attention. Or it can be accomplished by color, illumination, or some unusual form or arrangement. The use of revolving colored disks in front of a spotlight will combine the two factors of light and motion very effectively.

2. **Create interest.** After the attention of the customer has been attracted, then the florist must create an interest in his display so the customer will stop and look at it. This can be accomplished by the timeliness of the display if it ties in with a holiday or occasion. It can also be accomplished by the use of a demonstration on how to use the merchandise, or by the use of novel or unusual flowers or merchandise items in the display.

3. **Change the interest into desire.** The next step is to transform the interest in flowers to the desire for flowers or other merchandise on display. This is accomplished by stressing the use and need for flowers for a particular occasion. Try to sell the idea that flowers are

the *best bet* and better than anything else. Display flowers and arrangements in such an attractive way that the customer just can't resist them. Turn browsers into customers.

4. **Get the customer into the shop.** The final function of the window display is to get the customer to enter this store. This can be accomplished by the reputation of the store which has been built up through the years. It can also be accomplished by the physical layout of the shop to make the entry very easy. A wide level doorway and entrance is much better than steps or a narrow door. A light and pleasant store that looks inviting will also help to get customers into the shop, as will a shop that smells good.

The display is an information link between the consumer and the store. A display tells what is available, frequently at what price, and why it is available. The "why" factor (psychological motivation) is being emphasized in sales promotion today. Any florist can use it in his displays because it is mainly appealing to people's emotions.

The following principles of a good window display must be **kept in mind: (1) Each window should have a central theme or**

Figure 7-3. Interior displays can be seen through the window from the outside. (Courtesy, Silverblatt's Flowers, Pittsburgh, Pa.)

idea (and only one). (2) Avoid crowding because people will not stop and look at a cluttered window. (3) Design the window from the standpoint of the passerby. Remember the retailer has only 11 seconds to stop the customer and get across the message. (4) Have a definite sales appeal to the display. The ultimate aim is to sell the merchandise. (5) Use simplicity of design if it is to be most effective. (6) Make sure the glass and floor are clean at all times. (7) Use the principles of good design and color harmony. (8) Replace the old and wilted flowers as soon as noticed. This should be checked at least once a day. (9) Use price tags on the merchandise that can be easily read. Whether the merchandise in the window is priced or not will depend on the type of shop, and whether the owner thinks it is worth-while or not. Most florists and other retail merchants price all merchandise in their windows, and today's consumers like and appreciate it. Many florists price everything in the window and also in the store.

Do not give the windows a vacation in the summer, but make them work for the business. In summer, it is especially important that the window display be designed to catch the customer's eye. Flowers are just a bit harder to sell during these months when home gardens are filled with blooms, and when some of the customers are away on vacation. Therefore, the window should be as good or better than usual. Fortunately, summer is also the time when a florist ordinarily has more time than usual to spend on the window display. He should use this time to good advantage, set up some unusual displays, and keep it as clean as possible.

Window Backgrounds

The open versus closed background for windows has been debated for many years. There are advantages and disadvantages to both. Sometimes it depends entirely on the physical setup of the store. The open background is the more modern approach and of more advantage to most stores. It is less formal and lends itself to more casual shopping. It costs less to decorate since the owner can use the whole store for a background. Other advantages of the open background are as follows: (1) Displays can be viewed from both inside and outside the store. (2) The open background allows the passerby to see into the store. (3) Customers can see the displays in the store as well as other people in the store. (4) People seem to attract people and this can be used as a drawing power for the florist. (5) The open background makes for a brighter store and may even reduce the lighting bill. There are a few disadvantages to the open background, such as: (1) People are sometimes so interested in seeing what is going on in the store that they don't see the display in the window. (2) It is sometimes difficult to build a suitable background for a specific display. (3) The open background may result in more dirt and flies accumulating in the store (but not if properly cleaned each day). (4) The fact that people passing by can see the florist working in the store is considered a disadvantage by some and an advantage by others. Some florists are even remodeling their whole shop so that the designing is done where the customers can see how the artistry is accomplished. The advantages of the open background outweigh the disadvantages for windows in our retail florist shops of today.

Figure 7-4. A very modern store front. (Courtesy, House of Flowers, El Paso, Tex.)

Lighting

Window lighting is very important if the florist is to get the full value out of the window. Lighting works as a sales tool both for identification and attraction, but of first importance is identification. The first stress is on what is being sold; and secondly, the trade name of the shop should be visible, with the accent on flowers. New colors have been developed to increase the effectiveness of lighted plastic signs. A new and sharper white enhances the brilliance of the reds. Incandescent lights are again being used for outdoor lighting. In many shops, the entire store front is a merchandising tool, with wide glass fronts used as display cases which are invaluable when properly lighted. Size, brightness, contrast, and time are factors used in setting up eye-catching displays. In an average shop, 150 to 200 foot-candles of light are desirable. Deluxe cool white fluorescent lighting outstrips all others for store use. However, flowers react differently to various fluorescent lights so this should be discussed with an expert from the power company so that the colors of the flowers will be enhanced. Some lights will give red roses a bluish cast which can be disastrous, and may lose sales for the florist. Red poinsettias and red roses must have a nice bright clear red color if they are to sell.

In the window displays, colored lights should be used to attract attention and to bring out the colors of the flowers. Spotlights are best to use on the featured display items. If a florist uses spotlights of the same color as the flowers, they will have a more natural look. White light can also be used on the displays if the florist does not want to use a colored light. The lights should be recessed in the window ceiling or wall, and they should not shine or glare into the eyes of the observer on the street, or the customers in the store. The light intensity of the window should be sufficient to really show off the display to the best advantage.

CHECK YOUR DISPLAY

A check list can help you to evaluate your window display. Such a list should include:

1. Neatness and cleanliness. Sloppy housekeeping can reduce the effect of even an original display of quality merchandise.

2. Brightness. Colorful and appealing merchandise should be lighted so as to create the proper atmosphere. This increases the customer's ability to appraise the merchandise.

3. Selling message. Cards or props should clearly tell why the merchandise is desirable.

4. Focal point. Every display needs a central or dominant area to attract attention quickly. It should stop traffic so people will really look at what is in the window.

You may want to evaluate the factors that compose your display by scoring them as follows: 0—none, 1—poor, 2—good, 3—excellent. Total possible points is 51.

ARRANGEMENT

1. Window not too empty _____
2. Window not too full _____
3. Main items stand out _____
4. No clashes in color _____

CLEANLINESS

1. Window clean _____
2. Floor clean _____
3. Background clean _____
4. Props and fixtures clean _____
5. Merchandise (flowers) clean and not wilted _____

LIGHTING

1. Lights are hidden _____
2. Lights are clean _____
3. Some spotlights used _____

SELLING POWER

1. Background and props are seasonable _____
2. Selling points are stressed _____
3. Show cards tell the story _____
4. Props do not overshadow merchandise _____
5. Related merchandise is used _____

TOTAL POINTS _____

This means the window should have from 150 to 200 foot-candles of light, plus the spotlights.

One point frequently overlooked by store owners is the fact that as persons grow older they require more light with which to see. What may be adequate light for the store owner may be entirely inadequate for older customers. The window must be adequately lighted to attract attention. Women rarely stop at a dark, poorly lighted store and many florists' customers are women. A test was made recently of 100 persons passing a store window with ordinary lighting. Only 17 stopped. When proper lighting was installed in the same window, 46 out of 100 persons stopped. This was 2½ times more than with the ordinary lighting.

The exterior of the retail florist shop, including the display windows, is one of the most important features of the shop; often accounting for 35 per cent of the gross volume of sales.

The list on page 58 is one which should be checked periodically to find out the effectiveness of the window display.

References

1. Bluhme, A. "Choosing Your Location, Lighting and Layout," *Florists' Review*, Vol. 136, No. 3526 (June 24, 1965), pp. 19, 45-46.
2. Valencia, Sylvia. "Retailing from A to Z," *Florists' Review*, Vol. 135, No. 3500 (December 24, 1964), pp. 15-16, 38-41.

Chapter 8

INTERIOR SALES AND DESIGN AREAS; FIXTURES; EQUIPMENT

The interior of the shop with its physical features, equipment, and layout must be planned in advance. The layout of the shop is presented in Chapter 10, along with suggested model designs and remodeling ideas. This chapter will deal with the general interior for all shops with a discussion of the fixtures and equipment needed.

The interior of the store is very important because of the impression given a person when he (or she) steps into the shop. Will he be pleased or disappointed? The décor and style must tie in with the exterior and the windows. A customer does not want to step from an ultramodern front into a Victorian interior. The tie in must be graceful and subtle with the interior a continuation of the exterior.

The color scheme of the interior is important and must be one that enhances flowers and does not detract from them. It must not offend the customer. It must be well planned and executed. The ceiling should be white or off-white to make the store as light as possible. White on the walls, however, is bright, and will not show off the flowers to the best advantage. Most florists have found that a soft grey, green, or grey-green will be best and the one that makes most flowers stand out to the fullest advantage. Black is an excellent background for many flowers, but is not the most practical. Who wants the whole wall of a shop black? However, a small section of black for a special display or feature would be excellent. Some florists prefer paneling on one or two walls rather than paint, and redwood or walnut is very pleasing and can be used for a good display of pottery and flowers other than red. For utility as well as appearance, some florists are using pegboard walls which are painted off-white, beige, or grey-green.

Good circulation is an essential feature of the interior. There

must be ease of movement in the store for both the customers and
the employees. In a large store this is necessary so that the store
does not look crowded and cluttered with too many display tables,
plants, and other items or fixtures. In a small shop the best method
for good circulation is to have one open area in the center of the
store with the display tables and shelves along the walls. Customers
should have easy movement to see the displays and an open path
to the display refrigerator. Customers should be able to move
freely through the store without bumping into one another, unless
it is a holiday when the store may be crowded. Circulation should
also be provided for the salespeople so they can move around and
show various items to a customer without running into other customers. Employees should also be able to get to the wrapping
counter and cash register very readily. Naturally the circulation will
be curtailed or reduced at holiday time when the store will have
more merchandise on display than during the other days of the
year.

The interior of the store should be planned with ease of

Figure 8-1. Designing is done in the sales area in some modern retail shops.
(Courtesy, Fries Florists, Lancaster, Pa.)

cleaning in mind. Everything on display must be dusted periodically and this should be accomplished as easily as possible. The floor of the store must be cleaned frequently, and a well planned interior with this in mind will cut down on the hours of labor needed for this job.

Easy access to all supplies should be considered to cut down on the steps and time spent by employees both when waiting on customers and when making up design pieces.

There should be a systematic placement of articles of merchandise and supplies in the store. Items which are commonly used together should be displayed together. Displays should be grouped so that the customer can see all dish gardens in one spot, brass items in another, baby novelties in another, religious articles in another, and so on. There should be a systematic arrangement with planning ahead of time to make the store as attractive as possible to the customer. This will help to make it easier for the customer to buy. Impulse items must be easily seen to be sold effectively.

Heating and air conditioning must be provided and should be the best for the plants, customers, and employees. A cooler temperature is best for the plants and flowers, but not always for people. In the winter, heat must be provided, but the store should certainly be kept cooler than a person's home. Many retail florists are using air conditioning in the summer. It is beneficial to the plants, the customers, and the employees. Contrary to the belief of some retail florists, the air conditioning is not harmful to plants and flowers, and the cooler temperatures will make the cut flowers last longer. There is no evidence of injury to pot plants or foliage plants if the air conditioning is regulated properly.

Retail Shop Areas

The number of areas in the retail florist shop will depend on the size of the operation. There must be a sales area and a workroom or design area. The control center is very important and may be the office, a separate room, or just an area of its own which is convenient to both the sales and design areas. If the shop is large enough, a consultation room is very helpful for the discussions of funeral and wedding flowers. Sometimes this is a separate room, but often it is just one area in the salesroom, or the office itself. Storage rooms and restrooms must be provided.

The floor of the store should be a material which will not become slippery when wet, nor treacherous for walking. It should be a material that is easy to clean. Linoleum and rubber tile are better than wood. Asphalt tile is excellent but is more expensive. One of the best materials that is found in some of the smarter shops is carpeting. It is very attractive and easy to vacuum, but the florist must be sure to get a good grade of carpeting which will not spot with water. A new outdoor carpeting is on the market today and is excellent for retail florist shops. Concrete floors are very hard on the feet, particularly for the employees. Flagstone, slate, and terrazo are other materials which make attractive floors for retail florist shops.

Figure 8-2. Wall to wall carpeting can be used in the sales area. (Courtesy, Planter Florist, Bellevue, Wash.)

Mirrors in a small shop are good because they help to make the shop look larger. However, don't use them on more than one wall or the effect will be destroyed.

Lighting

Good illumination is necessary inside the florist shop. Customers like to see a well lighted store and want to see the merchandise easily. In the average retail shop, 150 to 200 foot-candles of light is desirable. In small shops the lighting will be about the same for the whole area. However, in larger shops the shop can be divided into different areas with various light intensities such as are recommended for most department stores. They use the 1-3-5-10 formula for foot-candles of light for lighting the store:

1—Circulation area, 20 to 30 f.c. (no selling)

3—Sales area, 3 times #1, 60 to 90 f.c.

5—Showcase and counter display, 5 times #1, 100 to 150 f.c.

10—Featured displays, 10 times #1, 200 to 300 f.c.

Retail florist shops do not have a separate circulation area as such, but they do have sales, displays, and featured displays to be lighted. Be sure there is adequate light in the shop. Light up the store, work area, and interior to the point where customers can see to make the right purchase of flowers, and employees can easily see to properly arrange the flowers.

Figure 8-3. Acoustical tile ceiling and indirect lighting are used in remodeling a retail shop. (Courtesy, Fries Florists, Lancaster, Pa.)

Fluorescent lighting, like all other elements that go into a store or display area, contributes towards a psychological effect called atmosphere. All atmospheres are described as warm or cool. The warm white lamps help to produce a warm mellow atmosphere which is not too applicable to a retail flower shop. The cool white light helps to produce a cool, crisp atmosphere of modern interiors, and blends well with the natural daylight coming from the windows. Illuminating engineers recommend the deluxe cool white fluorescent light for most retail florist shops. It combines excellent color rendition with good efficiency, to produce an interior atmosphere which is similar to natural daylight. Thus, florists can make their shops more attractive and enhance the appearance of their flowers, which will result in corresponding benefits to customers and the florist himself.

Incandescent lamps can be used very effectively in a retail florist shop. They will give the effect of sunlight on a foliage plant display. Featured displays can receive 200 foot-candles of light from the use of 150 watt R-40 floodlights.

Whatever type of light is planned for the shop, it must be adequate.

Equipment

In the sales area, *the display refrigerator is the most important piece of equipment.* (See Figure 8-4.) It should be located opposite the front door so that it will catch the eye of the customer and draw him to it. The display refrigerator is called the "silent salesman." Many florists keep a well filled refrigerator on display at all times. It should contain not only cut flowers but made-up floral arrangements as well. Display refrigerators range in size from 3 to 36 feet long with custom-built ones of any size. The 8-foot refrigerator is the most common one used in most florist shops although large shops will certainly need either a larger one or perhaps two of medium size. Many florists say that the proof of their profits comes from the excellent floral displays that they have daily in their display refrigerator. It is easier for the salesman to sell from this display, as well as to upsell various purchases. Often customers will spend $15.00 rather than $10.00 for an arrangement when they see the difference in the display refrigerator. The manager should check the display refrigerator daily to make sure it is always attractive. Frequently the display refrigerator is used for made-up arrangements, priced ready to go, while the stock of cut flowers is carried in another refrigerator called the storage refrigerator. The latter refrigerator is in the workroom.

Figure 8-4. Display refrigerator with shelves and heated glass doors. (Courtesy, Frederick's Flowers, Souderton, Pa.)

The second most important piece of equipment in the store is the cash register. It is important to spend the money to purchase a good one. The government requires accurate figures from all businesses today, and many states have sales taxes which must be collected and accounted for on their records. The cash register can help to give the florist a day-by-day accounting of his business, including cash and accounts receivable sales. Also he can keep track of his sales according to type of merchandise, if he wishes. The size and complexity of the machine will depend on the individual business. Fortunately, today's cash register not only keeps money but also can be a sales record keeper for the whole organization.

Florist shops differ greatly in the kind and amount of furniture and equipment that they have in the store. One will not find all of the things discussed here in all of the shops. The size of the store and the physical layout will, in a large part, determine how many of these things can be used.

A wrapping table and counter should be an integral part of every flower shop whether large or small. It takes too much time and is a nuisance to have to go to the back workroom to wrap each order. Frequently the cash register will be placed on the wrapping counter. The florist can take advantage of the space under the counter for shelves to hold wrapping paper, tissue, plastic, ribbon, string, scissors, boxes, foil, stapler, and other items commonly used in wrapping orders for the customer. Good packaging is essential to the success of the business.

A writing desk and chair should be part of the salesroom although some florists do not provide them. The desk should be well stocked at all times with plenty of the small cards for all occasions plus some plain ones. It is considered a courtesy to provide a place for the customer to sit down while writing a card

Figure 8-5. A consultation corner for discussing wedding and funeral flowers. (Courtesy, Royer's Flowers, Lebanon, Pa.)

rather than to expect him (or her) to stand up and lean on a desk or counter. (Not all florists agree with this.) The desk and chair should be placed out of circulation against the wall, so that a customer filling out a card will not feel that someone is looking over his shoulder to see what he is writing. The chair for the desk can also be used for consultation on flowers for weddings, for funerals, or for decorations, in a very small shop which may not have a separate room or area for this service.

Display tables and shelves are a necessary part of the sales area in a retail florist shop. The number and size will depend on the size of the shop. Normally a florist has as much display area in the salesroom as he can provide without giving the shop a cluttered look. There must be room to adequately display pottery, glassware, novelty containers, figurines, dish gardens, pot plants, permanent arrangements, and fresh flower arrangements. A florist may

Figure 8-6. A display area built into the wall during remodeling. (Courtesy, Royer's Flowers, Lebanon, Pa.)

also handle other lines of merchandise such as brass, milk glass, candles, and many other items to be displayed for the customer. The display tables or stands should be of a material which will fit in with the décor of the rest of the store. They may be wood, aluminum, wrought iron, or plastic and have glass, marble, formica, tile, or plywood tops. Some florists replace the glass with plywood at holiday times for display of plants and other items, with a minimum chance for breakage. The shape can be rectangular, round, square, triangular, dog-leg, or semicircular; and of a size that is convenient to the store. The display shelves can be of various materials and either built into the wall (Figure 8-7) or on brackets in a pegboard wall. With a pegboard, plus brackets and shelves, there are unlimited possibilities to the arrangement of the shelves for display. They can be easily changed as the display changes, whereas wood shelves are usually more permanent in nature. However, many florists prefer wood shelves since they consider them more attractive.

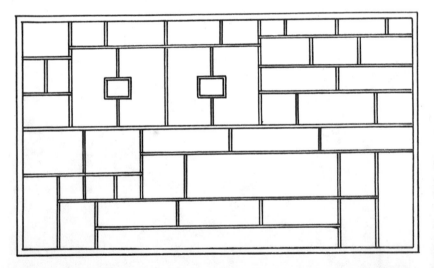

Figure 8-7. A 12-foot wall of wooden display shelves designed with various sized spaces for pottery and knickknacks.

There are also aluminum strips with adjustable shelves which can be used effectively. Shadow boxes of various sizes and types are used by retail florists for special arrangements. These can be recessed in the wall, set against a wall, or be free-standing in the middle of the room, held with a dowel rod from floor to ceiling. (See Figure 8-8.) Movable tables and carts are used by florists to increase their display space during the various holidays.

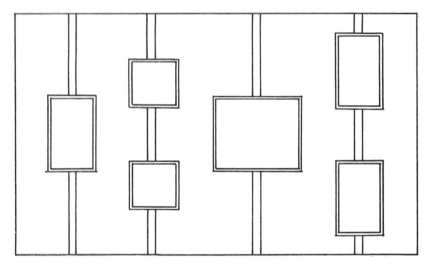

Figure 8-8. Free-standing shadow boxes on dowel rods along a 12-foot wall for feature displays.

The Workroom

The workroom is another very important part of the shop and must be planned carefully in advance, with efficiency in mind. Whether the area is large or small a florist will need certain items of equipment for a successful operation. The storage refrigerator is essential in the florist shop. It may be a separate unit, as is found in many shops, or it may be the rear half of the same refrigerator whose front part is the display refrigerator in the sales area. Many small shops find it more economical to have the latter. However, a shop doing a large gross volume of sales will find it absolutely necessary to have a separate storage refrigerator to handle the large supply of flowers and greens necessary for its volume of business. Some of the larger shops have two or more storage refrigerators plus one or two display refrigerators. The storage refrigerator should be large enough to walk into and have shelves around the sides to utilize as much space as possible. There should be a systematic arrangement of cut flowers in the refrigerator so the oldest material is on one side and the freshest on another. The florist might mark the cans so that the designers know which material to use first. Material which is too old to use at all, should be discarded quickly. This should be done daily so that the old, dead, smelly flowers do not accumulate. It is also wise to rearrange the flowers in the cooler every day to be sure they are in order. One person should be responsible for doing this or seeing that it is done daily. Sufficient lighting is important in this refrigerator so it can be kept neat, clean, and orderly.

The workroom also contains the work or design tables which should be of convenient height for the working comfort of the designers. There are newly designed tables on the market which are easily adjustable to the height of the designer. Ideally there should be one table for each designer. However, many shops have several persons working at one large table. A table 5 feet long and 3 feet wide is usually ample for most designers. If the table is larger than this, it takes up too much space, and there is the tendency for the designers to spread out more than is necessary. Tables have also been designed in a U-shape, S-shape, and E-shape which will accommodate more than one designer. The tables should have shelves and drawers for storing the materials commonly used in designing. The tables should be well lighted.

Figure 8-9. A design area with rolls of foil and ribbon neatly arranged. (Courtesy, Bonnie Brae Flowers, Denver, Colo.)

Ribbon storage shelves or a ribbon rack is necessary and should be centrally located and easily accessible to all designers. In some shops the ribbons are stored on shelves along the side of the room next to the design tables. Other shops provide a ribbon rack for each designer at the end of his own table or suspended from the ceiling over the tables. There are so many ways to design a work-room and arrange the fixtures and equipment that this will be dis-cussed in more detail in Chapter 10.

A water supply must be located in a convenient spot for the use of the designers as well as for the unpacking of flowers. Many shops have two sinks for these purposes. A new and more con-venient method is to run a pipe along the ceiling over the entire area, with a hose and spray or mist nozzle suspended beside each designer's table. Thus the designer can easily fill his vase or con-tainer right at his work table and then mist the flowers when he is finished. A deep sink is desirable at the table where the flowers are unpacked and put in water, so that tall cans can be filled easily. Hot water should be provided here because the stems of all fresh flowers (except orchids) should be put in warm water (100° to 110° F.) to harden them when they arrive from the whole-sale florist or greenhouse.

A separate corsage table or bar may be set up in one corner of the workroom where all the special materials necessary for corsage-making can be kept readily at hand.

An order board is kept in the control center or at the front of the workroom where it is convenient not only for the manager but also for the designers. There are many different ways to keep orders separated and in order.

Most of the rest of the space in the workroom is devoted to storage and circulation areas so that the employees can move around freely without getting in each other's way. As many shelves and cabinets for storage as are possible in the room should be provided. If the room is small, then just a few of such various items as pottery, brass, novelties, baskets, papier-mâché, frames, boxes, and other materials can be kept on the shelves. The remainder of the material will be kept in a storage room in the basement, attic, or garage. The more of the everyday materials that can be kept handy in the workroom, the better. It will save time and steps. If a designer must go to another room or downstairs every time he needs a container of some type, a lot of valuable (and expensive) time will be lost. Whether the bulk of the storage is in the work-room, downstairs, or in a separate room near the workroom, be

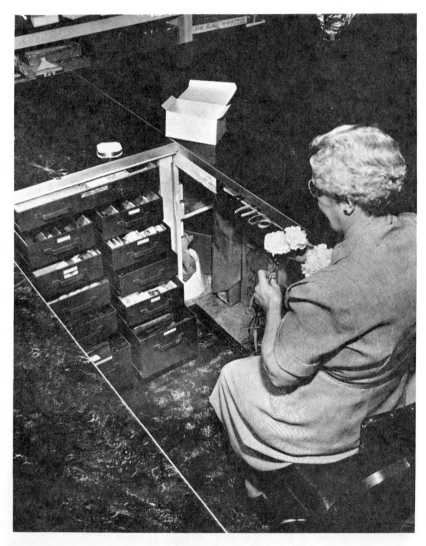

Figure 8-10. Supplies conveniently located for each designer. (Courtesy, Bonnie Brae Flowers, Denver, Colo.)

sure the items are kept in good order. Many florists have the materials systematically arranged on shelves with tags showing the date of arrival, the company, the number of the item, and the retail price. All materials should be priced immediately upon arrival in the store. Be sure to include postage or shipping charges in determining the retail sale price of these items. Many florists give each item a number and by using a card file system they are able to reorder certain stock items before they use up the last one or two, assuming an accurate count is kept of them as they are sold or used.

Retail florist shops differ greatly in size and arrangement. We have just gone over the main essential items of equipment in the store. Many more can be used if the shop is large enough; we have not tried to list all of these in detail. As far as supplies are concerned such as wire, ribbon, floratape, paper, containers, novelties, tape, papier-mâchés, dried material, Christmas, permanent materials, and the like, there are hundreds listed in the florist supply catalogs and each florist must determine his own needs for these items. It is doubtful if any one florist has every item that is available to the florists in the industry.

Chapter 9

EFFICIENCY; TIME AND MOTION IN FLOWER SHOPS

Efficiency

Efficiency is a hard term to describe because it includes so many facets, but it must be understood by the retail florist if he is to be a modern business man. It must be applied to retail methods. Basically, an efficient retailing method is one which will produce the desired result with a minimum of effort, expense, and waste. Efficiency applies not only to the designing area but also the sales area, office area, and in delivery. Every department in the retail flower shop can be made more efficient through proper planning and management.

In the sales area, efficiency can be improved through remodeling and rearranging the store. Suggested new store layouts for improved efficiency are shown in Chapter 10. That chapter also discusses efficiency in the design area by showing examples of more efficient arrangements of equipment in the workroom.

To illustrate efficiency, let us cite some examples found in new shops around the country. The Max Schling shop in New York City has incorporated the following in the moving of their shop after 39 years in one spot: Platforms in the display windows are on casters, and when they are pulled away from the window, they expose a continuous line of plant boxes which are filled with seasonal plants. The display refrigerator is so designed that the doors can be left wide open and the customers can walk in along with the salesmen to pick out their flowers. There is no sill to stumble over as the levels between the store and the inside of the box are the same. The designing space is out in the open in the store so that there is constant activity, which is of considerable interest to the customers. Heating, ventilation, and air conditioning are tied together in one thermostatically controlled system so that temperatures in the store are always cool and comfortable. Another example is in Cauthorn's Flowers, San Antonio, Texas, where they have devised a new and simple bookkeeping system to speed up efficiency in the office. It revolves around one simple statement form, designed to eliminate and/or speed up two office tasks: to eliminate the accounts receivable ledger and speed up statement preparation. Frederick's Flowers in Souderton, Pennsylvania, has almost 5,000 square feet of sales area in which all of the displays are movable to give greater flexibility to the shop layout.

Many retail florists have redesigned their shops with efficiency in mind both in the sales and circulation area, and in the workroom area. Some excellent examples are Royer's South Side Flower Shop, Lebanon, Pennsylvania; Surf Florist, Miami Beach, Florida; Quality Flower Shop, New Orleans, Louisiana; Sheherezade, Coral Gables, Florida; and Tubbs of Flowers, Corpus Christi, Texas. All of these have installed design areas with top efficiency in mind.

These florists and ideas are just a few of the hundreds of ideas which contribute to efficiency in a retail florist shop.

Time and Motion

Time is perhaps the most precious single commodity used in the retail flower shop. All florists are extremely conscious of time and its value and they are often faced with a lack of it which can mean loss of business, prestige, and money. Minor investigations in time-motion studies as applied to the retail flower shop have been carried on at Texas A. & M. University as an experimental problem at the undergraduate level, at Cornell University, and at The Pennsylvania State University.

Time and motion studies have as their salient purposes the *saving of time* and the *economy of motion* in any work operation. The study of saving time and economically using motion has evolved into the science of time-motion.

The procedure used in any study of a given operation or job may be divided into three general steps.

1. **Operation analysis.** Here the job is analyzed with the idea of eliminating every unnecessary movement and operation, without affecting the quality of the end product. Here also the best method of doing an operation is chosen as a result of scientifically measuring one method against another. This is ordinarily done by close observation of a trained analyst, by precise stop-watch measurements of time, and by analysis of still or motion pictures.

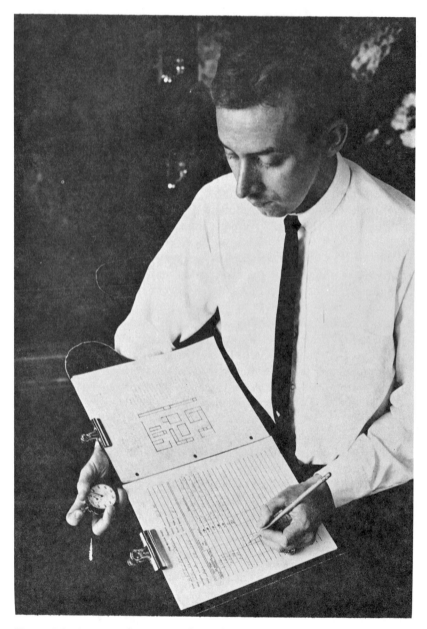

Figure 9-1. A time and motion study to determine efficiency in the design area of a flower shop.

2. **Work standardization.** Here a careful survey of equipment, methods, and working conditions is made with the view in mind of making improvements in materials, tools, equipment, and working conditions, so that a worker can do his best work without being hindered or tired by inadequate facilities. It is here, perhaps, that the greatest contribution may be made to the florist's field by time-motion studies.

3. **Determination of "standard time."** After the first two steps are completed and time-motion principles are applied to the data obtained, it is calculated how long it should take an average worker, working under average conditions, to do the job. This "average" time is known as the *standard time.*

Application of time and motion study methods to the flower industry is relatively new. Observations indicate that *too little attention is given in most flower shops to convenience or labor-saving in the arrangement of equipment or storage areas in workrooms.* Studies have shown that some designers make up floral pieces faster than others, an indication that improved work habits may be possible.

Labor costs of flower design are rising steadily; hence, any saving in labor which will increase labor output of salable floral arrangements promises to improve the net income from the individual shop.

An increase in net returns is possible from two sources: (1) greater output and more sales from the work of current employees and (2) the need for fewer employees in production of the present output.

For example, and a clearer understanding of time and motion, let's look at a study conducted by The Pennsylvania State University Floriculture Division on time and motion in two different retail flower shops. These same procedures can be used by any florist to discover the efficiency of his own designers.

Two types of retail flower shops—a family shop and a more formal business—were observed in this study. Measurements were taken of both shops, and scale drawings were made.

To limit the scope of the study only funeral vases and corsages were considered. Work on funeral floral pieces was observed on the day of the single, two-hour viewing. We will consider the corsage designer later in this chapter.

A modified flow process chart as shown in Table 9-1 was used. This shows the observations reported for an average operation. Figures reported on the blank labeled "Price Range" were approximations.

Table 9-1. Flow Process Chart of Observations Reported for an Average Operation. Standardized engineering symbols were used: → for initial travel, ← for return travel, and ● for operations.

Item: Standard funeral vase

Florist shop: No. 1

Designer: B

Date: May 3, 1960

Checker: H. W. Willits

Total distance: 235.8 feet

Total time: 18 minutes

Price range: $5 to $10

UNIT TIME (in minutes)	DISTANCE (in feet)	SYMBOL	EXPLANATION
	16.7	→	To vase storage
	16.7	←	Return with vase
	40.8	●	Cut, roll, and stuff wire into vase
	40.8	→	To front refrigerator
	40.8	←	Return with gladiolus
		●	Place gladiolus
	40.8	→	To front refrigerator
	40.8	←	Return with pompons
11:35		●	Place pompons and greens
11:35	39.2	→	To storage for delivery

During the preliminary observations when procedures were being established, the most common location for storage of various
items was established in order to record usual distances traveled
by designers in subsequent observations. For example, the papier-
mâché funeral vases had no standard location in either shop. When
arrangements were made immediately after flowers were delivered
by the wholesaler, the fresh supplies often were used before the
storage cans were placed in the refrigerator. When this occurred
during an observation, the most commonly used vase location was
noted and travel and time data to the proper flower storage area
were included in the record.

Shop No. 1 was owned and operated by a man and wife, who
shared the design duties; the man (Designer A) doing most of the
work on funeral flowers and the woman (Designer B) doing most
of the corsage assembly. Their son did the major portion of the
delivery work.

The physical layout of the salesroom was near optimum in size
and compactness for the average retail flower shop. The workroom
(Figure 9-2) had many inconveniences and considerable waste space
due to the lack of storage facilities.

The telephone was in a good position, easily accessible from
both the sales and work areas. The only water source—a small, old-
fashioned sink—was in a small closet behind the wrapping table in
the salesroom. Additional storage space, located in the basement,
was extremely cluttered, and much time was wasted looking for the
desired items.

Table 9-2. Travel Time and Data of Designers A, B, C, and D in Preparation
of Standard Funeral Vases. ("N" Stands For Number of Observations.)

SHOP NO.	DESIGNER	FUNERAL VASES				
		Distance (feet)		Time (minutes)		
		Mean	Standard Deviation	Mean	Standard Deviation	N
1	A	295.4	68.1	23.6	12.8	13
	B	241.9	50.4	23.2	4.3	5
	Average	268.6		23.4		
2	C	92.1	20.0	11.0	1.2	6
	D	89.8	17.0	18.5	6.9	8
	Average	90.9		14.7		

1-Secondary make-up table
2-Ribbon and netting supplies
3-Rear refrigerator
4-Miscellaneous shelves
5-Safe
6-Desk
7-File cabinet
8-Billing table
9-Auxiliary make-up table
10-Main make-up table
11-Storage shelves
12-Telephone table

Doors

A-To front of store
B-To cellar storage
C-To incinerator

Figure 9-2. The layout of a workroom in Shop No. 1 in study conducted by The Pennsylvania State University.

The workroom refrigerator was too small to hold an adequate supply of flowers. As a result, the designer often had to go to the salesroom refrigerator in the front of the shop for flowers.

Designer A took an average of 23.6 minutes and traveled 295.4 feet to complete a funeral vase. Designer B took 23.2 minutes and traveled 241.9 feet for a similar piece (Table 9-2).

At this shop, the designer placed chicken wire in each vase to hold the flowers, and only two types of greens were used: lemon leaf and a broadleaved fern. One of the most time-consuming operations was the trip to the sink to fill the vase.

The difference in the average distance traveled can be accounted for by two factors: Designer A always worked at Station 1 (Figure 9-2) and often made two trips for flowers, while Designer B frequently brought all of the flowers needed from the refrigerator in one trip. The similarity in time for design of funeral arrangements can be explained by the fact that Designer A did most of the funeral vases and thus made better use of his time while at the worktable.

Figure 9-3 shows average distance traveled for Designer A while arranging a funeral vase. The designer started at the order board (No. 6) and went to the design table (No. 1) with the order, then to the storage (No. 2) for a vase, and returned to the worktable. Then he went to the sink (No. 3) for water, to the front refrigerator (No. 4) twice for flowers, and then to the front of the store to the delivery table (No. 5). He then returned to the order board to start again. One trip to the refrigerator for flowers could have been eliminated.

Better use of the existing storage facilities could be made at Shop No. 1, and opportunities were ample for the addition of units that would increase capacity and efficiency.

The method of filling containers consisted of filling one small can several times and emptying it into the larger ones, which would not fit into the small sink. Facilities for filling containers with water could be vastly improved by the relocation, or expansion of those facilities now existing. With a slight change in present routine, a hose could be connected to the faucet for use in transferring water to vases, resulting in a marked increase in efficiency. A new sink could be installed in the workroom which would be much more satisfactory and more efficient.

At least one trip by the designer to the refrigerator could be eliminated by getting all necessary flowers for each arrangement the first time.

1-Designer
2-Vase Storage
3-Water Supply
4-Refrigerator
5-Delivery Table
6-Order Board

Figure 9-3. Travel pattern by Designer A in Shop No. 1 while designing a funeral vase.

By locating the vase storage under the design table, 33.4 feet of travel also could be eliminated.

The use of new, automatic boxes would considerably shorten the time required for packing operations.

Desk work should be kept on the desk instead of being allowed to clutter a worktable.

Since this survey, many of these conditions have been improved in this shop.

1—Waiting table storage
2—Novelty storage
3—Refrigerator
4—Ribbon storage
5—Storage
6—Ribbon storage
7—Storage
8—Table for storage
9—Storage
10—Potting table
11—Rear wrapping table
12—Storage shelves
13—Phone desk
14—Main make-up table
15—Bow storage
16—Can storage &
   Order Rack
17—Vase storage
18—Vase storage
19—Lavatory
20—Sink

Doors

A—To front of store
B—Down steps to cellar storage
   and outside

Figure 9-4. The layout of the workroom in Shop No. 2 in study conducted by The Pennsylvania State University.

Florist Shop No. 2 offered cards, pottery, and novelties for sale in addition to flowers. The owner (Designer C) had an assistant (Designer D), a driver, and two salesclerks, who served the customers entering the store. The physical space of the workroom was somewhat cluttered, but efficiently designed (Figure 9-4).

Due to the length of the shop, three phones were a convenience. One was located in the extreme front of the sales area, one in the office between the sales and work areas, and one in the rear of the workroom. Designer C always answered the phone when he was in the shop, and the salesclerks answered only when the two designers were out. This system worked well, because the designers were the only ones familiar with the availability of flowers in the refrigerator. The driver picked up the finished designs for delivery from the refrigerated storage, and the salesclerks came back to the workroom only when supplies were short in the display refrigerator in the salesroom.

Whenever business was slack, usually in the summer, the sales clerks were kept busy making bows, net puffs, and other storable items, and in dusting the shelved merchandise. The driver, on the other hand, kept the windows washed and storage areas in order, and performed other similar tasks. All of these are efficiency improvement factors which will result in a more profitable business.

Immediately after the lunch hour on the days that funeral arrangements were on order, the driver checked the number and size of vases needed, selected them from storage, filled them with vermiculite, water, and some greens. He then placed them on the designer's table. This job required an average distance of 29.4 feet and a time of four minutes per vase (Figure 9-5). The driver picked up the order (No. 1) and went to the storage (No. 2) for the container and took it to the worktable (No. 3), then to the sink (No. 4) for water, and return. Then he went to the refrigerator (No. 5) for greens and returned to fill the container. He could reduce this time by filling the container with water on his way from the storage.

Even though the observed number of vases completed per designer was about equal (Table 9-2), Designer D usually did the majority of the funeral work, with Designer C inspecting. The two designers worked from opposite ends of the table (Figure 9-4), with Designer C at Station 1 and Designer D at Station 2. However, their overall travel for the average funeral vase arrangement was equal, thus accounting for the similar distances recorded on the flow charts.

Figure 9-5. The movements of the driver in Shop No. 2 as he filled containers for the designer.

The average distance traveled and time required for funeral vase assembly (Table 9-2) for Designer C was 92.1 feet and 11 minutes and for Designer D, 89.8 feet and 18.5 minutes. The experience of the designers probably accounts for the difference in time required for each arrangement.

Figure 9-6 shows the travel of Designer D for an average funeral vase arrangement. The designer started at the order board (No. 1) and went to the design table (No. 2), then to the ribbon rack (No. 4), and to the container (No. 5) which he moved to his station (No. 2). Then he went to the refrigerator (No. 3) and re-

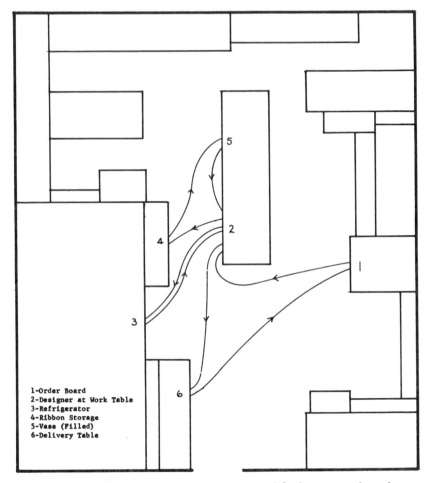

Figure 9-6. Travel by Designer D in Shop No. 2 while designing a funeral vase.

turned, and then to the delivery table (No. 6). He then returned
to the order board to start again.

A double nozzle on the hose which could be used for misting
corsages as well as to fill containers would eliminate the need for
trips to the sink to fill funeral vases.

Rolls of ribbon would be more convenient if placed nearer to
the design table.

The two firms studied differed widely in organization and in
methods of designing standard funeral vases and corsages. Shop No.
1 was a family business, and its operation had many of the ad-

vantages and some of the disadvantages that are characteristic of this type of establishment. Shop No. 2 was a more formal business unit, and it had the advantage of efficiency of operation.

Results of the respective travel and time observations of the two shops revealed a variation much in favor of the larger business firm. These figures also verified that individual designers differ in time required to make a design piece. Some of the differences are due to experience and pressure of the work load on a particular day.

The standard deviations (Table 9-2) showed a wide variation for each designer in distance traveled and time required between the several observations made in this study.

Changes in layout and location of supplies in Shop No. 1 could result in a much more efficient operation, with a resulting saving of labor.

Wages are constantly rising, and the number of paid employees in the retail florist shop is increasing. Wages account for more than 50 per cent of the florists' total overhead, which comes directly from gross sales. Since the designer is one of the highest paid employees, it is important to have him work as efficiently as possible in order to keep overhead costs to a minimum. One method of increasing his efficiency is by having him work in an efficiently designed workroom. Design tables should be located as centrally as possible between the sink, storage refrigerator, and storage cabinets. Some shops have sinks built into the tables themselves. Since the path from the storage refrigerator to the design table is the one a florist keeps the hottest, it should be as short as possible.

A study was developed at The Pennsylvania State University to evaluate efficiency in the design area of the retail florist shop in order to provide data to develop methods which would facilitate production by the following methods: (1) to establish time standards for designing several selected pieces in retail floral shops and (2) to design efficient workroom layouts which could be used as standards for renovating, modernizing, or designing the workroom in a retail florist shop.

Time studies were conducted in 15 retail florist shops, whose size categories were as follows: $50,000 to $75,000; $75,000 to $100,000; and over $100,000 annual gross volume of sales.

Six set designs were timed in each shop. Three funeral baskets or papier-mâchés and three artistic designs were timed.

The designers were timed with a stop watch, and the times were recorded on flow process charts. Elemental operation times,

elemental transportation times, delays, and explanations for the times
or delays were all recorded on the flow process charts. Flow diagrams
were made by drawing lines of the designer's travel patterns on
floor plans which were made prior to the actual timing of the individual. By measuring these lines, transportation or travel distances were determined.

After time studies were conducted in the 15 retail florist shops,
four efficiently designed workrooms (Figures 9-7, 9-8, 9-9, and
9-10) were simulated in the retail floriculture laboratory at The
Pennsylvania State University. Four different designers were timed
in the test shops. Each designer was timed making six set designs
in a particular shop: three funeral pieces and three artistic designs.
These designs were of the same quality and the same price ranges
as those made in the visited retail florist shops.

The results for the visited shops and the test shops were
analyzed statistically and comparisons made. In most cases, *test
shop times were significantly different from the visited shops.*

For artistic designs there was a 39.56 per cent decrease in
total time when comparing the visited shop times to the test shop
times. There was a 20.13 per cent decrease in operation time and
an 89.10 per cent decrease in transportation time. Transportation
distance decreased 76 per cent, showing the benefits of efficiently
planned work areas.

For funeral baskets there was a 34.92 per cent decrease in
total time, a 19.12 per cent decrease in operation time, a 91.85
per cent decrease in transportation time, and an 80 per cent decrease in transportation distance.

Time standards were computed for both the funeral baskets
and the artistic designs. Separate time standards were developed
for the visited shops and the test shops, since test shop times were
significantly different than the visited shop times in most cases.
Time standards were computed for the operation times as well as
the total times, since total times varied more between shops than
the operation times. A valid time standard could not be developed
if times varied too greatly between shops.

The computed time standards were as follows for the visited
shops:

> Funeral basket operation time, 16.79 ± 1.40 minutes;
> Funeral basket total time, 21.45 ± 2.64 minutes;
> Artistic design operation time, 9.44 ± 1.16 minutes; and
> Artistic design total time, 13.12 ± 1.72 minutes.

Workroom 15' x 25'   Scale: ¼" = 1'

Figure 9-7. Simulated workroom for two to three designers, with the design table along wall.

Workroom 21' x 24'   .   Scale: ¼" = 1'

Figure 9-8. Simulated workroom for two to three designers, with the design table in center of room.

Figure 9-9. Simulated workroom for three to five designers, with an E-shaped design table in the center of the room.

Figure 9-10. Simulated workroom for four to six designers, with paired design tables in the center of the room.

The time standards for the test shops were as follows:
Funeral basket operation time, 13.58 ± 0.48 minutes;
Funeral basket total time, 13.58 ± 0.53 minutes;
Artistic design operation time, 7.54 ± 0.54 minutes; and
Artistic design total time, 7.93 ± 0.51 minutes.
These are to be used for comparative purposes only with designers in a specific retail florist shop.

Since the visited shop time standards were computed for designs made in average shops under normal conditions, these standards would be of more practical value than the test shop standards. These time standards could be used for distributing the work load, determining cost, or detecting inefficiencies in the retail florist shop.

Another example is a time study conducted at The Pennsylvania State University, for making corsages. Many wasted motions could be eliminated by careful study of the problem and situation. At holiday times, the retail florist has an increase in business and could take advantage of the opportunity to run his operaton at peak efficiency and economy. By reviewing the records from previous sales, the florist should be able to estimate the number of expected corsage sales. Sufficient material should be ordered well in advance and trained personnel contacted prior to the holiday season. In order to fully utilize the additional labor and materials to fill the orders, it is essential that the work area be planned for greatest efficiency. Much time in many shops is wasted in hunting for materials and making unnecessary trips around the shop.

Figure 9-11. A corsage cabinet designed for efficiency.

A corsage table was designed so that all materials were readily available and arranged so that corsages could be made in a minimum amount of time. The corsage cabinet was designed in three sections each 24 inches high, 24 inches wide, and 8 inches deep. They were arranged like an upside down U with the sides angled so that all materials were within two feet of the designer. The cabinet was set so that it was 3 inches lower than the designer's elbow for maximum ease and efficiency. The center unit contained seven compartments across the top to hold various sizes of wire. Under this was a styrofoam block to hold corsage pins and dowel rods holding ribbon and floratape. Under this were compartments for made-up ribbon bows. The left section was composed of compartments for various colors of chenille stems and flocked wire, dowel rods for rolls of net, and compartments of ready-made net puffs. The right section contained six 10-inch cans or vases to hold the flowers used in the corsages (Figure 9-11).

For this experiment 400 corsages were made using roses, carnations, and cymbidium orchids. Rose corsages were made by two methods: (1) the standard method using #22 and #26 wire, floratape, tied with corsage thread, artificial rose leaves, and a bow attached and (2) the flocked wire method using a ready-made frame of flocked wire, roses placed on the ends of flocked wire, and a bow.

Carnation corsages were made by two different methods: (1) the standard method using #22 and #26 wire, floratape, thread, and a bow of ribbon and (2) the chenille stem method using two chenille stems with a flower at each end, and a bow.

Cymbidiums were made by two methods: (1) the standard method using #20 and #26 wire, net puffs, floratape for wrapping and tying, and a bow of ribbon and (2) the water tube method using #20 and #26 wire, net, water tube, floratape, and a bow of ribbon.

All of these methods were divided into two assembly methods. Half the corsages in each group were made and timed on an individual basis, and the other half made and timed on an assembly line basis wherein all the frames, bows, and net puffs were made ahead of time, and enough flowers were wired and taped for six corsages. Then the corsages were assembled and timed as a unit to be divided by six for an average. This was repeated four times for a total of 24 corsages of each type under each method.

Average time required to make a six-looped bow was 20 seconds, to make a flocked-wire frame was 45 seconds, with seven seconds to wire a rose or carnation, and six seconds to tape a rose or carnation.

Results showed that there was little difference in total time involved for orchids in the assembly line and made individually for both standard and tube methods. With the standard carnation corsage there was a reduction in assembly line time for total operations. Also there was a marked reduction in time with roses in the assembly line over the standard method.

Results showed that the time for making rose corsages with the standard method was cut in half on the assembly line and cut by three-fourths with the flocked wire method on the assembly line. The time for carnations in both cases was cut about one-quarter in time, and for cymbidiums the time was cut in half by use of the assembly line method.

Results also showed the real saving in time through the use of the assembly line method was when bows, net, and frames were made ahead of time. With roses there was a saving of 2 minutes 10 seconds for each corsage when done on an assembly line basis. On the flocked wire frame with roses there was a saving of 1 minute 18 seconds. The saving of 50 seconds by the standard method was not as great with carnations as compared with 20 seconds for the chenille stem method. The savings in time for orchids was 1 minute 30 seconds for the standard method and 1 minute 23 seconds for the tube method.

Results showed that for every 100 corsages made, the saving in time would be approximately 3-1/2 hours for roses made by standard method and 2 hours for roses on flocked wire frames; 1-1/3 hours for standard carnation corsages and 1/2 hour for carnations on chenille stems; 2-1/2 hours for standard orchid corsages and 2-1/4 hours for orchids in tubes. This assumes that the florist had all the net, bows, and frames made ahead of time and that the corsages were made by the assembly line method at least six at a time.

Making bows, net, and frames ahead of time lowers the time involved in the actual assembly of materials. The assembly line method of making corsages in units of at least six will greatly reduce the time per corsage for roses and carnations. This will result in a saving of several hours for each 100 corsages made. For 10,000 corsages this could mean a saving of 200 to 300 hours. The greatest difference in this experiment occurred with rose corsages made in the standard method and one at a time, taking 4 minutes 45 seconds as compared to rose corsages made on an assembly line on ready-made frames, taking only 32 seconds. The figures shown were for one particular designer and should be compared with the time it takes each particular designer to make a corsage. These are not stated as averages for any and all designers, but are to be used for comparative purposes only.

Motion Economy

There are 10 major principles of motion economy according to Niebel, many of which can be applied to a retail flower shop. They are: (1) motion of both hands simultaneously, (2) tools and materials located close to and in front of the operator, (3) a fixed place for all tools and materials, (4) gravity feed bins (not so useful to a florist), (5) the placement of tools and materials in a usable position, (6) drop delivery (not applicable to a florist), (7) let feet do the work of hands where possible—such as a pedal-operated sink, (8) locate materials and tools for best sequence of motion, (9) height of work space should be arranged to fit the operator (self adjusting design tables), and (10) lighting comfort should be provided. With these in mind a florist should go through his shop analyzing each operation along the following lines: (A) Materials— Can cheaper materials be used? Is material uniform? Are materials of proper weight, size, and finish? (B) Handling of materials—Can material handling be reduced? Can distances be shortened? Are there delays in getting material? Can conveyors be used to move materials? (C) Tools and fixtures—Are they the best for the work? Are they in good condition? Are there enough on hand? Can both hands be used? (D) Operation—Can an operation be eliminated? Can the work be done in multiple? Can the sequence of operations be changed? Can two or more operations be combined? Consider the type of work space set up? (E) Operator—Is the operator qualified for the job? Can work conditions be changed? Can the operation be improved by further instruction?

If a retail florist is really interested in saving time and money in his shop, a check-up through time and motion studies is almost a sure guarantee to improvement.

References

1. Heck, Bessie. "Shop Layout Geared for Efficiency," *Southern Florist and Nurseryman* (June 25, 1971), pp. 11, 21, 24.
2. Mutschler, Robert G. "*A Time and Motion Study in the Design Area of the Retail Florist Shop.*" M.Sc. Thesis, The Pennsylvania State University (June 1966).

3. Niebel, B. W. *Motion and Time Study*. Richard D. Irwin, Inc. (1958), 491 pp.
4. Tintori, Karen A. "Efficient Workrooms Increase Profits," *Florist* (July 1971), pp. 26-29.

Chapter 10

STORE LAYOUT; REMODELING; MODERNIZATION

Store layout, remodeling, and modernization are a follow-up to efficient retail operations as discussed in Chapter 9. Each shop, of course, is an individual case since there is no one average retail flower shop. However, efficiency is the keynote to the modern shop from the standpoint of management, operation of sales and design, and the customer. If the shop is averaging $15,000 gross volume of sales per full-time employee instead of $20,000, it is not enough and shows the need for study of more efficient methods.

Layout

Many retail operations spend thousands of dollars studying store layout in order to have a more efficient operation. The general retail store is most concerned with square foot return, and how many actual dollar-sales can be realized from any given space. Too few retail florists give enough consideration to how their space is utilized.

In every retail flower shop there is so much space devoted to selling, and so much to designing or the work area of the shop.

A good layout means putting the right equipment in the right places, where materials may be processed most effectively with the right method, requiring movements and transportation of the shortest distance, and in the shortest possible time.

In the general layout of the florist shop, an order must be sold, processed, made up, and delivered by the most efficient method with the least effort.

The selling area must provide ample area for circulation, display, and for taking an order. In most retail florist shops, this area is separated from the design area. However, some remodeled shops have put the design area in with the sales area.

Certain principles have been developed for doing work effectively at the design table: arrange for the worker to be in a position so that his hands do most of the work inside the most convenient area; arrange the materials in an arc approximating the arrangement; conserve energy, avoid fatigue, and save time by using minimum body movements; rearrange the shop to permit the most convenient location of all items and the easiest handling of them; improve working routines; and locate tools and supplies conveniently.

Remodeling

The important and expensive step of remodeling is taken for two reasons: first, to increase the efficiency of the shop; second, to attract new customers.

Figure 10-1. A remodeled office with windows into sales areas. Comfortable chairs for consultation. (Courtesy, Geralis Florist, Washington, D.C.)

When a retail florist is going to remodel he must put emphasis on the planning period. The shop owner must take time to go into all of the physical needs of his shop, the placement of all utilities to give ease of operation, and his own desires as to the kind of a shop he wants. Total store planning for a florist shop should include all of the following important factors that are functions of profits and sales: overall goals, location, store size, store equipment layout, lighting and electrical plan, heating and air conditioning, store décor, and financing.

Many points must be kept in mind for the successful remodeling of an efficient shop, or the designing of a new one.

All active storage should be located at, or close to, the design table.

Materials used only occasionally, which occupy space close to the design table, should be moved further away to make room for critical materials.

The fixed position of built-in refrigerators, in an established shop, should determine the relative position of the design area. The design table should be located as close to the storage refrigerator as possible.

In a new shop, the storage refrigerator should be located close to the design table.

If the designer is also a sales clerk, the design area should be located as near to the sales area as possible.

The cash register should be located toward the rear of the sales area to save steps for the designer-sales clerk and to induce customers to come further into the shop.

If the size of the shop requires more than one designer, there should be a sales clerk to wait on the customers. The designer will accomplish more if he does not have to take time off to wait on customers. The sales clerk can also assist the designer during lulls between sales. (Some shop owners who are also designers prefer to wait on customers in order to establish personal contact with the customer. This factor must be weighed in relation to the time and motion involved.)

Few florists have developed the habit of preparing stock containers ahead of time. Each morning before the business day opens, enough stock vases, papier-mâchés, and baskets should be stuffed and filled with water and flower preservative to carry through the day's business.

Prepared containers should be stored near the design table. Extra prepared containers for a big business day should be stored in the refrigerator or on the delivery table where they will be gradually replaced by completed arrangements.

All flowers and foliages for an order should be collected on one trip to the refrigerator. Correct amounts of materials should be carefully selected to prevent unnecessary repeat trips.

Flowers on display in the sales area, which are to be used during the day by the designer, should be considered as active storage, and should be placed as close to the design area as possible.

A designer's assistant should be employed, at least during the busy days of the week, to prepare stock containers, unpack flowers, and keep active storage containers filled.

"Hard" foliages, which will not wilt down if they are kept out of refrigerated storage, should be stored close to the design table.

Some space near the design table should be available for completed arrangements so that the designer can make up two or more designs before taking them to the delivery table.

Both hands should be used to carry completed arrangements to the delivery table, or to replenish active flower storage whenever the designer moves to other areas in the shop.

If completed arrangements are stored in the refrigerator, the designer should collect materials for the next order and return with his arms loaded instead of empty-handed.

There should be a definite space for completed arrangements conveniently located to the design table. This space should be designated as the delivery table. Much motion is wasted in some shops by scattering completed arrangements around the sales area and the storage area.

The sink should be located as close to the design table as possible. If relocation of a poorly placed sink is not feasible, plastic or copper pipe should be extended to a spot convenient to the design table. A large tub or dry sink with a drain faucet could serve as a catch-basin.

Enclosure cards, bills, and delivery tags should be written at the time of selling. The designer should not have to take the time to write, or waste the motion to get cards, bills, or tags. However, a small supply of these enclosures, along with a pen and pencil, should be kept at the design table for emergency use.

A telephone extension should be placed near the design table.

Each person in the shop should have his own knife, scissors, and pencil with him at all times. A belt sheath or pocket sheath where these tools are always kept would be the best solution.

Heavy shears, wire snips, pliers, and similar tools should be given a permanent place at the design table.

If it is possible, one should avoid locating in, or building, a long narrow shop. This arrangement elongates the various shop areas and promotes extra time traveling between work stations.

Besides a wrapping counter in the sales area and general work area, a small wrapping table close to the design table would serve the designer when designs need special wrapping.

When many similar orders are to be filled consecutively, large refrigerator storage cans of flowers and foliage should be removed from the refrigerator and placed near the design table.

The display refrigerator should be kept for display purposes only. Arrangements as well as a selection of cut flowers and corsage flowers should be on display. Flowers to be used for make-up should be kept in the storage refrigerator.

Large shops are not necessarily an indication of an efficient layout. Small shops may be more concentrated. This cuts down on distances and may save motion, time, and energy.

If two or more designers work side by side, or facing each other, there should be a complete set of tools for each. Each designer should have his own design space, as much basic equipment, and as many active storage materials located convenient to him as possible.

Make all trips count. Try to avoid going empty-handed, and try to bring something back on the return trip.

All basic units such as sink, refrigerators, telephones, and delivery table should be located as close to the design table as possible.

It is difficult to give specific details on the remodeling of a shop, because each one is an individual case. There is no one perfect plan. However, there are basic considerations which would apply to any shop. Many shops can be modernized with a resulting increase in business through remodeling.

The first place to start is with the front and exterior. It has been estimated that 35 per cent of an average florist shop's sales are a result of the front of the store. A good coat of paint may be all that is necessary to improve this.

Most modern retail florist shops today have an all glass front or as much glass as is practical. Whether the shop has one, two, three, or more display windows in the front does not matter. The main point is to take those down to the floor and up to the ceiling, so that most of the front of the store is glass. In this way, a passerby can see into the store and see other persons in there. People attract people. The store itself will be lighter and will form a background for the window display. The whole store will look more inviting.

The exterior construction of the store may need to be changed to fit in with modern ideas. Materials should be used which will tie in with the other buildings in the block, particularly those recently modernized. There are many choices, including black granite, marble, wood siding, stone, brick, concrete block, or any of numerous materials. The main idea is to tie in with the other buildings in the neighborhood.

A new sign should be included in the plans. Be sure that it is neat, large enough to be seen, and tells the customer that this is a flower shop besides giving its name. The sign should be lighted at night.

The best entrance to a retail shop goes into the store without ramp or steps. The door should be glass to see through and wide enough so that materials can be easily carried in and out. It may be single or double.

The floor inside the florist shop should be easy to keep clean and yet not too slippery if a little water is spilled. There are several new vinyl materials which are excellent for florists' shops. Pick a design which has a color and pattern that do not show every footprint or speck of dirt. Many customers will come in with wet and muddy feet. A floral design or leaf pattern is attractive, and may enhance the beauty of the shop.

The décor of the interior must tie in directly with the exterior. The walls may need to be repainted. A neutral color like grey, grey-green, or tan is always good. Black, however, would be a good choice for a special display, because most flowers will stand out against it. Redwood or knotty pine paneling should also be considered. For a simple job of remodeling, a good coat of paint may be all that is necessary for the floor, walls, and ceiling.

If the store has an old-fashioned ceiling, it can be easily remodeled by use of any of the new ceiling tiles. If the ceiling is too high, a lower false ceiling will give the shop a feeling of intimacy. The new acoustical tiles will improve the appearance of a shop, as well as help with acoustics. The tiles come in plain colors, as well as in many patterns. While planning the ceiling, be sure to consider lighting. Most customers hesitate to enter a dimly lit retail shop. Plan the lights in the window display as well as the rest of the store.

The furniture must tie in with the décor of the rest of the sales area. The furniture needed depends on the size of the store and volume of business. Probably the simplest would be one wall of display shelves, a writing desk, one or two movable display tables, a wrapping counter, and a display refrigerator. For larger shops, more display shelves, more tables—possibly tiered, a flower cart, writing table and chair, and several chairs for customers would be added. The only limit to the number of display tables is the shop size.

Although a whole wall may be utilized for shelves and irregular spaces for pottery (see Figure 8-7), some areas may have just shadow boxes, with dowel rods from floor to ceiling, for particular displays, as shown in Figure 8-8. The arrangement of display areas, shown in either of these two figures, can be symmetrical or asymmetrical. The shadow boxes will give a modern look, particularly if painted black, and if they fit the rest of the décor.

Sales Area

The sales area is very important. It must be attractive, inviting, not cluttered (except perhaps at holidays), and conducive to flower sales. There should be enough circulation area so that the customers can move around freely. If the store is large enough for browsing, plenty of room is needed for customers to move around. In a small shop, the circulation area would be simply the open space in the middle. But, in any case, enough room must be provided to be able to handle customers on an average day without excessive crowding. The most important piece of equipment in the sales area is the display refrigerator. This should be opposite the front door, so that it is easily seen by the customers entering the shop. This is the "silent salesman" and should be so well lighted and attractive that it draws the customers to it.

Although some florists wrap all orders in the back room, an item to be taken by a customer should be wrapped in the front where he can see it being done. This will save time and steps for the salesperson. The wrapping counter should be easily accessible to employees, but not open to customers. It should have shelves under it for wrapping supplies and is a good place for the cash register— an important item.

Several possible plans have been designed for a workable sales area and are shown in Figures 10-2, 10-3, and 10-4.

Figure 10-2 shows the arrangement of a small sales area 20′ x 28′ with just one large window display and three display areas. There is good circulation in the shop even though it is small and

Figure 10-2. An example of a sales area 20′ x 28′.

has an open path back to the display refrigerator. A writing desk is to the right of the refrigerator and the door to the workroom and office on the left. The wrapping counter is in the back left corner.

Figure 10-3 shows a larger store (30′ x 40′) with two display

Figure 10-3. An example of a sales area 30′ x 40′.

windows. Again there is circulation with an open path to the display refrigerator which is located in the far right corner. Besides the two window display areas, there are six display tables (including a flower cart) of various shapes and sizes to show the variety that might be found in the store. There is also a wrapping counter, desk, and three chairs for the customers.

Figure 10-4 shows the largest shop in this series (40' x 40') with plenty of circulation, and both an office and consultation room behind the display refrigerator which again is directly opposite the front door. There is a very symmetrical arrangement of the many

Figure 10-4. An example of a sales area 40' x 40'.

display areas and tables to give some more ideas for the shop. The round tiered tables with glass shelves, can be replaced with round plywood shelves at holiday time for the pot plants, to reduce the chance for breakage.

These are just a few of the many plans which could be applied to stores of these various sizes. Each shop would be an individual case.

Workroom

The workroom is where the florist can increase or lose his profit. In remodeling the workroom, it should be designed with the designers' efficiency in mind. The equipment should be so arranged that time and steps are utilized to the best advantage. More production from the same number of employees means that a florist can increase his total sales volume without an increase in overhead. Thus, an efficiently planned workroom is important, and the time to consider this is when a shop is being remodeled. There is no one model to use for a perfect workroom.

Figure 10-5. A sample work counter along the wall with all supplies conveniently located for designer efficiency.

The design tables should be centrally located between the storage refrigerator, sink, and storage cabinets. The design tables should each have drawers and shelves either above or below, so that each designer will have his own equipment. They should be of the correct height for the designers. A table 5 feet long and 3 feet wide is considered ample. The control center and order board should be easily reached from the salesroom, workroom, and office. Each designer should have a clipboard to keep his orders where they can be seen. Bolts of ribbon and net should be on shelves or racks within reach of all designers. Many shops have a separate table for corsages, where all materials can be kept within easy reach of the designer.

Some design tables are in the middle of the workroom, and some are against the wall. Both arrangements have advantages and disadvantages. The ones along the wall may have more drawers and shelves for materials used in making designs (Figure 10-5). However, these take up space which may be needed for storage.

The plan to use depends on the volume of business and the physical layout of the present store. Some florists have separate tables for each designer. Others are using U- and E-shaped tables, while others have designed S-curved worktables. Tables should be so designed and arranged as to give the greatest efficiency. It would

Figure 10-6. Individual work tables with sink for each designer. (Courtesy, Royer's Flowers, Lebanon, Pa.)

Workroom 20' x 30'   Scale ¼" = 1'

Figure 10-7. An example of a workroom 20' x 30'.

Figure 10-8. An example of a workroom 30' x 40'.

be worth-while to provide an overhead water line with a nozzle above each designer's table.

Provision should be made near the back door of the workroom for receiving supplies and merchandise, with the water supply and refrigerator vases nearby. Also, an area is necessary for the placement of orders awaiting delivery.

Several workrooms planned for efficiency are shown in Figures 10-7, 10-8, and 10-9 which fit with the sales areas shown in Figures 10-2, 10-3, and 10-4.

Figure 10-7 shows a small workroom (20' x 30') with a storage refrigerator connected to the display refrigerator in front and an office beside the door to the sales area. Two design tables are in the center of the room with a U-shaped corsage counter, with the order board at one end and the water supply at the upper end of the U. The other areas are storage and counter space.

Figure 10-8 has a larger workroom (30' x 40') with a separate storage refrigerator and a large office which also doubles as a consultation room. There are three design tables with two water supplies at the ends of the first and third tables.

Figure 10-9 is the largest workroom (40' x 50') and shows an office opening into both the sales and workroom, with a separate consultation room. The design tables are E-shaped and there are three sinks for convenient water supplies. An overhead line with three hoses over the designers' tables would be more economical. Then, just one sink near the rear door would be sufficient. The storage refrigerator is large and in the rear right corner of the room.

These are just a few ideas as to how sales and workrooms can be designed for efficiency. Four other plans designed for efficiency are shown in Chapter 9 (Figures 9-7, 9-8, 9-9, and 9-10).

Store layout is important for both areas. Efficiency is the keynote for employees and the circulation for customers.

The U.S. Department of Commerce has published a "Store Modernization Check List" which spells out the hows and whys of modernization through the following five goals: (1) better physical appearance, (2) better utilization of space, (3) up-to-date fixtures and equipment, (4) better heating, ventilation, and air conditioning, and (5) soundness and safety. The booklet suggests that the retail shop owner should look at his office as if he were a competitor making an inspection.

Small Marketers Aids No. 54, prepared by the Small Business Administration, Washington, D.C., gives an excellent check list for retail store modernization.

Figure 10-9. An example of a workroom 40' x 50'.

Store layout, remodeling, and modernization are most important in today's retail flower business with the keynote on "efficiency."

References

1. Bluhme, Alice. "Choosing Your Location, Lighting, and Layout," *Florists' Review*, Vol. 136, No. 3526 (June 24, 1965), pp. 45-46.

2. Fox, Raymond T. "Motion Economy in Retail Flower Shops," Erie County (N.Y.) *Farm News* (September 1966), pp. 8-10.
3. Pfahl, Peter B. "Remodeling a Flower Shop, Part I," *Florists' Review*, Vol. 132, No. 3413 (April 25, 1963), pp. 19-20.
4. —————————. "Remodeling the Workroom, Part II," *Florists' Review*, Vol. 132, No. 3414 (May 2, 1963), pp. 51-52.
5. Richards, Ed. "Total Store Planning," *Teleflora Spirit* (July 1971), pp. 18, 19.

Chapter 11

MANAGEMENT

The management of a retail florist shop is a complicated procedure since it involves so many areas, from taking care of customer complaints to showing someone how to sweep the floor.

In most retail florist shops the owner is also the manager and must do many of the jobs himself. In larger shops the owner will hire a manager to oversee the many operations of the business. But whether the manager is the owner or not, he has a big responsibility.

A successful manager is one who knows what he is doing, with very little guesswork involved. His primary concern is to operate the business at a *reasonable profit*. The manager can never be down. He should be ready to take on any job in the place and do it in a way that puts employees and customers in a good frame of mind. The flower shop should establish a fair and profitable price for everything that it sells. It is up to the manager to see that the price will take care of the overhead, and all services which are performed by the florist. The price of an arrangement must include the cost of the flowers, cost of inventory items used, the cost of labor, the overhead, and a profit. This is the basis for managing a successful operation. The details of pricing are discussed in Chapter 14.

To manage properly, a florist must keep an accurate record of his sales volume, and know the sources of income. These sources of income are as follows: flowers or perishable merchandise, inventory merchandise, labor, wire orders, and transmittal charges. Every order filled can be divided into one or more of these five categories. A florist cannot manage successfully, and know that he is operating with the proper markup if he does not know the amounts in each category. Herb Mitchell suggests that each florist have a rubber stamp made as follows:

Perishable merchandise	$_____
Inventory merchandise	$_____
Labor charges	$_____

Wire-order sales	$_____
Transmittal charges	$_____
Total sales	$_____

This should be stamped on the back of each order and filled in by the designer and the sales person. The manager can take all of the orders for one day and add up how much of the sales were in each category, and determine whether or not he is operating profitably. The figures for the wire orders must be figured on the net, not on the gross, since the florist does not retain the full amount from these orders (see Chapter 22). Otherwise his gross might look larger than it really is for the business.

The secret of a profitable operation is increasing volume without increasing operational overhead. This calls for careful study by the manager so that this may be accomplished. There is a break-even point in any business where the income equals the expenses. Anything above this is profit, and this can be increased by increasing the volume without increasing the overhead. It depends on sound management.

The manager must know all of the mechanical aspects as well as the financial manipulations of his business. He must be astute in the all-important phase of buying; whether it be cut flowers, plants, supplies, pottery, or gift items. He has to be a good judge of stock, and familiar with the price situation. He must manage his inventory profitably so that he does not end up with too many nonsalable items. He should plan how to move the merchandise before it is purchased and not vice versa. He must be a disciplinarian with his time because *time is money*. Many retail florists, unfortunately, seem to feel that their time is worth nothing. Every man's time is worth something, and should be figured in the cost of doing business. It is important that every florist plan his own work as well as that of his employees. This is particularly true on slow days. Good planning is essential.

The manager is responsible for the hiring of regular and extra help. He should be able to recognize the potential in applicants, and be able to explain the business to them. It is usually the job of the manager to properly train the new employees. He must also know how to handle the employees so that they are satisfied with their jobs. He should keep a record of the work done by each employee to see that each one is working to maximum capacity. As explained in a previous chapter, most florists can expect to gross from $16,000 to $20,000 per full-time employee including himself. The better florists try to attain a figure of $20,000 gross per employee.

The average in 1970 was $19,368. If a florist shop does not come up to the $20,000 figure, then it is time for the manager to analyze the situation and make some changes. He may have too many employees for the volume of business, some of his employees may not be working as hard, and producing like they should, or his markup may not be high enough to provide a reasonable profit. He should explain to all new employees that they will have to work overtime at various times of the year.

In a managed shop every employee should be hired to become a specialist in some phase of the business, and the manager must spend time tying the work of the specialists together. The sales people must sell what is available, the greenhouse must grow the right crops for the designer, and out of town deliveries must be made-up before the delivery that goes across the street. The manager must control and coordinate all of the activities for all of the employees. Inability to communicate effectively is one of the most prominent factors in *decaying* managerial skills.

The modern florist of today (and the successful manager) must know how to *merchandise*, whether through cash-and-carry specials or by other means. Along with merchandising, the manager must be able to advertise profitably. He has to know the basic principles of advertising as well as which media will bring in the expected return.

The manager must manage the shop, instead of just designing or doing odd jobs. The manager and owner must get along and resolve differences of policy. The employees must be happy. There should be a manual of procedures and policies for new employees to read. It is also the manager's duty to supervise the deliveries, particularly at holiday times.

It is extremely important for the florist or the manager to cultivate ideas that will give the florist a guaranteed weekly income. These might be weekly bouquets of flowers in commercial places of business, weekly church banquets, reminder services to regular customers, cash-and-carry weekly specials, or other ideas for a steady income for the florist. The manager should be alert to new ideas and possibilities that can be expanded into a guaranteed weekly income.

The manager, if he is the owner, must make the most of public relations and be active in civic affairs. He must decide which public relations promotions will bring in the desired publicity, and be worth the effort. These promotions should also be tied in with his advertising program.

Another job which the owner-manager of a small business has to do is that of credit manager and billing clerk. He must determine the credit policy of the store and in small shops may find he is also the bookkeeper, sending out the statements each month. As such, he must have a basic knowledge of simplified accounting and bookkeeping procedures followed by small retailers. These are discussed in Chapter 25.

Operating a retail flower shop is hard work for the most part. This fact alone makes it imperative that most operations in the shop be so planned that things can be done the easiest, and most efficient way. There are several fundamental things that make any job hard, such as: (1) lack of interest, (2) lack of skill or knowledge, (3) improper tools and equipment, (4) makeshift equipment, (5) crowded working space, (6) poor working conditions, (7) poor working methods, (8) wasted motions, and (9) interruptions. Any or all of these factors may occur in the average florist shop. Improving retail store operations involves itself in overcoming these obstacles, and this falls to the owner-manager to accomplish. This can be done by careful attention to four considerations, including: (1) careful planning, (2) proper selection of personnel, (3) adequate training of employees, and (4) proper work incentives for the employees.

Complaints

Handling customer complaints is another big job for the manager and should be handled by him alone. The following eight recommendations are aimed to enable florists to make adjustments, and still retain the good will of the customer:

1. **Don't get excited.** The first job is to calm down a person who resents the inconvenience and loss of money that he believes (rightly or wrongly) is the fault of the florist.

2. **Listen courteously and appear attentive.** Listening to the customer is to the advantage of the florist because the customer can talk and get it off his chest and become calmer. This may show both of them that the grievance is exaggerated.

3. **Assuage his injured feelings.** Use soothing phrases if and when he pauses: "I know how you feel," "That's a good point."

4. **Get the important facts.** Now is the time to get the important facts by asking diplomatic questions without arousing his ire again.

5. **If he is in the right,** and the florist is wrong, many florists simply admit this and make a settlement that's fair. The florist may

Figure 11-1. Flower store owners and managers attending a retail florist conference.

have to do more than this to retain the customer's good will, but it will be worth it for the sake of future business.

6. **If the customer is wrong,** and the florist is right, don't show smugness. The florist should still make an adjustment even if it costs him some money in order to keep a *good* customer.

7. **Never underestimate the human element.** If a retail florist has only one complaint after selling 50 or 60 plants, it probably is not the fault of the plant, but just lack of care by the customer. The florist may revive the plant and save the sale. Explaining how to care for the plant or sending along one of the "care" tags will often forestall these complaints.

8. **Make the solution work to the advantage of the florist.** Don't say "I think you're in the wrong, but I'll give you a new plant anyway." Instead, remark enthusiastically, "this is a wonderful plant for the living room, and because I know you agree, I'm going to give you a new one free of charge. It needs special care so let me tell you how to take care of it properly."

Management Efficiency

Since poor work habits cost money, it is up to the manager to discover and correct them. This is particularly true today if a florist wishes to compete successfully with other businesses and other florists in his area. With rising operating costs it is essential that every employee operate at top efficiency. The manager must watch each employee and analyze the work habits of each. Herb Mitchell has several suggestions for increasing the efficiency and fostering better work habits with employees. He suggests the following: "(1) Watch the work pattern of each employee. There is a definite pattern for each job. (2) Always replace a bad habit with a good one. Don't just criticize without offering a solution. (3) Start the new employee out on the right foot. (4) Give a reason, and be sure it is a good one, for changing a work habit. (5) Be a good example himself. This may be the hardest one to follow. (6) Get participation from everyone. It takes only one person to upset the whole organization."

Figure 11-2. The owner supervises all activities in the retail flower shop. (Courtesy, Planter Florist, Bellevue, Wash.)

How much time should be spent by the owner-manager on managerial jobs and how much should be spent on small details?

Since the majority of our florists are small businesses with the owner acting as manager, the following figures will give some idea as to the amount of time that a small florist *might* expect to spend on various phases of the operation.

A survey from The Pennsylvania State University showed that the owner-manager of an *average small retail flower shop* spent 32 per cent of his time doing miscellaneous odd jobs around the store. The survey was conducted over a 12-month period. Ten random observations were made each day during 14 working days each month for a total of 1,680 observations. Whatever the owner-manager was doing at the time of the observations, it was recorded. All observations were made at random between 8:00 a.m. and 5:00 p.m. on randomly chosen days. This included holidays as well as normal days.

The operations in this shop were divided into 25 categories and then condensed later into 12 groups. The percentage of time an owner-manager of a small average florist shop spent in each operation is shown in Table 11-1.

Table 11-1. Per Cent of Time Spent on Specific Jobs by an Owner-Manager of a Retail Florist Shop.

Job or Operation		Per Cent of Time Spent
1. Selling		20.0
2. Designing:		16.5
Corsages	2.0	
Funeral papier-mâché vases	8.0	
Funeral sprays and wreaths	3.0	
Home and hospital vases	2.0	
Weddings	1.0	
Novelties	0.5	
3. Business operations:		16.0
Accounting and bookkeeping	11.5	
Mail	1.0	
Pricing	0.5	
Writing orders	3.0	
4. Telephoning (sending and taking orders)		12.5
5. Employee and customer consultation		3.0
6. Unpacking flowers and merchandise		9.0
7. Packing orders		5.0
8. Personal delays (meals, haircuts, etc.)		5.0
9. Idle		4.0
10. Emergency delivery		1.0
11. Inventory		1.0
12. Miscellaneous		7.0
		100.0

The survey showed that approximately 20 per cent of the owner's time was spent on waiting on customers, 16.5 per cent at the design table, 16 per cent working on the books, 12.5 per cent on the telephone and 3.0 per cent on consultation for a total of 68 per cent on the main operations involving the retail flower business.

Thirty-two per cent of the owner-manager's time was spent on miscellaneous items such as packing orders, unpacking merchandise, inventory, cleaning, personal delays, and meals. The personal delays are found in every shop as a part of the daily routine. They should be kept to a minimum.

The 4 per cent idle time could be spent more profitably in planning for specials, and other merchandising ideas to stimulate sales. This is too much time for a florist to be doing "nothing." Better planning would eliminate this.

The 7 per cent miscellaneous and 14 per cent packing and unpacking orders in many stores is done by employees which would leave 21 per cent more time for the owner-manager to spend on more important items of managership.

Successful management will mean more profits for the store. The following is a check list of factors which may mean more profits for a retail florist who follows them: (1) Is the merchandise priced to give the profit expected? (2) Is the buying being done carefully and economically? (3) Does the manager keep a careful check on all orders and merchandise, and keep dumpage to a minimum? (4) Are all salespeople trained to upsell items and sell the merchandise which is in largest supply? (5) Do they try to sell related merchandise with each order? (6) Does the manager periodically check the inventory to be sure all items are selling? (7) Does he take advantage of good buys to increase the markup when possible? (8) Does he check all employees to see that they are really productive? (9) Does the manager keep a constant watch over all the various operations of the store?

Mismanagement caused over 90 per cent of the more than 12,000 small business failures in one year according to Dun and Bradstreet as reported by Alvi Voigt. Forty-nine retail florists in the United States failed with a resultant loss of $900,000 to creditors. Many others failed without any loss to creditors, but with a loss of their own investment. Improved management organization and management development are, therefore, of great importance to the retail flower industry, which is primarily made up of small businesses. The report of Dun and Bradstreet stated that the most common factors in business failures were inadequate sales (50%), heavy operating expenses (3%), difficulties in collecting receivables (6%), poor inventory (7%), excessive fixed costs (4%), poor location (5%), competitive problems (21%), and others (4%). Management weaknesses were listed as plain incompetence (43%), unbalanced management experience (18%), inexperience (18%), lack of know-how in the particular field (13%), and other reasons (8%). (These two sets of figures are approximate figures only.) It is assumed that two out of five businesses failed because the *owners should never have been in business at all.* This shows very clearly the importance of management to the small retail business.

Why do customers leave a particular retail store? A survey in Oregon gave the answer to some of the problems which occur in retail stores. These figures are for all retail shops, not only florists, but they are worth considering by retail florists. The figures show the percentage of people that gave each reason for leaving a retail shop and going somewhere else (Table 11-2).

Table 11-2. Reasons Why Customers Leave a Retail Shop.

	Per Cent
1. High prices	37.44
2. Poor quality of goods	11.87
3. Delay in store service	8.98
4. Indifferent salesmen	6.08
5. Errors	5.17
6. Substitutions of goods	5.02
7. Tricky methods	3.95
8. Store appearance	3.34
9. Misrepresentation of goods	3.04
10. Haughty salespeople	2.89
11. Overinsistent salespeople	2.73
12. Wrong management policies	2.73
13. Reluctance to exchange	2.13
14. Poor advertising	1.97
15. Ignorance of goods	1.90

The manager's job in any small business is unique. Although he may be called upon to do many jobs if he is the owner too, his primary function is to see that all the work is done properly, smoothly, efficiently, and profitably. All of this takes planning, but more than that it also takes execution and evaluation. The job of the manager will vary in time from about 20 per cent doing, with 80 per cent planning and evaluating in a large shop; to 80 per cent doing, and 20 per cent planning and evaluating in a small shop. It's up to the manager to budget his time according to the operation of the retail florist shop.

Tie in all the aforementioned duties of the small shop owner and manager with the fact that he must be concerned with delivery, general maintenance, and a host of other things, plus being a good designer; and you must be quite an unusual person to be a successful retail florist.

Reference

1. Voigt, A. O. "What Causes Business Failures?" *Florists' and Nursery Exchange,* Vol. 145, No. 21 (May 21, 1966), pp. 16, 18.

Chapter 12

HIRING AND TRAINING EMPLOYEES; DESIGN SCHOOLS

A successful manager or owner of a retail florist shop will try to divide his employees into groups according to the job. In very small shops this may be difficult because one person may be selling, designing, and answering the phone. However, in most shops each person is usually assigned to one main job. In the larger shops (over $125,000 annual gross volume of sales), each employee should have a specific job and title, as mentioned in Chapter 11.

A look at each of the major types of employees seems to be in order, with a listing of some of the qualifications for each.

Designer

1. The designer must have good artistic sense, and good designing ability. He must know the fundamentals of the principles of design if he is to be above average as a designer to become a retail florist.

2. He must have imagination and originality so that he can create new designs, and not have them all the same.

3. He should have had some previous experience, and have worked in a retail florist shop during most of the seven major holidays.

4. He should be quick and efficient in his designing so that he can get the work done on time.

5. He should be enough of a businessman to be economical in his designs to preserve the margin of profit. One extra flower thrown into each design will eat up most of the profits. (Table 14-1).

Salesperson

1. A salesman must like people, and have the initiative for selling.

2. He must be ambitious and a go-getter, not just an order-taker.

3. He must be an employee who is dependable and reliable.

4. He must be efficient in serving the customer, and know how to use the rest of his time wisely.

5. He should be a person of good health since he is in contact with the public daily; and one who will not miss work very often.

6. He must have a knowledge of prices, types of designs, names of merchandise, delivery schedules, selling methods, and general store policies.

7. He should have a pleasing personality, and a pleasing appearance to make the best possible impression with the customer.

8. He should be diplomatic and courteous with all customers. One dissatisfied customer can lead to more.

9. He should be able to get along with other employees.

Buyer

1. There should be just one person to do all the buying, and preferably it should be the manager. It is often the owner of a small shop.

2. He should be familiar with the market and prices so that he can purchase economically.

3. He should be familiar with the type and amount of merchandise that his customers will buy.

4. He should know whether he can *merchandise* an item that is in great supply on the market during a glut. He has to know when he can sell the material, and how much he can sell at one time.

5. He should be able to recognize a *good* buy when he sees one.

6. He should impress his wholesalers with the fact that he never wants old, or poorly grown merchandise.

Bookkeeper

1. The bookkeeper must be familiar with the fundamentals of accounting and bookkeeping.

2. He should know how to file properly.

3. He should know how to post entries and to keep the ledger sheets.

4. He should know how to make out the periodic Profit and Loss statements for the manager or owner.

5. He should be dependable in doing the work on time. The statements must be sent out on time each and every month.

6. He must be honest.

7. He should know how to answer the telephone properly, and be able to take an order or call a salesperson to the phone.

Delivery

The delivery man or truck driver is more important than some florists realize. Many florists will hire just any high school boy, or unemployed person, without realizing his importance to the store. The delivery man is often the main contact between the store and the customer, or between the store and a potential customer.

1. He must make a good impression.

2. He should be neat and clean.

3. He must be reliable. If the designs do not reach the customer the same way they left the store, there will be complaints and many dissatisfied customers.

4. He should be pleasant and courteous to help set a good image of the store.

5. He should have a thorough knowledge of the streets, and know how the streets are numbered in the town. He can save time by efficiently delivering the orders without a lot of backtracking.

6. He must be honest, so that he can collect C.O.D.'s and delinquent accounts for the shop.

7. He should be a good driver, and obey all of the traffic laws.

8. He should take pride in his truck, and see that it is kept clean, greased, and filled with gas.

9. He should be able to help out in the store when he is not out on deliveries.

Manager

In a large shop the owner may employ a separate manager to oversee all of the operations, as discussed in Chapter 11.

1. He must have all of the qualifications of a retail florist.

2. He will supervise the salespeople and designers, and set up the delivery schedules.

3. He will often do the buying, and regulate the advertising program.

4. It is up to him to operate a smoothly efficient and profitable shop.

Selecting Employees

"Ninety per cent of your employee troubles can be eliminated at the time of hiring" according to one florist. Make certain to pick the right person in the first place. This is never easy for a small retail florist who must do a hundred things at once. The following are some of the things to look for in a new employee: (1) productivity—the ability of every employee to *produce* for the business; (2) good will building—every employee represents the business and his attitude towards his employer is mighty important; (3) care of equipment—the employee should take pride in, and care of, the materials he uses; (4) cooperation—necessary for an efficient and productive business; (5) loyalty—a must; (6) honesty —expected from every employee; (7) ambition—the desire to get ahead; and (8) compliance with rules—they must be obeyed.

The following definite steps to be followed when interviewing an employee will result in a minimum of wasted time:

1. Make sure the interview is relaxed.

2. Get the applicant to talk about his work and experiences. Don't get off on too many extraneous matters except to get him to relax.

3. Get the facts. Don't waste too much time on idle talk.

4. Check the employment record of the applicant.

5. Quickly check his personality and skills by careful observation.

6. Check appearance of the applicant.

7. Find out his attitude towards work and long hours. Explain the working hours, and that overtime is expected at holiday times.

8. Make sure he knows what the job is and what is expected of him.

9. Get him to ask questions.

10. Keep control of the job interview so that there is not a lot of precious time wasted.

11. Analyze results and let the prospective employee know the decision as quickly as possible.

12. Have the applicant fill out a simple application form which will always be of value to the employer.

Labor Market

Where does the retail florist get his new employees? Colleges, high schools, trade schools, design schools, and neighbors are a good source of supply. Young people in high school and the early college years, young housewives, and older women are probably the easiest available labor market in local areas. If a retail florist needs more employees due to increased business, he should hire these people on a part-time basis first and train them, before they become part of his regular staff. Some universities operate their own flower shops to give experience to the students. One of these is Mississippi State University, which trains over 275 students a year in the basics of floral design.

Figure 12-1. Students learn floral designing at The Pennsylvania State University.

Besides high schools and colleges, there are now available other means of finding employees for the retail florist business. Several cities have set up schools with backing from Washington, D.C., under the Manpower Development and Training Act, and several florists have been paid to offer on-the-job training to future florists who want to learn the business. Many high schools are offering vocational horticulture courses with specialties in floriculture. The number is increasing every year as are government supported schools, which train students to become retail florists.

Training Employees

When florists hire employees, permanent or part-time, it is up to the owner-manager to train them properly. Regular help should be taught the value of a prompt and courteous approach to the customer, the manner in which to develop and close a sale, the proper way to answer the phone, the value of merchandise and how to handle it, and all the many other things he should know about the retail florist business. Extra help should be trained well in advance of the holiday.

It is a costly job to train an employee. Good, well-trained flower shop employees are hard to find. The shop has an investment in the employee once he is trained. He is a valuable asset to the shop, and it is in the best interests of the employer to do everything possible to keep him. Usually an employee in a flower shop finds something more than just wages and other benefits to attract him, if he is to stay in the retail florist business. He catches a glimpse of the beauty of the merchandise (every florist enjoys working with flowers), of the fascinating work of creating an artistic design, and of the importance of serving his customers. But, it quickly can be clouded by an employer who shouts instead of instructs, who bosses rather than leads, and who distracts rather than inspires his help.

A wise employer recognizes that each new employee starts his first day with apprehension mixed with enthusiasm. Aloofness has no place in a flower shop, either with the employer or the employee. Everyone likes to be called by name, so the florist should be sure to apply this to each new employee from the very first day. Every employee is a human being and he expects to be treated like one. Commands are given in the Army, not in a flower shop. Once a florist has started an employee off on the right foot, he is well on the way to the all-important objective of keeping him permanently employed.

Take time. Part of the fault with training employees seems to lie with the florist himself. Either he thinks he doesn't know how to train new employees (which is wrong in many cases) or else he just doesn't take the time to do it. Why try to train a new employee for either full or part-time work the week before Christmas or Easter? This is the worst possible time, and yet this is exactly what some of the retail florists try to do and then wonder why they fail. Every florist is much too busy for the few weeks prior to a major holiday to spend time to properly train a new employee. Some

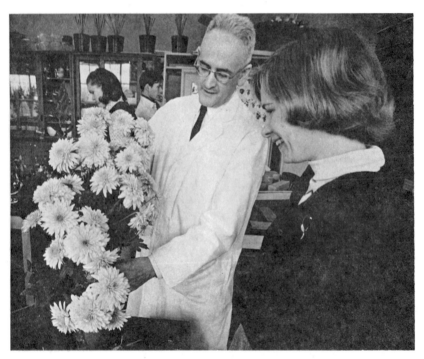

Figure 12-2. The author gives personal attention to a future florist.

florists, however, do this year after year and then complain that they can't get competent help, and that the new employees are not worth what they have to pay them. Often they wait until 10 days before Christmas and then try to get cheap help. "Forget the cheap help," says Bill Curtis of Phoebe Floral in Allentown, Pennsylvania. "There are many sources of good part-time help such as school teachers, college students, retired clerks, and housewives."

Be systematic. A retail florist should train new employees in a systematic businesslike manner, and do it at a time when he can concentrate on this and little else. He should consider the training of new employees as a regular part of the business, and not something to be squeezed in on a hit or miss basis.

Procedure.

1. Pay the employee a minimum wage while he is learning; with a promise of higher pay for the holiday or for when he becomes more experienced, and becomes a regular full-time employee of the shop.

2. Arrange for the new employee to work in the shop every day for two weeks at least. This should be several weeks prior to a holiday. The summer is a good time to train and line up extra holiday help for later in the year. In fact, the summer is when the retail florist has the most time to train any new employee, and yet florists seem reluctant to hire a new employee in the summer.

3. Give the employee time to become acquainted with the merchandise, prices, charges, delivery, and other standard practices in the shop. A mimeograph of procedures and practices should be given to the new employees to read over, and study at home. (It won't hurt to let older employees read them once in awhile too.) Be patient until the new person learns the job. Don't be afraid to let him observe a little, and absorb the atmosphere of the shop. This is a vital part of the training process, if it is not carried to excess.

4. Introduce the new employee personally to the rest of the employees, and use first names so they will be friendly, and make the new employee feel more at home.

5. Be definite with the new employee as to exactly who is the boss, and from whom he is to take orders. It should be preferably just one individual.

6. Tell the new employee exactly what his duties will be and what is expected of him. Also be sure to tell him that there will be times when he will be asked to do other jobs—even some quite menial tasks. Explain that at holidays *everyone* has more work to do, and will have to work longer hours.

7. If the new employee is to do any designing, be sure to give him plenty of time at first to design several test arrangements. Stay with him and help and guide him. Some florists walk away, come back and say "it's terrible," or else just tear it apart and do it themselves. Help to build *confidence* in the individual and show him where he is going wrong at the time he is doing it, not later. A florist may let the new employee watch the main designer for awhile so that the new employee can see the style of arrangements done by this particular shop.

8. Do not "bawl out" an employee (new or old) in front of other employees.

9. Don't expect miracles the first week. Give the new employee a chance.

10. Tell the new employee how he is expected to dress. He should realize it just through observation, but he may not.

11. If the shop is large enough for separate designers, salespeople, packers, and delivery men, then have a mimeographed set of procedures for each group to give to the new employees.

12. For part-time holiday help, go over the specific details for the holiday with all new employees several weeks before the holiday. The florist should take a half-day and spend time explaining what he wants done, the prices of various items, the merchandise that has been ordered which will be for sale, delivery schedules, and other procedures. If all the employees and part-time workers know these things, then they won't be asking so many questions during the rush of the holiday. Many florists post several copies of prices of plants and cut flowers for the holiday around the shop so there will be no mistakes.

13. Stress to all new employees that they should be friendly, personable, and efficient when waiting on customers. Also, they should use common language. Employees should be salesmen, not order takers.

14. Older and retired ladies make an excellent source of part-time employees, as do college students home on vacation for the holiday.

Most retail florists are well qualified to train new employees if they will just *take the time to do it.* They know their business better than anyone else, they know what they want done and how it is to be done, they know the merchandise and prices, they know how to design, and they should know how to sell. All that is required is to take a little time to systematically impart this knowledge to the new employees.

Training an Assistant

Many retail florists find themselves in a dilemma when it comes to vacations, attending meetings, and just taking some time off. They need an assistant, and yet feel that none of their regular employees can fit into that category. Thus, they go on for years without a real vacation or attending florists' meetings which would benefit them and their business. The following suggestions would be helpful in training an assistant.

1. Immediately after hiring a new assistant, acquaint him

with the store in the simplest way—by sitting down, and discussing the business with him. Describe its routine, problems, principles of management, present policies, and the plans for the future. Tell the new man how and where he fits into the picture, and what jobs he will take over. Take plenty of time for this discussion.

2. Acquaint the new assistant with the principal people with whom he will work, and be sure they understand they will be taking orders from him. Introduce him personally to all employees.

3. Assign job responsibility with intelligence. Don't give him too much to do at once. Don't check his every move, but oversee his progress in a general way.

4. Expect the assistant to make mistakes. Everyone does at one time or another. He doesn't have the experience of the employer. Errors can't be prevented but the assistant should be taught to *learn* from them. Discuss the mistakes with him quietly and in private.

5. Always work in harmony with an assistant and share all knowledge with him.

6. Encourage the assistant to improve himself. Be sure he sees, and has time to read, the various trade publications. He should have the opportunity to attend some of the conferences and conventions of retail florist organizations.

7. Give the assistant a decent salary commensurate with his responsibilities.

Checking Top Salespeople

The importance of the sales personnel cannot be overemphasized in today's business. The success of any retail florist shop is determined in large measure by the quality of its salespeople. While they are being trained and going through a probationary period, there are at least 50 items which should be checked by the manager. These included items of sales ability, handling of customers, personal appearance, habit, honesty, doing extra jobs when not waiting on customers, proper handling of merchandise, satisfaction with the job, and many other items which will result in better business for the store.

Design Schools

After leaving high school or college, it is usually advisable for a prospective retail florist to attend one of the many fine design schools located all over the United States. Even if the employee has worked part-time in a flower shop, or has taken some design courses, the experience and practice at one of these schools will be worth-while. Also he will be able to pick up new ideas and techniques which will help him to be above average as a designer. There are at least 25 such design schools in the country offering courses several times a year for from two to six weeks in length. Many of them are advertised in the trade papers such as *Florists' Review*, *Florist and Nursery Exchange*, *Southern Florist and Nurseryman*, and *Flower News*. The advantage to a prospective employee or future florist is well worth the cost. If the prospective employee is looking for a job, it is worth his spending the money at one of these schools to help him get a good job. It is also worth-while for a retail florist to pay the way of a new employee, so that he himself will not have to spend so much time teaching the employee how to design. Some retail florists will also send older employees, and pay their way so that they will learn new techniques of design.

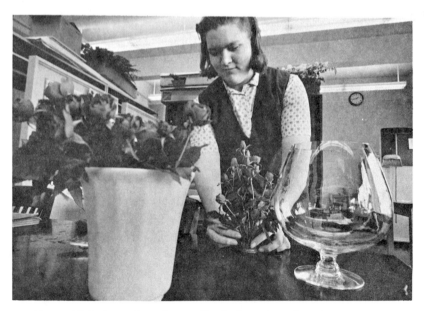

Figure 12-3. A student learns floral designing through experience.

The hiring and training of employees is important to a retail florist and should be given serious consideration. Too many retail florists do not spend the time trying to find the right kind of employees for their shop or take time to train them properly once they have been found. The ultimate success and profits of the business rest with reliable, well-trained employees.

Dismissal

Today's laws are extremely complex in terms of employer-employee relationships. This means that mishandling an employee's dismissal may be costly to any business. Take precautions to avoid this by never dismissing an employee during a heated argument, and be sure all terms of the original employment agreement have been complied with. It pays to have every agreement in writing. Be sure to check all records of payment to ascertain that nothing is due him. Dismiss an employee only after carefully considering the case from all angles.

References

1. Anonymous. "Mishandling Employee Dismissal Can Be Costly to Businessmen," *Florist and Nursery Exchange* (January 6, 1970), p. 12
2. Anonymous. "Stopping Employee Turnover," *Teleflora Spirit* (July 1966), p. 24.

Chapter 13

BUYING

Buying is one of the most important functions of the manager or owner of a retail florist shop. Many florists have increased their net profit by careful buying, and knowing when and how to take advantage of gluts and discounts.

There are four areas of buying for the retail florist, and each requires a different set of skills and information. They are as follows: (1) the purchase of perishable merchandise for resale, (2) the purchase of non-perishable merchandise for resale, (3) the purchase of expendable supplies (staples) for use with the perishables, and (4) the purchase of equipment and fixtures.

Perishable Merchandise

Buying perishable merchandise is one of the most important and most difficult practices involved in operating a retail florist shop. The skillful buying of flowers and plants requires a good deal of study, as well as considerable planning and experience. Buying is either done directly in person or by phone. A person buying by phone has to depend a great deal on the salesman on the other end of the line. It is important for a florist to stay with one salesman (when he finds a reliable one) and instruct him on the florist's likes, dislikes, and type of merchandise preferred. Reliability of the salesman is extremely important in the retail florist business. Tell him about the business so he will know the quality of merchandise wanted, and the quantity and type of items which can be sold in this particular shop. Telephone buying may cost about 10 per cent more in the long run, unless the florist has a contact with a good reliable salesman. Prices of cut flowers vary from hour-to-hour and day-to-day in the wholesale market, so timing is important. In general, personal visits to the wholesale flower markets and greenhouses are desirable and necessary, when possible, if the retailer is to be well informed about actual price conditions, and the quality of merchandise available. However, a lot of valuable time is wasted in the wholesale market, so make the time count. Only a well informed retail florist can operate a profitable business in a highly competitive market of plants and flowers.

Figure 13-1. Salesmen receiving orders from retail florists in a wholesale commission florist company. (Courtesy, Denver Wholesale Florists Co., Denver, Colo.)

A retail florist should plan his buying ahead of time since it will be to his advantage in the end. Accurate records on what portion of his business is funeral, wedding, hospital, gift, and cash-and-carry will be of value in planning what merchandise to buy. If the florist is located in a large city with several wholesalers, he should contact all of them to see what quality, quantity, and price of merchandise is available. Salesmen may alter the price depending upon the supply and demand for the product. This occurs hour-by-hour and day-by-day. He should try to get the best buy possible. If he is ordering in advance for a wedding, the florist must see what each wholesaler can do, and be sure to order ahead of time. The larger the order for flowers, the better the price should be. A retail florist ordering 50 roses will usually pay more per rose than a retail florist ordering 1,000 roses.

Nothing is a bargain if it can't be used or sold. When there is a glut or an oversupply on the market, the wholesaler will try to sell in quantity. For this reason the florist must decide what he can sell and decide in advance what he is going to spend. By doing so, he will come out with less loss and more profit. This may not be true, however, if he is buying flowers with a long life. Experience tells which flowers will keep the longest. But to keep ordering more than is planned each time, can lead to losses.

For sales promotions such as weekend cash-and-carry specials, plan ahead, and buy in quantity at a price which the florist can afford for offering the merchandise at a low cash-and-carry figure. The florist must buy only what he will be able to sell in his special. If too much is left over, it may have to be dumped. This type of merchandising is discussed in Chapter 16.

When buying in quantity offer the salesman a price below the set price, according to many florists. It depends on the salesman, but each one has his own price to which he can go if he feels he can make the best sale. It is the old question of supply and demand. The retail florist knows he will always be able to buy at the set price, and the salesman may not offer any less for it unless the florist asks for it. However, during a glutted period the salesman will then tell him that there is a better price for a certain quantity and will make him a good offer.

Non-perishable Items

Every supply magazine and every trade fair for florists has hundreds of items which can be used and sold in the retail florist shop. The best advice on buying these items is to purchase wisely and well.

The actual job of buying is easier if enough time and effort have been devoted to planning, according to Herb Mitchell. He says: "the biggest job is selecting items which will move in a specific flower shop." Most of our successful florists do not buy what they like personally. They try to purchase what their customers like. Some florists rely on the salesman to tell them what a comparable shop is selling. The salesman often will know which items are moving. Some florists ask their wives, salespeople, and a few good customers for their advice on some items to find out their likes and dislikes. However, no matter how hard he tries, the retail florist will have a *lemon* now and then. Merchandise must be selected for its sales appeal, and experience seems to be the best teacher for this.

One of the biggest problems in buying is deciding whether to buy a few items in depth, or to select many items and buy only one or two of each. It is usually wise to buy some each way. Mainly it is important to buy enough of any item or group of similar items to make an attractive display. It is important to plan ahead and know how the merchandise is going to be sold. Old stand-by items will be known, but new items are always a gamble.

Knowing *when* to buy is another important consideration. Planned buying demands that purchasing be accomplished on a definite schedule. If orders are placed with every salesman who comes into the store, it is practically impossible to keep an accurate inventory record. Certain items should be ordered each month, while other merchandise is only purchased once a year.

Prompt payment of these items to take advantage of cash discounts will add to the margin of profit for the retail florist.

Staples

In the buying of non-perishable staple items such as wire, ribbon, papier-mâché containers, floratape, chicken wire, and other necessary items, there is usually a fluctuation of price. The larger the quantity, the better will be the price. Many small florists buy these items one at a time as they need them, and this is the most expensive way to do it. If a florist's credit with the company is good, he will get a better price for the items. Many florists will buy a year's supply of these items if they have plenty of storage space. Sometimes he can save up to 15 per cent in this way, and this will often more than pay the shipping charges. Prompt payment also is an important buying procedure and one which will help with the profit picture. If a florist can get a discount by paying promptly (often within 10 days) this will increase his profits. So, it is essential in a florist's planning to have cash on hand to take advantage of discounts. Cash discounts are extremely important to his business and he should take advantage of them. **Even borrowing from a bank is well worth-while. You may compare a cost of 6 per cent interest for borrowing money from the bank as opposed to 2 per cent saved if the invoice is paid on time. Even though the rate of interest from the bank is** greater, according to Jack Carman, when speaking of cash discounts, 2 per cent for 10 days is equivalent to 36 per cent true interest per year. Compare 6 per cent per annum with 36 per cent and in the course of a year, it can be seen that there will be a considerable saving of money when the florist borrows from his local financial institution in order to meet his payables. If he buys a year's supply of staples and saves up to 15 per cent, the saving is even greater.

Equipment and Fixtures

The purchase of equipment and fixtures will be determined by need. A good buyer knows when to replace equipment. If he has properly depreciated the items and set aside money to replace these items, then he should not have any trouble paying for the new equipment and fixtures. As mentioned in Chapter 6, the florist must set aside money for equipment, and not take too much out in personal withdrawals. Whether he buys new or used equipment will depend on his needs, the cost of the item, and the amount of available capital. As in other buying, prompt payment may give him a discount which is well worth-while.

The Purchasing Decision

For every purchase, the retail florist must make the following decisions: (1) what to buy: quantity, quality, color, and type; (2) when to buy: date or time of year to purchase material, or day of week; (3) when to receive: specify delivery dates for non-perishable items; (4) where to buy: contact several wholesalers and suppliers; (5) how to ship or deliver: the most economical way, but with proper handling; (6) how to pay: plan and budget ahead; (7) what to pay: price must be competitive. Try to get the best buy.

Buying is important and a good retail florist should never hesitate to ask for a better price.

Stock Turnover

Increasing the rate of stock turnover in a business is one of the keys to higher profits. The businessman will make more profit per dollar invested in stock if he gets a fast turnover of his merchandise inventory.

To improve the stock turnover, he has to know the current rate. In the retail florist business the rate of turnover, of course, for flowers and plants (perishable merchandise) is very rapid. However, on the non-perishable items it may be very slow. So, here we are talking about the non-perishables or inventory items, termed "hard goods" by many florists.

There are several steps in determining a florist's stock turnover rate: (1) Determine the dollar volume of the average inventory for the year. As an example, say $25,000. (2) Divide the average inventory into the cost of goods sold. For example, divide $25,000 into a theoretical $75,000 cost of goods sold. (3) The turnover rate is three, or three times a year he will have a turnover of stock.

The turnover rate can be increased by two methods: (1) increase the sales and keep the average inventory the same or (2) decrease the average inventory, and keep the sales the same. In this example, if the cost of goods sold increased to $150,000, the stock turnover rate would be six instead of three. Thus, the dollars invested in the business will *work harder for the florist* if he increases the rate of stock turnover in the business. If he controls all other elements, and increases his stock turnover rate, then his profits will improve. Eliminate old stock, and eliminate odds and ends to reduce the inventory. Too many florists keep lemons around longer than necessary and have money tied up in inventory. It is best to get rid of the lemons periodically in a reduced sale table in the store.

It should be obvious that the job of buying is one of the most important responsibilities of the manager or owner of the retail florist shop. Careful buying can greatly increase the net profit for the business.

Reference

1. Carman, J. "Why You Should Take Advantage of Cash Discounts," *FTD News*, (July 1962), p. 25.

Chapter 14

PRICING; MARKUP; PROFIT

Pricing

Pricing is one of the most important functions, along with buying, of the owner or manager in the retail florist shop.

Nearly 40 per cent of the retail florists in the United States charge the same price for arranged as for unarranged flowers according to a recent U. S. Department of Agriculture survey. This is not a good business practice.

Most prices in the retail florist business are figured on the cost of merchandise while profits are figured on sales. The majority of florists price their flowers on the basis of the wholesale price or cost of merchandise. However, the economists tell us that the price for flowers should be based on sales and the profit which the florist wants from his business. Although pricing will not affect the actual cost of the merchandise to the florist, it does affect the cost of merchandise *percentage* as shown in the following example. A. Voigt has shown that with a business of $60,000 gross volume of sales, a 10 per cent increase in prices will result in a 100 per cent increase in net income. Thus, the cost of merchandise changes from 55 to 50 per cent and the net-to-owner from 10 to 18.2 per cent. (Even a 5 per cent increase in prices will result in a 50 per cent net income increase.) Example:

A. Current situation:

Sales	$60,000	100%
Merchandise cost	33,000	55%
Gross profit	27,000	45%
Operation costs	21,000	35%
Net-to-owner	6,000	10%

B. New situation:

Sales	$66,000	100%
Merchandise cost	33,000	50%
Gross profit	33,000	50%
Operation costs	21,000	31.8%
Net-to-owner	12,000	18.2%

Thus, with an increase in price or sales, the percentage of merchandise cost was changed and the net profit was increased.

Markup

How do retail florists determine what they shall charge customers for their merchandise? Most of them have a definite policy, or think they do. Many florists claim to use a specific markup, but few of them actually follow it. There are several rules of thumb used by many florists which, unfortunately, do not lead to the desired profit. Surveys have shown that markup ranges from 50 to 200 per cent by various individual retail florists. The rule of thumb used by many florists for years has been 2 to 1, 2-1/2 to 1, 3 to 1, or 4 to 1 markup. The average is 3 to 1. But the price should not be based on a simple markup. Most of them use a 2 to 1 on pottery and pot plants. This means they buy the item for a dollar and sell it for two dollars. The markup is based on the cost of the item. The 2 or 3 to 1 markup started some 50 years ago at a florists meeting when a speaker mentioned that he used a 2 to 1 markup for pricing his flowers. Even though florists will tell you that they use a 3 to 1 markup, they don't do it all the time. They use it as a basis for pricing and it is probably a legitimate markup *when the flower market is normal*. However, when the florist gets a *good buy* and pays 5¢ for a flower which normally costs 12¢, he does not reduce the price to the customer, unless it is for a cash-and-carry special. Thus, if he sells the flowers for the same price per dozen all year, his markup at this time will be much greater than the 3 to 1. Likewise, when the market is tight or when there is a holiday, the wholesale price goes up, and since the retailer cannot raise his prices too far out of line, his resulting markup will be less than 3 to 1. Many florists try to hold the prices for the standard flowers at the same retail price all year, hoping that the markup will average at least 3 to 1 for the year. They hope, but many just don't know, and this is a poor business practice.

The florists, besides trying to start with a standard base, also determine the selling price for flowers by what they think their customers will pay. Many times they are wrong. It has been proven that too many retail florists are order takers, and not salesmen. They are afraid to upsell. At least 80 per cent of our florist shops are charging the same price for arrangements that they did 5 and 10 years ago. Yet, every other commodity in the United States has increased, some even doubled, and tripled. Expenses and overhead costs for the florists have gone up tremendously in the past 10 years, but not the retail price on flowers. A survey in 1963 showed that in suburban shops the average minimum funeral piece was $7.50, and a hospital piece was $4.50. In rural shops, the average minimum funeral arrangement was $5.75, and a hospital piece was $3.50. The downtown shops reported an average minimum funeral piece was $6.60, and a hospital piece was $4.50. These were *minimum* prices for orders which were charged and delivered, and *these prices are very close to what they were 10 years ago.* Retail florists have not kept up with increasing costs and prices in most instances. Many florists will deliver *any order without charge,* while others use a $3.50, $4.00, or $5.00 minimum for delivery.

Times are constantly changing. Transportation costs and methods for handling flowers are changing, and retail florist shops themselves are not the same. They no longer cater only to the old-time carriage trade. With all of these changes, the cost of labor over the past 20 years has at least tripled, the cost of flowers on the wholesale level has increased, and the necessity for purchasing all sorts of supplies has become part of the retail florists' business. However, the one thing that has not increased substantially is the *retail price for flowers.* If the profit that is expected at the end of the year is not there, the florist must check the records, and find out whether somewhere along the line he had forgotten to make needed changes in pricing. If this is true, now is the time to make this change and step up the markup.

Profit

A selling price is a combination of four factors: cost of merchandise, overhead, labor (salaries and wages), and profit. *The price should not be based on a simple markup no matter how high it is.* Remember that keeping profits is as important as making profits. One way is to reduce your tax cost wherever practical. Profit should be planned. Profit comes from efficient control of overhead and labor, as well as the buying of quality merchandise at an economical price. Net profit should be separated from salary. A good businessman, even if he is the sole owner, must pay himself a decent salary. Labor is the biggest expense item and must be included, along with profit, in determining the selling price of the item. An average florist shop will spend between 15 and 30 per cent of the gross volume of sales for the payroll, depending upon the size of the shop. Overhead is the cost of doing business, including rent, advertising, utilities, delivery, and minor items of expense. Overhead must also be considered in the pricing of items for sale. Although many florists figure the markup will take care of this, it often does not.

If a florist figures his profit at 10 per cent, from the start, then he will have the following to guide him in determining the selling price: profit 10 per cent, labor 30 per cent, and overhead 27 per cent; leaving 35 per cent for the cost of merchandise. Since the markup on cash-and-carry items, and the markup on hard goods like pottery is a standard 2 or 2½ to 1, then the markup on the perishable items must be more than 3 to 1 in order to keep the total cost of merchandise at 33 per cent for the year. As it goes higher, the profit goes lower. Thus, a retail florist should start with the selling price and work backwards to find how much merchandise to use, rather than starting with the purchase price and trying to use a standard markup. Unfortunately, today the majority of retail florists use the old system of a 3 to 1 or 4 to 1 markup, hoping it will give them a profit. For some shops this works, but for others it doesn't. It is usually just a guess.

The pricing should be figured as shown in the following example. A $10.00 sale would be broken down into the following:

Profit (10 per cent)	$1.00
Overhead (27 per cent)	2.70
Labor (30 per cent)	3.00
Inventory (container)	1.00
	$7.70
Cost of merchandise	2.30
	$10.00

This method leaves $2.30 to be spent on the cost of merchandise. The total of the inventory merchandise plus the perishable merchandise equals the 33 per cent mentioned previously. *The perishable merchandise factor is the one that must be variable and reflect the proper markup to determine a decent profit.* Many florists will figure their markup on a monthly basis rather than on an annual basis. This is good business because the percentage of overhead varies from month to month. According to a Michigan State University survey it varied from 30.7 per cent to 50.9 per cent in one store during a 12-month period, as follows: January—41.8 per cent, February—41.8 per cent, March—37.2 per cent (Easter), April—42.6 per cent, May—30.7 per cent, June—37.6 per cent, July—49.7 per cent, August—46.3 per cent, September—50.9 per cent, October—41.1 per cent, November—45.1 per cent, and December—35.6 per cent.

The hardest part for most retail florists is to charge for the labor, delivery, and other expenses. They find it difficult to charge different prices for flowers if they are arranged, charged, and delivered. And yet, this is exactly what must be done, or at least it must be included in the selling price. As mentioned previously, a national survey showed that 40 per cent of the retail florists in the United States are charging the same price for arranged as for unarranged flowers. It is an unprofitable way to run a business.

Another hard job for florists is to figure the pricing of flowers for weddings. Instead of breaking it down into labor, cost of merchandise, overhead, and profit, they use a markup of maybe 5 to 1 or even 8 to 1, hoping this will cover everything. Some florists figure in the cost of setting up the wedding decorations, but forget about the time and labor involved in tearing them down and returning the materials to the store. All of this should be figured in the final price.

Another place where retail florists do not figure properly is in pricing pottery and other hard goods. The 2 or 2-1/2 to 1 markup is fine, but many florists forget to include delivery charges. These must be added to the cost of the item before it is priced. Transportation charges can be quite high on some items and must be included in the sale price, otherwise the markup will be less than 2 to 1, which is the minimum. With increased costs in today's business world, a 2-1/2 to 1 markup is a better base for pottery and hard goods.

A survey of retail florists in 1963 showed the following average markups from approximately 75 florists surveyed: (1) average markup on cost for flowers boxed and wrapped was 2.68 to 1, (2) average markup on cost for flowers in corsages was 3.86 to 1, (3) average markup on cost for flowers in arrangements was 2.98 to 1, (4) average markup on cost for flowers in wedding work was 4.07 to 1, (5) average markup on cost for flowers in funeral wreaths and sprays was 2.93 to 1, (6) average markup on cost for flowering pot plants was 2.25 to 1, (7) average markup on cost for green plants was 2.28 to 1. By comparing these figures with those in the preceding paragraph, it is easy to see why the average florist of today is not making a 10 per cent profit. (Chapter 6 shows 4.9 to 7.8 per cent.) These figures for markup are much too low. If a retail florist were to take the money he invested in his business and put it into a building and loan or other

Table 14-1. Money Lost with Extra Flowers Thrown In.

Yearly Volume	Average Order	# Orders Yearly	Average Cost per Flower					
			3¢	5¢	8¢	10¢	15¢	20¢
$ 25,000	$ 3.50	7,142	$214.26	$ 357.10	$ 571.36	$ 714.20	$1,071.30	$1,428.40
35,000	3.75	9,333	279.99	466.65	746.64	933.30	1,399.95	1,866.60
50,000	4.00	12,500	375.00	625.00	1,000.00	1,250.00	1,875.00	2,500.00
75,000	4.20	17,857	535.71	892.85	1,428.56	1,785.70	2,678.55	3,571.40
100,000	4.50	22,222	947.34	1,578.90	2,526.74	3,157.80	4,736.70	6,313.60

form of investment, he would receive at least 4 per cent return with no risk involved. Therefore, the retail florist is entitled to at least 6 per cent (net profit after taxes) plus a fair salary for himself.

If he finds that the markup is actually below that which is needed to insure a profit, it may be due to any of the following: (1) the prices are too low, (2) the florist is not buying properly, (3) he is throwing in too many extra flowers, (4) he has not coordinated his buying and selling, (5) the dumpage is too great, (6) someone is failing to ring up sales, (7) someone is taking flowers without recording them, or (8) the overhead is too high.

Table 14-1, prepared by Professor Paul Krone, shows how the profits will suffer by throwing extra flowers into floral designs.

The following example will show how the way material selected for the design will determine whether there will be a profit or a loss on the order. Two or three extra flowers (depending upon the price) will turn the profit into loss.

Example: Two $10.00 baskets.

A		B	
12 glads	1.00	10 glads	.80
9 asters	.72	6 asters	.48
1 bu. pomps	1.00	3/4 bu. pomps	.75
6 mums	1.80	3 mums	.90
Container	1.00	Container	1.00
Greens	.50	Greens	.50
50% overhead	5.00	50% overhead	5.00
Total	11.02	Total	9.43
Loss	1.02	Profit	.57

Profit should be figured on the selling price, not the cost of merchandise. Profit is not made until the sale is completed and'paid. The figures for most other retail businesses are based on sales, so why not in the retail florist business?

Along with proper pricing to obtain a fair profit, go the subjects of selling and merchandising. All of these go together to give the retail florist a fair profit.

Profit is a legitimate element of the selling price, so be sure it is indexed with every article sold.

References

1. *Profile of the Retail Florist Industry.* U.S. Department of Agriculture Marketing Research Report #741 (1964).

2. Tolle, L. J. "Cost of Labor Variations Are Indirectly Reflected in Modern Pricing Theories," *Florists' and Nurseryman Exchange*, Vol. 143, No. 19 (May 8, 1965), pp. 24-26.
3. Voigt, A. O. "Your Retail Business-Merchandise Costs," *The Exchange*, Vol. 143, No. 7 (February 13, 1965), pp. 10, 12.

Chapter 15

ADVERTISING AND PUBLICITY

What is the difference between advertising and publicity? The end result is the same—to sell a product. In the case of the retail florist, it is to sell more flowers and related items to the consumer. The means by which this is done will differ. *Advertising means offering a product to the consumer which results directly in selling merchandise. Publicity,* on the other hand, *sells ideas* which eventually lead to selling merchandise. Advertising is done to get results *now,* which will make money for the business man. Advertising should be considered as an investment, not an expense.

Publicity is usually a means of promoting the idea of flowers, and trying to build a favorable image of the retail flower shop. It is an indirect way of selling. Many merchants and industries use flowers in their ads to sell furniture, clothing, liquor, and other items, and yet many florists are reluctant to use flowers for their own advertising and publicity. Fortunately for the industry, many of our more progressive florists realize the value of publicity and public relations. A retail florist a few years ago donated several hundred bulbs to beautify the grounds around city hall. The resulting publicity cannot be measured in dollars and cents to this florist, but there is no doubt as to the increase in business which resulted from this act. Another florist helped to landscape and beautify the area around a local bank which in turn improved the whole downtown area of his small town. Public relations, through publicity, is of great value in making the general public more flower conscious. Corsages have been donated to guest stars appearing on television shows by some of our retail florists. There are many ways to gain publicity for a retail florist shop.

Advertising

Advertising is a more direct approach to induce people to buy flowers *now.* A good advertising campaign must be planned carefully in advance. Advertising should start readers thinking about the merchandise offered for sale. A good ad will attract attention, be brief enough to be easily read and quickly grasped, and bring results. A good ad should aim to leave the readers, who cannot be sold at once, with a favorable impression, so that sooner or later, as the need or occasion arises, they will remember *a particular ad and store.*

There are four key principles which form the basis of successful advertising: (1) Good advertising informs the consumer, and helps him or her to buy more intelligently. (2) Good advertising tells the truth. (3) Good advertising conforms to the generally accepted standards of good taste. (4) Good advertising recognizes both its responsibility to help pay its own costs, and its social responsibilities in serving the public.

Considerations

There are several major points to consider when planning the advertising campaign for the year, as follows:

1. **The area to be covered with the ad.** What group of people is the florist trying to reach?

2. **The cost in relation to the expected return.** The decision here will be based partly on past experience, and partly on future expectations. What results are expected?

3. **How much to spend?** The general average quoted by most successful florists is approximately 3 to 5 per cent of their annual gross dollar volume of sales. This should include all types and forms of advertising, and particularly the cost of window displays. This should include the cost of flowers used, which are dumped after they have served their purpose.

4. **The age and reputation of the store.** A new business should expect to spend more (3 to 5 per cent) than an older established shop (2 to 3 per cent).

5. **Location of the store.** This will be a big factor in determining which type of advertising to use.

6. **When to advertise?** This seems to be the major question. Many florists and authorities will say to advertise *between the holidays,* many say only *at holidays,* and others will say to do both. Each florist must make his own decision. Each shop and location is different and we have very little concrete evidence to guide us. The author believes that a retail florist should have a planned advertising program all year, and advertise both at, and between, holidays.

7. **Determine both the long and short range objectives** for the program. Plan for the holiday as well as for the whole year.

Advertising must be well planned in advance. There are many factors to be considered when planning the advertising program for the year, including the following: (1) Compare the advertising expense with the gross volume of sales. What was the percentage spent last year? (2) Calculate the advertising expenses for each month during the year. (3) Determine what percentage of advertising expense will be used for each type of media. (4) Make sure the florist has the best space contract possible with the newspaper. (5) Be sure he is satisfied with the position assigned to his ad in the newspaper, or the spot on the radio. (6) Review and revise the direct mailing list to be sure it is reaching all the potential customers. (7) Be sure the mailing list is up-to-date. (8) Use the most effective postage rate on direct mail advertising. (9) Make a list of the non-productive advertising from last year. (10) Be sure the advertising job is as effective as that of his competitor.

Here are a few general advertising rules which will be wise to keep in mind when planning the advertising campaign. (1) Try not to get tied up with any real long term contracts. (2) Consider most advertising as an experiment and evaluate its effectiveness periodically. (3) Always advertise flowers and their uses.

Media

There are 17 different types of media from which to choose. The advisability of each must be considered for each particular shop and location. They are as follows:

1. **Window display.** This is one of the best for most shops if they are in the right location. Arrangements displayed in the store are considered in this category because they often are part of the window display.

2. **Newspaper ads.** They are very good in small towns, but may not be as good in the larger cities where the florist may be trying to reach only one section of the population. It is best to use many small ads rather than just a few large ones in the newspaper.

3. **Direct mail.** This seems to be the one advertising media which will work for all retail florists. Here, they can select the audience and aim the ad at a selected list of customers, and potential customers. Each florist can measure the return with the cost of the ad very easily. Brautigam Florists of Chicago send out 11,000 direct mail form color ads during the Christmas season.

4. **Radio.** This is good in small towns, but usually too expensive in large cities. Some florists allocate up to 75 per cent of their total advertising budget to radio advertising.

5. **Television.** Television is good for Allieds, or a large retail florist if he can afford it.

6. **Store front sign.** This is very good with little expense.

7. **Sign on truck.** This is good advertising with little cost.

8. **Yellow pages.** The advantage to this type of advertising in the phone book will depend on the size of the town, and the type of store. There are pros and cons on this type of advertising. Some florists feel it is a waste of money, and claim people do not use the Yellow Pages for a florist. Others feel that new people, particularly, in a community will go there first to find a florist, and feel it is well worth the money spent for this advertising. The florist must remember that he must do $1,000 worth of business to pay for a $100 ad.

9. **Street car and bus ads.** These are prohibitive in cost to most florists. They are good for the Allieds.

10. **Outdoor billboards.** These are prohibitive in cost to most individual florists, but good for Allieds and national advertising. They can be coordinated with television, and the Society of American Florists' campaign. The message must be brief, so the passerby can read it quickly.

11. **Magazines.** High schools and local clubs will ask for ads. Consider these as a donation (not advertising) since they will be a waste of money in most cases.

12. **Motion picture houses.** The success of this depends on the community.

13. **Organizational magazines.** An ad in *FTD News, Teleflora Spirit,* or *Florafacts* may increase the business from other member florists. Whether to pay for an ad in one of these magazines will depend on the size of the city, and just how much of this business a florist wishes to handle.

14. **Flowers.** The condition of the flowers, and the artistic designs constitute an excellent means for advertising floral products and the store, without any additional cost to the florist. Nothing can take the place of the reputation a retail florist builds for himself with his flowers. This is the foundation of the retail florist business, and its future success.

15. **Word-of-mouth.** The advantages of this type of advertising are that it is spoken as friend to friend and attracts attention, arouses interest, creates conviction, and is very effective.

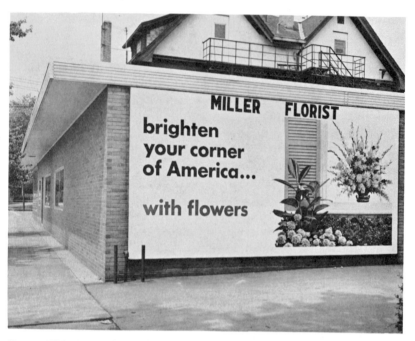

Figure 15-1. An outdoor billboard tying in with S. A. F. national advertising. (Courtesy, Miller Florist, Warren, Ohio.)

16. **Phone call reminders.** Such calls to regular customers can be an effective way to advertise.

17. **Cooperative advertising.** This can be very effective through Allieds and other groups. The Society of American Florists and the Florists Transworld Delivery Association both advertise nationally in a cooperative effort to help all segments of the florist industry. Colorado Carnation Growers advertise nationally, as do the Florida Gladiolus Growers Association. The latter two advertise a particular flower and the advertising is aimed at the retail florist as well as the consumer.

How does a retail florist determine which type of media is best for his shop? Nearly three-fourths of the florists advertise in paid media one or more times a year according to a U.S. Department of Agriculture survey. Over one-third feature specific floral products in their advertisements. Newspapers are the most popular medium used by retail florists to inform their customers of items featured. Nearly 40 per cent advertise in this way. Other frequently used media are window signs, radio, and direct mail. To determine the proper media depends on the size of the city in which a florist is located, the type of the shop, the volume of business he expects, and the age of the store.

Through results of various surveys we have come to the realization that the best advertising media for the florists in the smaller areas are: (1) newspaper, (2) direct mail, (3) window display, and (4) if the advertising budget allows it, radio. Television in most areas is prohibitive in cost. A consistent newspaper advertising campaign, backed up by direct mail advertising seems to be the most effective for many florists. This is in addition to a good window display as discussed in Chapter 7.

Newspaper Advertising

There are certain specific advantages of newspaper advertising to the retailer in a small town, as follows: (1) He reaches the largest number of potential customers. Probably no other single medium could deliver a message so completely and to so large an audience at one time. (2) He builds good will and prestige as well as sales. The mere fact that a small retail merchant has his name in the newspaper lends a high degree of prestige value to his business. The continued appearance of his name under an advertisement, even if only a small insertion, in the local newspaper places him and his wares in an acceptable position in the community, and thus builds good will for himself. (3) He can tie his advertising message in with the news of the moment, thereby making it more effective. There are unique possibilities offered by the timeliness of the newspaper. (4) He can receive valuable aid in his advertising from the newspaper. Publishers have wide experience with preparing advertisments for insertion in their papers. The skill acquired from this experience is at the disposal of the advertiser, usually free of charge. (5) He can capitalize on the buying state of mind of the newspaper reader when inspecting the advertisements for bargains. (6) His ad stays in print and can be seen whenever the newspaper is read.

Be sure to select the best ad mat. Professionally prepared advertisements in mat form will help to develop a strong selling ad at a minimum of work and expense, and it will be an ad that increases sales for the flower business. Advertising mats that are distributed by suppliers are exceptionally good in a high percentage of cases. The advertising experts who prepare these mats devote their full time to the study of advertising problems to determine the best buying motives, to select the strongest selling appeals, and to create a good advertising message for local retailers. Tie in with national advertising when possible. A good example here is to tie in with the advertising program of the Society of American Florists whose national advertising is expanding each year. Use timely mats or seasonal mats to tie in with the various holidays. Be sure to use a variety of appeals to be successful with different customers.

Many retail florists belong to an Allied in their own locality whose members are retailers, wholesalers, and growers all contributing a percentage of their gross sales to the advertising of flowers. This benefits everyone in the industry. All retail florists should join their own Allied.

A retail florist can have a powerful, consistent, advertising program with a limited advertising budget when he uses small space newspaper ads for his flower business. Successful advertising is based on the three profit P's of success. Good ads are: Planned, Persuasive, and Persistent. Remember that *repetition builds reputation*. Small ads will help to stretch the advertising dollars. Here are some good rules to follow: (1) Stick to one idea and one only in a small space ad. (2) Select the readers. Pinpoint the appeal to one group of customers; *i.e.*, an ad on the society page or the sports page. (3) Frame the ad so it will stand out. (4) Don't divide the ad into several parts—it is too small a space. (5) Don't crowd the ad. (6) Make sure it is easy to read. (7) Include only the essentials. The advertisement should appeal to the readers' self-interest, offer a product he really wants, be unique, picture the product or service, state the price, tell where to get it, and urge the customer to act *now*.

Direct Mail

Direct mail advertising is simply any sales message carried by mail to a regular or prospective customer. It is neither complicated nor difficult to use. It can sell, promote, introduce, or inform. Results depend on how well the program is planned and produced to do the job for which it is intended. The heart of any direct mail effort is the mailing list, which can be set up or obtained in many ways. Timing and cost are also important considerations.

Whatever form of direct mail advertising is used, be sure to remember the following key qualities, if the effort is to be rewarded with increased business: repetition, quality of the ad, be sure the list is one which is reaching the people that the florist wants it to reach, and select the best items to put across the message.

In order to be successful, direct mail advertising must do the following: (1) Be sent to a select list of customers and prospects who can be given strong reasons for coming to a particular store. (2) It must be kept accurate, and up-to-date. (Sending a notice to someone who is deceased is irritating to the survivors.) (3) The sales message which is sent to them must tell them "what they want to hear," or benefits which they will gain from shopping in this store. (4) The sales message must be personal. (5) The mailing list must fit the personality of the store, the merchandise, and the services advertised, as well as the people to whom it is addressed. (6) Each piece must be a selling piece. Ask for the order!

Direct mail advertising is similar to other advertising with some distinctive characteristics which can be extremely valuable to retailers. These are: (1) It is a personal contact with a selected prospect. (2) It can be sent to a limited number of especially qualified prospects. (3) It can be concealed from competitors. (4) It can be scheduled to reach the prospects on any given date. (5) Retailers can easily measure direct mail's effectiveness, and keep its cost in balance with sales and profits.

To set up the direct mailing list, the retail florist should start with his own customers, add people to whom he has delivered flowers from his customers, use lists of business executives, country club members, garden club members, new businesses in the area, and include members of various civic organizations. These lists should be screened to make up a particular list of special potential customers.

The Value of Advertising

Many retail florists do not realize the value of advertising. As a result, too little advertising is done by the florists. There are many florist shops that do not spend enough money on advertising. Many successful florists and experts in the field of advertising have said that a florist should spend from 3 to 5 per cent of his gross volume of sales on advertising. Yet, the surveys show 1.5 to 2.4 per cent is usually spent (Table 6-1, Chapter 6). The survey figures, of course, may not include all the expenditures which should be charged to advertising; such as flower donations, cost of window displays, and flowers used in these displays. When all expenses and monies are figured in that should be charged to advertising, the figure should approach 3 to 5 per cent of the gross volume of sales for the shop, including the planned advertising campaign discussed previously. However, it is hard to develop an advertising program around a percentage allotment. This is used as a basis for comparison with others. Advertising must be planned in advance, so that too much money is not spent before the year is out. It may be figured monthly, quarterly, or yearly, but it should be planned at least six months in advance. It must be planned and controlled by appropriations and budgets. It must include all the costs for planned advertising, promotions, publicity, and public relations. The important thing is to stimulate in the public mind an awareness of the pleasures to be derived from the increased use of flowers in daily living.

Promotion and Publicity

Obtaining newspaper publicity for the shop will help a retail florist with his business. The best way is to make himself known to more people by gaining publicity for his shop. Most newspapers are glad to print items of news, if they are news, and not just an attempt to get free advertising. Meet the editor of the newspaper and cultivate a nose for news. Give stories a professional touch, and be sure to offer genuine news. Publicity is indirect advertising in that it sells the idea of flowers, not the flowers themselves.

Open House

One of the best promotion ideas is to have an open house before Christmas and again before Easter. Planning is important here, just as in any advertising campaign. Everything should be priced that is on display and plenty of made-up items should be available for customers to see how to use the merchandise. Some florists, if the open house is held on Sunday, do not sell any of the merchandise, but will always take orders. Others set up several cash registers and do a booming business. The newspaper publicity will be tremendous from this. The florist might invite the local radio station to broadcast from his shop during the open house. It is impossible to measure the value of this in dollars and cents. Provide the opportunity for people to return to buy something they saw and liked but didn't get a chance to purchase. An open house can be an excellent traffic builder, but the event must be well planned and executed, and merchandised for maximum results.

Promotions are used for several reasons: to create more busi-

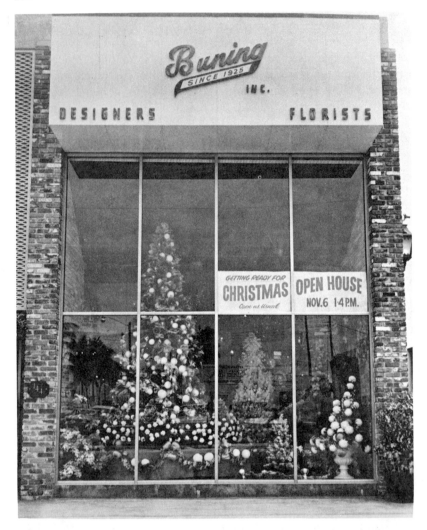

Figure 15-2. Christmas open house. (Courtesy, Buning The Florist, Fort Lauderdale, Fla.)

ness, to realize more profitable orders, to move over-supplies, and to eventually sell merchandise. Each promotion begins with an idea which is expanded by the florist. As an example, in the fall when automobile dealers are featuring new cars, the promotion manager can be approached and sold on the idea that a window full of flowers shows activity, and that something unusual is taking place. Sell dealers on mass display. Identify their salesmen with boutonnieres, and the women employees with corsages. Some florists have

talked automobile salesmen into giving the customer an orchid corsage or a pot plant each time a new car is delivered. Or sell them
on the idea of giveaway items, such as individual roses or carnations, to each customer during the sale.

Figure 15-3. An open house can draw tremendous crowds if the florist has
the space. (Courtesy, King Floral Co., Forty Fort, Pa.)

Another promotion idea to keep the volume steady is to sell a
man on sending his wife 10 arrangements throughout the year. These
arrangements can effectively tie in with anniversaries, birthdays, and
the major holidays, and are excellent for husbands who are forgetful.

Window displays can be used to promote flowers by tying in
with a local event, movie, or news item of national importance.

Another method for publicity is to provide some free flowers
or corsages for special programs on television. This can be done by
an individual florist, by a group, or by an Allied.

Publicity and promotion can help sell flowers for any shop, but they must be planned in advance, and correlated with the advertising program and expenditure of the shop.

Public Relations

Public relations is a form of publicity, and an indirect form of advertising. Basically, it is a method to interest people in a particular shop. It can be done by supplying bulbs as mentioned at the beginning of the chapter, by speaking to various groups, giving demonstrations, donating plants and flowers to public officials, or any of a hundred other ideas.˙ The florist should charge a fee for any talks and demonstrations that he gives. A fee will cut down on the number ˙ of requests, all of which cost time and money. A florist has to weigh this against the benefits from the advertising value gained.

Herb Mitchell says: "Public relations are activities performed in an attempt to create a favorable public opinion among customers and potential customers." He gives the following 16 examples: "(1) Giving care information for cut flowers and pot plants. (2) Guaranteeing the merchandise. (3) Filling out the sympathy card on the reverse side with all pertinent information. (4) Providing adequate parking for your customers. (5) Advertising in local programs and yearbooks. (6) The use of credit cards which can be very advantageous to your business. (7) Acknowledgment of new accounts. (8) A follow-through to see that orders are satisfactory. (9) Servicing weddings. (10) "Thank You's" for business. (11) Contact inactive accounts. (12) Proper telephone atmosphere and techniques. (13) Checking driver contact with the customer. (14) Checking to see how your packages look. (15) Sending flowers from *you* to the customer on special occasions like birthday and anniversary. (16) Giving customer service." Many of these are just good business practices as well as being good public relations.

Advertising boils down to the question of "does a retail florist really want his business to grow?" If so, then he must plan his campaign carefully. Decide *What* to sell, *When* to advertise, to *Whom* to advertise, *Where* to advertise, and *How* much to budget for advertising? It is up to each florist to plan his advertising, and do it carefully. Advertising, promotion, public relations, and publicity are all part of a well-organized successful florist business.

References

1. Anonymous. "Select the Best Ad Mat," *Flower News* (February 5, 1966), p. 1.

2. Conn, G. *Retail Florists Should Not Advertise Unless.* Talk, given at the Pennsylvania Retail Florists' Conference (July 18, 1966).
3. Havas, N. *Profile of the Retail Florist Industry.* U.S. Department of Agriculture Marketing Research Report #741 (1964), 27 pp.
4. Mitchell, H. "Public Relations," *Florists' Review,* Vol. 136, No. 3519 (May 6, 1965), pp. 54-55, 69 and Vol. 136, No. 3521 (May 20, 1965), pp. 37-38, 82.

Chapter 16

MERCHANDISING; CASH-AND-CARRY

Merchandising

Merchandising today is a far cry from the pushcart selling of flowers of our forefathers, and yet they employed some of the same principles used today. Their success was based on letting the people see the flowers, plus personal contact, and asking them to buy. Today we must do the same.

If we are to merchandise flowers, we must display them and use salesmanship to complete the sale. Merchandising means offering the right product to the right people, at the right time, in the right place, and at the right price. We already have the right product: flowers—a universally liked commodity. We do not have to sell people on flowers. We also can sell the merchandise at the right price. Many recent studies have shown the most popular range for merchandising flowers to be between 90 cents and $1.50. So, two merchandising criteria can be met very easily by the retail florist. Now the florist has to find the right people, the right time, and the right place. Mass market outlets are a part of the answer, but do not apply to the retail florist business except from the competitive angle. Advertising will help to find the people. A U.S. Department of Agriculture survey showed that 86 per cent of the florists contacted, reported they used floral designs in their shop windows as a regular part of their merchandising program.

In shifting the emphasis from artistry to merchandising, the retail florist does not need to lessen his efforts in design. In order to direct his business and orient it toward the requirements of the new market, he must become a merchant, not just in name, but in fact.

Effective merchandising depends on the establishment of a positive firm image in the public mind. To the man on the street, every retail establishment carries an image.

The tools of the merchandiser fall into four broad areas: price, advertising, display, and salesmanship. Price is the most powerful merchandising tool of all and will be discussed later in detail. Advertising was discussed in Chapter 15. Display is an important part of merchandising, and no other product lends itself so well to display as flowers. Good merchandisers recognize that displays are the first step in getting the product into the customer's hands. Salesmanship must be developed by the retail florist if he is to become a successful merchandiser of floral products.

The big sales expansion for flowers today lies not only with special occasion or holiday buying, but with the *everyday use of flowers in the home and place of business*. Promoting flowers for everyday use means publicizing flowers as a part of today's modern living.

In order to merchandise flowers and increase the use of flowers by the average consumer, we must endeavor to establish a buying habit for flowers. Merchandising is one way we can get people into the habit of buying flowers regularly. The florist must concentrate his efforts towards selling flowers for the home. Between 80 and 90 per cent of the people in a survey indicated that they would buy flowers regularly if they were available at a low price. They indicated they would be willing to spend 90 cents to a dollar per week on flowers if they were available. Most of the purchases would be for the home.

Roses have been shown by several studies to be a good item for a special sale. Consumer preference studies have also shown that the number does not need to always be a dozen. Pompon chrysanthemums and gladioli have had wide acceptance. In pot plants we find that pot chrysanthemums, kalanchoes, and petunias are the best sellers in some shops.

Merchandising can be done all the time, and not just to move surplus stock. To merchandise economically, a florist needs flowers that are attractive, will last more than a few hours, are low priced, and are attractively displayed. They should be in constant supply, and sold in such a way that they are easy to buy.

Supermarkets place their products before 35 per cent of the consumers, while retail florists' shops attract only about 3 per cent of the consumers. This drawing power can be increased in the flower shops by following some of the ideas adopted by the supermarkets. Supermarkets are now reaching a hitherto florally untouched segment of the buying public. Surveys have shown that most people who buy flowers in supermarkets never patronize a retail flower shop.

Mass Market Outlets

The mass market outlets offer a means of broadening the market. This can cause a significant increase in the sale of flowers for home use through the means of impulse sales. There will be increased profits to the growers through this increased volume of sales. It will ultimately increase profits to retail florists by increasing the consumer's awareness of flowers, and by influencing his buying habits to include flowers. If people are more flower conscious, then they will purchase more flowers in retail flower shops for special occasions as well as for home use. Any promotion of flowers will eventually stimulate the sale of flowers through the regular conventional channels.

Flowers are being sold in convenience stores, drugstores, and supermarkets in the Denver area through two non-traditional firms.

Mass market outlets have been successful because they have created a demand for flowers through advertising and promotion. Their setup is entirely different from that of the retail florist. They depend on mass display, large store traffic, and a low markup.

The supermarkets use advertising and promotion to the utmost. This integrated program of advertising and promotion can be used by retail florists on an industry level. The supermarkets recognize differences in people according to social class, religious groups, and regional groups. They isolate groups for their own business, and concentrate all their efforts on that group. Supermarket "competition" is not as real as one might think

The advertising and promotional program must stimulate the buyer to want the product, or to want the satisfaction it provides. Stimulation so far has not been provided successfully by floral promotion and packaging. This is something which needs to be developed in the retail florist industry. Packaging lends the goods to better merchandising, one of the avenues to increased sales.

A recent study at the University of Illinois showed that flowers competed favorably with other merchandise in both a variety store and a supermarket, for net returns and gross profits per square foot of display space. Special sales of pot plants and small bunches of cut flowers were studied in these two stores, and compared to sales in a retail flower shop. It was found that less expensive items sold better in the variety store, while more expensive items sold better in the supermarket and retail flower shop. Holidays, weekends, and special occasions had the largest influence on weekly sales. The quality of the merchandise was found to be of prime importance.

To encourage the everyday use of flowers and plants, an adequate display of good quality merchandise should be maintained in the store at all times. This seems to be the area in which the mass markets fall down in most instances. And this is where the retail florist shop can have the advantage. An adequate selection of colors and varieties is also needed.

What about competition between retail flower shops and the big chain stores? In order for a retail florist to merchandise flowers he must concentrate on the reluctance of consumers to enter a retail flower shop. Recent studies have shown that the average person will not enter a florist shop to browse. He does not feel welcome, and this condition has been brought about by the florists themselves. If florists are to merchandise flowers and increase sales in their shops, they must *make people feel welcome.* Successful merchandising depends on volume selling, which can only occur through increased store traffic.

A retail florist can increase total sales through cash-and-carry sales, as well as realizing profits through the selling of other items at the same time. If the florist can produce speed and ease in purchasing, as well as attractive displays, he will bring more people into the retail shop.

A spectacular new mobile merchandising innovation is called "Flowerama." It is designed for merchandising outdoor flowers in such areas as shopping centers, supermarkets, nurseries, and garden centers. The structure is pre-cut of translucent Filon panels and opens to a 24' x 32' selling area. It folds up to 8' x 32' and is mobile so can be moved to where the action is. Bachman's Bouquet Boutique is another new idea in merchandising (see Chapter 3).

Cash-and-Carry

Cash-and-carry is probably the most common form of merchandising practiced by many retail florists. Cash-and-carry specials are applicable to almost all retail florist shops. Each florist must decide for himself what is best for him. A lot will depend on the type of store, location, and customers, but any florist can merchandise through cash-and-carry specials if he wishes. However, if a florist does decide to try cash-and-carry specials, he should give it a fair trial. Don't try it once and say it isn't any good. It has to be tried *every weekend* for at least six months to be successful. The florists who are successfully offering cash-and-carry specials to their customers do it every weekend of the year including holiday weekends with the possible exception of Easter and Mother's Day. Some florists offer a cash-and-carry special even on these weekends.

Why Cash-and-Carry?

Many florists wonder why they should try cash-and-carry weekend specials. There are several reasons why a retail florist should try them. One is that it will increase the total gross sales which in turn should increase the net profit to the business without additional costs to the overhead. Secondly, it will get more people into the store which in turn will lead to more sales. With more people in the store, the florist will sell more related or impulse items if they are on display. Thirdly, these are cash sales which will put actual cash in the cash register without any expense for the bookkeeping. Fourth, these are sales which do not need to be designed or delivered. Fifth, flowers can be purchased in larger quantity, and at a lower price than usual. Sixth, the flowers not sold for cash-and-carry can be used the next day in funeral work. This means a higher profit on these design pieces because the material was purchased at a lower cost than usual, and sold in funeral work at the normal price which results in a greater markup. And, lastly, the florist will be helping more people to buy flowers more often.

Saving the Customer Money

One of the best advertising gimmicks to use is to show the customer how cash-and-carry is saving him or her money. It saves the customer money because there is no delivery charge figured into the price of the merchandise. (Florists have reported delivery charges range from 35 cents to $1.25 per piece depending upon the city.) There is no bookkeeping or mailing of statements involved. Since there is no labor in designing, the flowers can be offered to the customer at a lower price. There is no container or box to be paid for. All of these items reduce the cost of the merchandise to the consumer. The retail florist should tell the customers that he is buying large quantities of flowers cheaper, and that he is passing the savings on to them. They will understand and appreciate this.

The success of the program depends upon a good advertising

policy, attractive display, and sticking strictly to the *cash-and-carry* for everyone. If the florist explains the facts to the customer, even the best customer, she will not insist that he deliver, and put it on her charge account without an additional charge. If a florist starts making exceptions, then the success of the program will be impaired and he will find himself losing money instead of making it.

The success of tie-in promotions to take advantage of traffic drawn through cash-and-carry specials, depends upon the following: (1) Select an item which adds to the appeal of the special, or has a strong latent appeal of its own. (2) Price it and advertise it as a bargain. (3) Set up a mass display of the item. (4) Use personal salesmanship to the fullest. A good advertising program is necessary to tell the customer about the product, tell why it is a bargain, tell the customer which of his wants it will satisfy, and tell as much as possible about the retail operation which affects costs and the retail price.

How Much to Charge?

The cash-and-carry specials should be offered every weekend of the year and at a price between 90 cents and a $1.50. Studies at several universities have shown that when specials were offered at 35 and 50 cents, the people felt it was too cheap for a retail florist shop and hesitated to buy them. When the price rose over $1.50 then the number of sales was curtailed. The success of cash-and-carry lies in volume business. Most florists who offer cash-and-carry specials on a regular basis keep the price around $1.00. Some sell them for 95 cents, which, if the sales tax is five cents, brings it to an even dollar. Others sell at $1.00 plus the tax. Others use an uneven figure such as 97 or 99 cents. Each florist must determine his own price. Florists do not agree on whether to keep the price the same every week or vary it with market conditions. It is up to each florist to determine which policy he thinks will work best for him. Some florists try it each way for six months to see which is best. Pricing is based on the cost of merchandise. Most florists use a 2 or 2½ to 1 markup. This should take care of all costs and expenses, since there is reduced overhead with this type of selling.

What to Merchandise?

This is a hard question to answer although we do have some guidelines. The first of these is to work with the wholesaler and offer material that is in oversupply on the market. If there is no oversupply, then decide on some other flower. Flowers should be offered that are commonly known to the general public. Stay away from exotic flowers or flowers that are relatively unknown to most people. Roses have been shown by many studies to be one of the best all-year-round items for cash-and-carry specials. Pompons, gladioli, snaps, and carnations are also good items. A florist does not need to sell in dozen lots. If the wholesale price is such that the florist can offer only nine roses or one-half bunch of pompons, then he should advertise it this way. If he can't merchandise at a markup of at least 2 to 1, then it will not be profitable. The florist, however, must always use quality merchandise (even if short-stemmed) or he will defeat the purpose of the program.

Will It Work?

Yes, for many florists, and not at the expense of normal sales. In a program in Pennsylvania a few years ago, all of the retail florists in a certain town offered cash-and-carry specials every weekend for a year. Aggregate dollar volume sales from all six shops increased 14.8 per cent over the preceding year. Net profits increased 19.3 per cent. Not all of this was due to the cash-and-carry specials themselves, but a good percentage was, according to the participating florists.

The potentialities of self-service in the flower industry are grossly underdeveloped. For instance, only a few florists among the many that offer specials today have the cash-and-carry items out where the customer can help himself.

Successful Examples

Many florists all over the country have been trying cash-and-carry specials for years with great success. A florist in Nashville, Tennessee, sold 100,000 roses during the summer months and merchandised gladioli from November through May at $1.00 a dozen. A Chicago florist sold 6,000 roses, cash-and-carry, on Sweetest Day back in 1955. A survey of special sales in eight major cities showed that cash-and-carry specials were successfully improving business in four of the cities where the florists were trying this type of merchandising. New York City florists are changing their selling methods to keep up with their growing city. Many are trying merchandising through cash-and-carry sales. They insist on using prime quality material and most of them do not charge over a dollar.

A particular retail florist was losing business to a supermarket across the street from his shop. He started offering flowers that were priced for home use through weekend cash-and-carry specials. He offers these every week of the year and furnishes no greens, designing, or delivery. He has educated his customers to the term cash-and-carry. His total sales have increased by 15 per cent in a six-month period due to special sales. He says that people will return week after week to take flowers home. He also said that some of his summer weekends would be dull without these specials. He says these sales do not interfere with his usual flower sales. *He has competed so successfully with the supermarket, that the supermarket has discontinued the handling of cut flowers.* This florist is successfully merchandising flowers with advertising, display, lower prices, and quality merchandise.

Many florists have tried weekend cash-and-carry specials and are convinced of their success in helping to sell more flowers. The following are some typical remarks made by retail florists concerning special sales: "Specials have increased store traffic by 400 per cent." "Total sales have increased since I started cash-and-carry sales." "The sale of other items in the store has increased." "Advertising for special sales keeps my name before the public." "These specials create customer buying habits." "Specials do not cheapen the store name."

A few retailers have started to develop real techniques for merchandising, and others are following. Many retail shops, however, are not located in positions favorable for store traffic and merchandising. Some retail florists are not interested in low-mark-up sales.

The florist must separate his business into two types: service and cash-and-carry. He cannot live on special sales alone, but they can add to his gross income and net profit. The success of this program rests not alone with advertising, display, and pricing, but also the enthusiasm and initiative of the store personnel. Price alone is not sufficient for a successful merchandising program.

The study mentioned previously showed that gross income and net profits could be increased in every shop in one town and not at the expense of another. Each store showed an increase. This program also showed the importance of coordinated effort in purchasing, advertising, and an all-out promotion as a group.

The results of this yearlong study of cash-and-carry specials showed the following: added gross income was accomplished with little additional capital and operating costs, merchandising helped to move the additional flowers on the market, a definite promotional appeal is needed to get people into the habit of buying flowers weekly, cooperative buying and advertising by a group of florists will greatly reduce the cost of the promotion, and the effectiveness of cash-and-carry specials depends upon the quality of merchandise offered at a retail price under $1.50, and for every weekend of the year.

Another successful cash-and-carry florist is The Rialto Florist in New York City, which is open 24 hours a day, seven days a week. "Quality" is the firm's key word in marketing its cash-and-carry specials. Average price for the specials has risen from 98 cents to $1.29 per bunch.

Supermarket Competition

Irwin A. Cochrun gives retailers the following 10 steps to increase sales if they wish to compete effectively with the supermarkets: "(1) Make use of the power of pre-sold merchandising through the media of mass communications. (2) Speed the flow of goods to the selling shelves, and use bigger displays. (3) Use the power of lowered prices. (4) Make it easy for the customers to shop, and provide adequate parking. (5) Make it easy for customers to go through the store, and draw them past the merchandise items to the service counter. (6) Expose customers to the power of mass display. (7) Make the product saleable by packaging cut flowers for ease in self-service. (8) Do not rush customers, but let them browse around. (9) Use alert, courteous, and helpful salesclerks. (10) Remove any bottlenecks in recording sales and the checking-out operations." Many of these points can be used by retail florists.

Increased Sales

Other ways to increase sales in existing retail flower shops are through the use of seasonal flowers, displaying arrangements of varying sizes to give a choice, separate pricing of flowers and services, and pricing all merchandise so the customer can make his own selection.

Another way to increase the sale of flowers is by increasing the number of florists' holidays from the traditional seven to 10 or 12.

Why not promote flowers, as some florists are already doing, for other holidays and special occasions? Some suggestions for other holidays would be St. Patrick's Day, Sweetest Day, National Secretaries' Day, Father's Day, and National Flower Week.

Planning ahead for features of specials when the market is low in price and high in supply can be beneficial to the retailer, wholesaler, and grower; whether specials are a part of each florist's operation or not. Any florist can use these times to advertise real values to his customers to get more of them to come into the shop. This is all part of a successful merchandising campaign.

Merchandising does not only revolve around cash-and-carry specials at $1.00. Other quantities of merchandise can be successfully merchandised at $3.50, $5.00, $7.50, and higher if the florist has the right kind of customers who will purchase these items. It all depends on how the merchandise is advertised, displayed, and offered for sale to the customer.

Physical Layout

Another rule of merchandising is that a physical layout should draw the customer naturally and unconsciously into all parts of the store. Every possible item should be displayed so it is easily seen. Goods well displayed are half sold. The following list of important consideration is from Robert Ench, S. Klein Department Store.

A. An attractive and appealing interior:
   1. Provide a convenient, symmetrical layout.
   2. Have amply wide aisles.
   3. Modern display fixtures and equipment are necessary.
   4. Have low fixtures in the center, so that the whole area can be seen.
   5. Most of the merchandise should be in plain sight and properly priced.
   6. Attractive and orderly arrangement of displays and stock will increase sales.
   7. Have an appropriate floor in good condition.
   8. Use harmony of colors and forms so that the whole store makes a pleasant picture.
   9. Have plenty of light so the merchandise is seen to best advantage.

10. Cleanliness of merchandise, fixtures, displays, and floors is essential.
11. The store should be properly ventilated or air-conditioned.
12. The floor space must be large enough so that people do not feel crowded.
13. The store personnel shall be neatly and inconspicuously dressed, courteous, and eager to serve.

B. **Traffic control:**
   1. Right or left hinging of entrance door.
   2. Wide or narrow aisles.
   3. Location of service counter and cash register at rear of store.
   4. Locate staples or items most frequently asked for in out-of-way corners of store.
   5. Change location of merchandise once or twice a year.

C. **Eliminate blind fixtures and other hiding places for merchandise:**
   1. Have 90 per cent of your merchandise on display.

D. **Install open fixtures and make other provisions for display:**
   1. Self-service fixtures.
   2. Low display tables.
   3. Island displays.
   4. Wall displays for tall merchandise.

E. **Allot space to items in accordance with their sales volume and sales possibilities:**
   1. Locate merchandise for convenience.
   2. Group related items together.
   3. Locate seasonal items in greatest traffic area.
   4. Locate specials in greatest traffic area.

F. **Interior displays:**
   1. Price mark every item displayed.
   2. Accompany merchandise with a sign telling what it is and its possible uses.

G. **Window displays:**
   1. Make the windows advertise the merchandise and the character of the store.
   2. Mark prices plainly.
   3. Display related items together.
   4. Tie in displays with local events.
   5. Tie in with national advertising.
   6. Put human interest into display.
   7. Do not crowd the window.

8. Make displays simple.
9. Improve the window lighting.
10. Change displays frequently.
11. Keep everything clean.
12. Motion attracts attention.
13. Make the displays sell merchandise.

Summary

Merchandising means offering the right product to the right people, at the right place, at the right time, and at the right price. It can be done by retail florists as well as by mass market outlets. Successful merchandising depends on advertising, promotion, display, easy access, low prices, and quality merchandise.

Each florist must study his own situation to determine how he should best merchandise in his shop. His employees must have the desire to merchandise flowers and use their salesmanship on these as well as other items.

Hundreds of regular retail florists are successfully merchandising flowers through cash-and-carry specials. Other methods will be developed in the future. Retail florists are proving every day that cut flowers and pot plants can be merchandised successfully with a minimum of effort and operating expense, even in the face of supermarket competition.

References

1. Ench, R. "Store Merchandising Outline," Pennsylvania Retail Florists Bulletin No. 79 (October 1965), pp. 4-5.
2. Havas, N. *Profile of the Retail Florist Industry*. U.S. Department of Agriculture Marketing Research Report #741 (1964), 27 pp.
3. Norland, Jim. "Convenience Flowers," *Southern Florist and Nurseryman* (March 6, 1970), pp. 14-16.
4. Pfahl, P. B. *Merchandising for Profit in Retail Flower Shops*. Penna. Agr. Exp. Sta. Bul. 659 (August 1959), 25 pp.
5. White, L. T. *Merchandising: The Key to the Future*. Talk, given at the Pennsylvania Retail Florist Conference (1964).

Chapter 17

SALESMANSHIP

Salesmanship—the art of selling—is one of the weakest links in the present retail florist industry. Most retail florists are excellent designers, many are good businessmen, but few are top-notch salesmen. It has been said by many people that most sales people in the retail florist business are *order takers*, not salesmen. This is unfortunate, because the success of the business, and the profits realized, depend on the successful selling of the merchandise. Retail florists are caught between rising costs and shrinking profits, and one solution is a rise in sales. We have mentioned in Chapter 12 the qualities that a florist should look for in hiring his sales personnel. To review: a salesman should have the initiative for selling, and must like people; he should be ambitious, dependable, efficient, have good health and appearance; have a pleasing personality; be diplomatic and courteous; be able to get along well with others; and have a thorough knowledge of store merchandise, prices and policies.

Salesmanship is actually one element of good merchandising. A person cannot be a good salesman unless he knows what he is selling. Besides selling flowers, a retail florist is selling what flowers can do for people. It is the job of the retail florist to translate the characteristics of flowers themselves into the intangible messages they carry. This calls for selling skills far beyond that of an ordinary merchant. The better a florist knows the product he is selling, the more successful he will be. He must tell people about his product and what it costs, and then get them to buy it. Eighty per cent of the retail florists in the United States, according to a recent survey, price mark all items displayed. A retail florist should not be afraid to price his merchandise so that the customer can easily see it. It will greatly help in the selling of flowers and other merchandise.

To be a good salesman, a person must want to be a salesman. He must like his product and believe in it, and he must like and trust people. Salesmanship is an art that takes practice. He must work at it to become a good salesman. Many of the points of good salesmanship are just plain common sense.

It has been stated many times that a salesman can sell anything if he makes it attractive, and shows a prospective customer how he can use the item. Many florists have installed large, walk-in refrigerators for the customers. Allowing a customer to really see and handle the flowers fits in with today's philosophy of selling flowers. A florist should utilize the five senses as much as possible if he wishes to succeed in selling.

The following highlights on selling are from Herb Mitchell. There are three types of salesman: the order taker, the negotiation type, and the creative salesman. The order taker is just what the name implies. The negotiation type tries to bargain with the customer. The creative salesman, however, is the one who makes more sales for himself and the store, and is the one who upsells the merchandise and gets the customer to spend the most money for what he or she wants. Maximum satisfaction is the aim. Courage and confidence in himself and his product are two important factors in becoming a successful salesman. He should not be discouraged if he doesn't succeed at first. Throw out the attitude that "this won't work" and say instead, "it is worth a try."

The salesman should serve every customer in the best way possible. He must develop a winning personality and constantly strive to improve his personality. It also pays to cultivate a persuasive personality. Selling depends on communications. A good salesman must learn to communicate with his customers. They must know what he is saying, as well as what he means. Communication is a two-way street between the salesman and the customer.

First impressions are always important and the first 30 seconds that a customer spends in the shop may be the most important. There are four vital components of an approach to a customer which lead to a sale: (1) *The shop's name.* Use it in all discussions. (2) *The salesperson's name.* The customer likes to know the name of the person to whom he is speaking. (3) *The customer's name.* Find out what it is, use it, and remember it. (4) *The need.* Find out what the customer's need is and try to fill it.

All retail florist salesmen have a five point selling job: (1) sell himself, (2) sell the store, (3) sell his ideas, (4) sell the product, and (5) sell customer satisfaction. Successful salesmen use various buying appeals to create a favorable impression for flowers and services. They try to convince customers that flowers are the best thing to buy for the occasion. They appeal to the aesthetic or utilitarian factor of flowers. Selling is both an art and a science. It calls for careful planning. There are three important steps to every successful sale: (1) The salesman must interest his customer in his merchandise and his ideas. (2) He must convince the customer that he needs the products and services that are offered by the florist. (3) He must ask for the sale—ask the customer to buy—*now*. This is where many sales are lost. Many sales training authorities say that 90 per cent of the sales are sold in the first 30 seconds. This is where the salesman must sell himself and his store, and create the impression of his ability to serve and deliver the goods. Use the "you" approach to selling, and bring the customer into the discussion. Sell quality and not price. The six points for selling quality are as follows: (1) Establish a quality atmosphere. (2) Sell significant benefits of the merchandise. (3) Point out the superior features of quality flowers. (4) Always emphasize exceptional values. (5) Sell the experience and reputation of the store. (6) Sell friendly and reliable service. Many florists do not understand certain values of their business and of selling. They don't under-

Figure 17-1. An attractive and spacious area for selling. (Courtesy, Frederick's Flowers, Souderton, Pa.)

stand the value of their own time. They don't understand the
value of their own ability. They don't understand the value of
their own product, and services. An understanding of all these values
is essential if the florist is going to be a good salesman. *He must
believe in himself first.*

Upselling

Upselling is the mark of a successful salesman. This means
selling a $15 arrangement to a customer who had expected to
spend $10. The salesman must use the power of suggestion and
use enthusiasm in his selling. He should be able to give ideas and
suggestions. He must show the customer how beautiful the flowers
are. It is always best to take the flowers out of the refrigerator,
and let the customer see them and smell them. Don't just point
to the flowers. Don't mention price unless forced to do so. When
price is mentioned try to give the highest price to give the most
customer satisfaction. Don't ask a question which gives the customer a chance to say "no." Close the sale by asking the customer
"which one" they want, not "if." Try to put the customer
into the mood to say "yes" not "no." A demonstration will help
to make the sale. This is very effective in store selling. Handle the
new merchandise with respect. Demonstrate a finished product
whenever possible, not just the ingredients. Put the merchandise
into the customer's hands as soon as possible. Sell the good features
by telling the customer the benefits of the flowers, and of this
particular arrangement. Mention the features of the product, such
as: fresh, long lasting, well designed, unusually arranged, colorful,
newest variety, and other salient points which will help to complete the sale. The idea of the salesman taking the customer into
the delivery room to see the higher priced arrangements is also
a part of successful selling. All of these practices will help the
salesman to upsell his merchandise. This is also called *upgrading
the sale.*

Men are easier to sell to than women, but over half of the
customers in a flower shop are women. A florist needs patience
with all of his customers. Don't try to high-pressure the customers
as it is not expected nor appreciated in a retail florist shop. A
modern approach to selling in the flower shop is to encourage
browsing, and to make the customer feel welcome. Try to greet
all regular customers by name. Remember their likes and dislikes
in flowers. It is best to find out the occasion for the flowers, and

make two or three suggestions, letting the customer make the final decision. Always give a range of prices where possible. For example, a man went into a retail flower shop recently to get his wife some flowers for Valentine's Day. He asked the saleslady what she had and she said, "We have roses for eight dollars." That was all she said. The customer did not wish to spend eight dollars for Valentine's Day, and yet he did not want to be made to feel *cheap* by asking for something less expensive, so he said he would think about it. He left the store and bought his wife a three dollar box of candy. The florist lost that sale, and many more. The man is afraid to try flowers again.

Use the common names of flowers and plants, and not the scientific name unless specifically asked by the customer.

Use the psychology of selling by appealing to all of the senses. Color slide presentations of designs make impressive shop sales aids for all designs, not just wedding work.

Good manners are very important in successful selling. The following practices are considered *bad* manners and should be discouraged in the retail florist shop:

1. Being indifferent to a customer waiting for service.

2. Using a cold, impersonal manner with customers.

3. Arguing or contradicting a customer.

4. Interrupting another employee when he is waiting on a customer without first asking permission from the customer.

5. Allowing friends to visit on the telephone.

6. Carrying on personal conversations within hearing of a customer.

7. Loud talking and laughing in the store.

8. Whistling or singing when there is a customer in the store.

9. Loud shouting or calling out instructions in the workroom or sales area.

10. Referring to customers or other employees as "honey," "dearie," "kiddo," or "my dear."

11. Chewing gum, smoking, or eating in the presence of a customer.

12. Men lounging around with their hands in their pockets.

13. Women powdering or putting on lipstick on the sales floor.

Pitfalls in Selling

A survey of Michigan florists by a mystery shopper a few years ago brought out the following points on poor selling: (1) Many florists neglected the customer. She waited over 10 minutes for a clerk in one shop. (2) Florists were not careful enough about distractions and confusion in the store. (3) They didn't try to upgrade the sale. In most shops, she did not spend as much money as she had been prepared to for the items she purchased. (4) The florist did not try to sell related merchandise by suggesting other items to go with the flowers purchased. (5) Many florists did not know enough about their merchandise. Some salespeople did not even know the names of some of the common flowers in the shop. (6) They didn't suggest the uses to which flowers can be put. (7) They didn't attempt to close the sale in many cases. She walked out of nine shops without making a purchase. (8) They didn't show the merchandise to the customer, nor get it into the customer's hands. (9) In some shops, there was so much extraneous conversation that it took too long to make the sale. (At $1.20 an hour, it costs the florist 30¢ in labor time when the clerk takes 15 minutes to wait on a customer.) In an FTDA survey of over 100 retail florist shops in Kansas City, more than $400 extra business was lost by seven out of the 100 shops in one day. Professional shoppers were used and they did not spend the $15 plus tax and service charges that they were allotted, except in just a few of the 100 shops.

ABC's of Selling

Understanding the fundamentals of any science makes it possible to learn the more technical aspects. Here are some ABC's of selling more flowers to more people, suggested by J. Bedford:

Appreciate the opportunity you have to be engaged in the greatest business in the world—selling flowers.

Believe in what you are selling.

Compliment your customers honestly and sincerely every time you can.

Dedicate yourself to making a successful career of selling.

Enthusiasm is contagious and will help your sales.

Find the key reason why your customer wants to buy.

Give a little more attention and service to your customer, and you won't have to worry about competition.

Hesitate before you answer any question your customer asks. It will avoid arguments and give you time to think of the best answer.

Imagine your customer enjoying the benefits of what you are selling.

Justify every sales point you make so your customer is convinced of the truth of what you are saying.

Know all you can about your merchandise.

Listen for key words your customer uses when talking.

Memorize your customer's name when you first hear it.

Nail down each sales point in step-by-step strategy.

Obligate your customer to buy with an extra bit of service to him.

Persuade with all of the enthusiasm you can generate.

Quote authorities who are well known to your customers so you can prove your sales points.

Refrain from knocking your competitor.

Say it with flowers.

Trade the benefits of what you are selling for your customer's dollar.

Use all the tricks of the trade in selling: enthusiasm, tact, confidence, and sincerity.

Visualize your customer owning and enjoying the benefits of your merchandise.

Work at selling.

X-ray your customer's buying mind to discover the real reason why your customer will or will not buy.

You are the key to more sales.

Zip up the sale quickly.

Telephone Selling

Real salesmanship counts more than ever today, and this applies especially to orders given over the phone. The telephone should never be answered by an inexperienced clerk who does not know what flowers are available, their prices, and cannot make suggestions as to their use. Also, select a quiet location for the telephone, away from the cash register and other distracting noises.

There are many suggestions to follow when trying to sell by phone, including the following:

1. Answer the telephone promptly.

2. Speak clearly and distinctly so that you can be easily understood.

3. Give the name of your shop and your name.

4. Be cheerful and friendly, and speak with a smile in your voice. This is very hard for some people to do. A person should never sound annoyed at having to answer the phone.

5. Be courteous and handle wrong numbers in a courteous manner.

6. Avoid coughing into the mouthpiece.

7. Never drop the receiver while the customer is on the line.

8. Always let the customer hang up first. The salesman may even get an extra sale that the customer thinks of at the last minute. If he hangs up first, he will lose it.

9. He should have knowledge of available merchandise and prices at his fingertips, or on a sheet posted by the phone.

10. Be sure and spell names and addresses correctly and get the customer's name for billing. Repeat the order, so that there will be no mistake.

11. Be sure the delivery date is correct.

12. Be helpful, and treat the customer with as much consideration on the phone as if he or she were in the store.

13. Use the same good English as if face-to-face with the customer in the store.

14. Help the customer to decide on the order by making several suggestions.

15. Acknowledge the customer's likes and dislikes.

16. On funeral orders, it is not in good taste to say "thank you." Rather say "we will take good care of this order for you."

17. Be sure to get the message for the card.

18. Always ask if there is anything else the customer needs—flowers for herself—or any other way you can be of service.

Seven Faults

The Bell Telephone Company's research experts have found that there are seven common faults that are basic to poor telephone salesmanship. They are as follows: (1) Slow, indifferent, and incomplete answering of the phone. (2) Failure to listen to what the customer wants. (3) Failure to use word pictures. (4) Failure to sell extra items, larger quantities, or better grades. (5) Failure to ask the customer to buy. (6) Winning the argument and losing the sale. (7) Failure to follow through.

Salesmanship in the retail florist shop, whether in person or by phone, is a very important part of the business. Some florists are order takers rather than salesmen. They simply wait for a customer to come in and give them an order. More profits could be realized by many retail florists if they would increase their sales; even by as little as 5 per cent. The chance to upsell most customers is there for the retail florist if he really tries to be a good salesman. Sales techniques are published in many books. All it takes is for the florist or sales employee to follow through, close the sale at the proper time, and *ask the people to buy*. The retail florists have the best product in the world to sell.

Chapter 18

CUSTOMERS AND CONSUMER PREFERENCES

The customer is the mainstay of the retail florist business. He is the one to whom the florist caters, and for whom the flowers and plants are produced, marketed, and sold. He is the ultimate consumer of the florists' products, and it is he who influences the whole operation and management of the retail florist business.

Customer Importance

The purpose of every sale is to satisfy the customer, not only with the merchandise that the florist sells, but with the services that he provides, so that the customer will want to continue to come back to his store. *The store exists for the customer, not the customer for the store.* If the store, the merchandise, and the services do not please the customers, they will take their trade somewhere else. Customers say that they want salespeople to be interested, courteous, and intelligent. Each of these is important, and can be developed by study and by noting how other successful salespeople use their traits in pleasing their customers. Salesmanship has already been discussed in Chapter 17.

The Customer's Image

The image created in the customer's mind by a particular shop is of utmost importance. What do people think of a florist and his shop? A retail florist should try to find out. It has been said many times that the success of a sale rests with the first 30 seconds that the customer is in the shop. Does the florist greet all customers promptly, or at least acknowledge their presence if he is busy with another customer?

This is most important. Here is a true story that occurred recently to the author in a Florida retail flower shop. "The flower shop was one of the most attractive shops I had seen in a long time. Since it was in a shopping center mall the front display windows were open. The display was simple in design, and very striking. The entrance was along a curved path through this attractive display, and into the retail flower shop itself. The whole picture was so inviting, it seemed to say 'Welcome, come on in.' So, my wife, son, and I went down the path and into the shop to see this wonderful looking florist shop—and there the image changed. The shop itself was attactive enough, but being *ignored* by the store personnel ruined the entire effect. At the rear of the store was a latticed partition and we could see three people working in there. Through a glass partition we could see a man sitting in the office watching the people in the workroom. The three of us wandered around the shop looking at the flowers, plants, and gift items, and I spent considerable time looking at the fresh flowers in the display refrigerator. (I know that people like to browse around in a shop, but they do not like to be *ignored.*) We were in the shop between three and five minutes and still no one came out to greet us. If we could see them through the lattice, I'm sure they could see us. After five minutes (remember the first 30 seconds are the most important), we left the shop and no one even tried to stop us. Once outside, I thought to myself that I have worked with retail florists for over 15 years so maybe I should try again. So I returned to the shop. As I came through the door, a man was standing behind the wrapping counter and I thought 'fine, I'll talk to him about the shop.' However, as I came through the door he turned around and walked into the back room and joined the two who were still in the work room. The man in the office still sat there. No one was busy on the phone or waiting on another customer as far as I could see. I wandered around for two minutes this time and decided to leave again. Just as I was leaving a woman came out and called to me to see if she could help me. There was no smile, nor any apology for keeping me waiting. I told her this was the second time I had been in and wondered why no one came out to wait on me, and she just said she was sorry. Her manner showed she didn't really mean it or care at all. She was quite unfriendly. I told her I was sorry because I worked with retail florists and liked to talk to them about their shops. She didn't reply to this at all. We both turned away and I really felt badly about this experience. I'm sure if I were an ordinary customer, not acquainted with many retail florists, my image of that shop, and florists in general, would be pretty poor. I probably wouldn't try to buy flowers again. There are many other gift items from which to choose, and I hate to see people turn to these other items because of the unfriendly attitude of a florist or his employees. Anyone could come out and greet a customer and say that someone will be with them in a minute."

Americans resent the attitude of impersonal contact and are returning to more fundamental values according to Chuck Johnston, President, TELEFLORA. Let the customers know you care about them and appreciate their business. Browsing is good for business and should be encouraged.

Many retail florists do not realize the importance of greeting the customer immediately, and also do not realize the importance of the image they create. Unfortunately, the preceding related incident is not an isolated case. It happens much too often in our business and should *never happen at all*. People must be made to feel welcome in retail florist shops.

Consumer Behavior

Motives for buying may be conscious or subconscious. Why do people act the way they do? Why do people buy certain products and not others? The answers to these questions lie in the area of social-psychological behavior according to our economists and psychologists. Money is the medium of exchange used between consumers and producers. How can we get more of it for flowers? Flowers must be made more important in the customer's mind than other items, and it must become a habit to buy flowers often. Consumer behavior is related to habit based on various social ideas or values.

Values

Our society is ruled by a set of social values which determine why people do things, and why they buy things. Some of these values are as follows: (1) status symbol—people buy a Cadillac as a status symbol, (2) expected—people send flowers or other items on certain occasions because it is expected, (3) function—people buy things because they perform a function in life, (4) self-esteem—people buy certain items for their own personal satisfaction, (5) historical—this is for sentimental reasons because they enjoyed some past experience, (6) modern—many people buy up-to-date products because they want to feel they are keeping up with the modern world, (7) expression—to express an emotion such as at the time of a death in the family, and (8) aesthetic value—in order to make their environment more pleasing. Status and prestige have become fixed symbols in American life today. These are things which motivate people to spend their money and buy things. Therefore, the florist should use his advertising and promotions to appeal to these different values. Flowers fit into some of these values more readily than others. Flowers do not perform a *function* as such, only in an indirect way; but they are a status symbol to some people. They are certainly used to express sympathy and other feelings. The sentimental value has been the greatest in the past, while the aesthetic is the value on which florists should be concentrating today. Flowers for gifts and home decorations should be pushed more and more. Flowers can be used for many occasions. The habits of people which make them spend money on flowers rather than something else, are the following: (1) People like to live comfortably. (2) People like to possess things. (3) Flowers appeal to romance. (4) Flowers have always expressed love. (5) Flowers remember—they say "I am thinking of you." (6) Flowers express sympathy and say things that most people find hard to put into words. (7) Flowers help in the desire to make money, as in commercial accounts (see Chapter 36). A retail florist should keep these ideas in mind when he is planning his advertising campaign.

Appropriateness of Flowers

Flowers are very appropriate for any occasion. Florists should try to work on the value of *habit*. Habit is a great force in our present-day society. Florists should try to get married men into the habit of buying flowers for each holiday, and then they won't be able to quit. Flowers are appropriate for men too, although not for as many occasions as for women. Factors which govern the appropriateness of flowers are: (1) class of people—flowers are more appropriate for some classes than others; (2) type of occasion—wedding, funeral, anniversary, sickness, and birthday, are all appropriate; and (3) various situations—more flowers are sent from men to women; and married and unmarried people differ in their desires for flowers, and the amount of money to spend on flowers. Married men buy more plants because they last longer, while unmarried men buy more roses and cut flowers because of the expression of love. The florist should emphasize *utility* to the married and *sentimentality* to both. Sick people and the aged are very receptive to flowers.

Another motivation for flower selling that the florist should

Figure 18-1. Attractive display of merchandise for the customers. (Courtesy, Miller Florist, Warren, Ohio.)

cultivate is the smell or fragrance of flowers. People expect this with flowers and expect to find it in a florist shop. It can serve as a good selling tool.

Consumer Preferences

Several surveys have been conducted to indicate the preference of consumers towards flowers. Interviews with people who purchased flower specials have shown that only 12 per cent of the purchasers had planned to buy flowers before they saw them displayed. Between 80 and 90 per cent of the people indicated that they would buy flowers regularly if they were available at a low price. (Advantage of cash-and-carry specials, Chapter 16.) They indicated that they would be willing to spend 90¢ to $1.00 per week on flowers if they were available, and most of these purchases would be for the home.

In a study on consumer preferences for flowers conducted by Dr. C. E. Trotter of The Pennsylvania State University, 1,152 individuals were asked to choose which of various gift items they would give for various occasions. The people did not know at first that it was a flower survey. The gifts listed were: personal clothing, candy, flowers, ornamental knicknacks, toilet articles, jewelry, and household items. The occasions were birthday, Easter, St. Valentine's Day, Mother's Day, Father's Day, wedding, anniversary, illness, expression of affection, and expression of appreciation. Of the 1,152 interviewed, 56 per cent had made one flower purchase in a year, and only 10 per cent had made three purchases of flowers in a year. They indicated flowers were appropriate, but they only purchased them half as often as they said they thought they were appropriate. In most of the situations presented, less than half of the people indicated they would select and send a gift of any kind. For example, only 40 per cent said they would send a gift at all on St. Valentine's Day and only 10 per cent indicated it would be flowers. The implication of this study is that there is a broad market to be developed. If consumers were educated to give flowers on more occasions, this would have a tremendous influence on flower sales. The following were three main reasons why flowers were given for a particular occasion as a gift: (1) the use of flowers for a particular reason, (2) the anticipated reaction of the person receiving flowers as a gift, and (3) the respondent's idea of the characteristics of flowers suited to the desired need. Flowers were considered highly acceptable gifts for women, but unappropriate for men, unless sick or old.

Flowers are the principal choice for certain holidays like Easter, Christmas, Mother's Day, and Memorial Day. There is no substitute for flowers for weddings. Flowers are highly acceptable at funerals, but the "Please Omit" phase is reducing this market. The use of flowers for gifts for birthdays, anniversaries, and other occasions is the market which should be developed by the retail florist industry. The degree of competition between flowers and other items depends upon the social commitment associated with the event, and the nature of the event. Education of the public to the proper use of flowers for various occasions is needed, along with a vigorous advertising campaign to sell more flowers to more people more often.

Retail Florists' Preferences

Consumer behavior and consumer preference studies have been conducted in many areas but not often in the florist industry. Retail florists are too often *apt to sell what they want to sell* rather ·than *what the customer wants to buy*. A study in Texas by L. J. Tolle on the purchasing habits of retail florists (not the florists' customers) showed that 32.4 per cent of the florists preferred carnations, 22.8 per cent preferred gladioli, 7.9 per cent preferred chrysanthemums, and 4.3 per cent preferred roses. Yet, from the standpoint of sales, we know that most people prefer pompons, carnations, and roses to all other flowers. The reasons given for these preferences showed versatility, keeping quality, ease of use, and the ability of flowers to make a "show," to be the most important reasons for florists' flower preferences aside from their personal likes. This same study showed the breakdown of florist sales by merchandise classes to be the following: funeral 59.98 per cent, arrangements 22.21 per cent, party decorations 16.70 per cent, weddings 8.75 per cent, corsages 6.89 per cent, and bunches of cut flowers 5 per cent. All of these areas (except funeral work) could be increased by finding out what consumers prefer for these occasions. (These are estimates from the florists who responded to the questionnaire.)

New and Tolle reported in 1964 that studies proved that the carnation was among the most popular and versatile flower sold by retail florists. Out of 36,024 orders, 5,863 or 16 per cent used carnations. Forty per cent of all corsages contained carnations and 34 per cent of all arrangements (including funeral) had some carnations in them. We don't know if this is the preference of the customers or of the retail florists.

Consumers know and appreciate the value of flowers and want to enjoy them more often in their homes. Several surveys on consumer preferences for flowers and pot plants have been conducted in the past 10 years. Mississippi research workers found that foliage plants were preferred over azaleas and pot mums while red roses, yellow mums, red carnations, and pink gladioli were the favorites among cut flowers. Ninety-two per cent preferred a pot plant over an arrangement as a gift. A study in Memphis showed that roses were preferred over all other cut flowers; followed by pot plants, pompons, carnations, and gladioli in that order. The Memphis study also showed that flowers were a favorite gift during an illness in any and all income groups of people. The retail flower shop was preferred by far, over supermarkets, five-and-tens, and variety stores for the purchase of plants and flowers. Most people in this survey preferred to receive a pot plant rather than cut flowers as a household gift, but preferred cut flowers for home decorations. Seventy-four per cent of the people surveyed had no desire to see their flowers arranged before buying them. (This seems to be opposite to the views on salesmanship that people like to see made-up arrangements.) Most people interviewed felt roses and snapdragons were the cut flowers that would last the shortest time while chrysanthemums, gladioli, and carnations were expected to last longer. Although keeping quality was a factor in selecting some flowers, roses were still listed as a very popular flower. (The latest census figures for 1966 indicated all chrysanthemums first, carnations second, and roses third in sales.)

A study in Texas conducted by three panels of 25 members each found the following points of interest on consumer preferences, and buying habits for flowers: (1) The general public likes flowers, especially for the home, and will use them if they are readily available at a reasonable price. (2) Customers want to know how to care for their plants. They prefer instruction cards which include scientific and common names, some history, and complete directions for plant care. (3) Customer habits in using flowers can be changed or developed. Once the habit has been established, it should be cultivated continuously. (4) In purchasing flowers, customers prefer a variety of choice, and *prefer the price to be plainly marked.* (5) Consumers are concerned about the keeping quality of plants and flowers. This affects some of the purchasing selections.

Customers like to have merchandise displayed and priced. With flowers, they like to make their own decision on what to order. Yet, a recent U.S. Department of Agriculture survey showed that less than 40 per cent of the florists displayed prepared arrangements in their shops for customers to see and buy when placing an order in person. However, over three-fourths of the florists who did display floral arrangements put a price on them for customers to see. We need more studies on consumers, to determine more of their preferences in relation to variety, color, type of flower, length of stem, price, and other factors.

Garden Clubs

A retail florist should cultivate the members of garden clubs and handle the materials which they want to buy.

When a friendly, inquisitive, probing garden club member wanders into a retail florist shop the owner should not run and hide, rush around frantically covering up his supplies, close his eyes and hope she will go away, or hound her so closely she will leave. He is turning his back on a wide-open source of additional sales for his shop. The National Council of State Garden Clubs, Inc., alone boasts a total membership in excess of 418,000 and there are thousands of others who do not belong to this national organization.

The retail florist should take advantage of the volume sales potential they represent by attending their meetings, and learning firsthand their problems and needs. They will not be a nuisance as some florists think, if allowed to browse and pick out their own materials and supplies. They don't have to have extra services.

Stock salable supplies such as wire, tape, chenille stems, water picks, preservatives, clay, pin holders, styrofoam, and other items that they want to buy. They will find them elsewhere if not in a florist shop. Let them browse and buy just one or two flowers at a time. This all helps to increase the volume of business, and will lead to *impulse* sales.

A retail florist can be his own public relations man. He can offer his services as a guest speaker, which will afford him a fine opportunity to publicize his own shop.

A successful florist will cultivate the garden club members, not fight them.

Education

All florists should embark on a consumer education program for the florist industry. This should be aimed to make the public more favorably disposed towards flower purchases. The retail florists should strive to change the image in the minds of the general public and make them feel *welcome* in their shops.

Understanding why consumers buy the way they do is important in any industry. We know people like flowers, so all the florist has to do is concentrate on increasing sales by encouraging them to buy more flowers for more occasions, more often.

William Cronin suggests that each retail florist should find out what the town thinks of his shop and determine what he can do about capitalizing on his image. He suggests that each florist consider the following questions: (1) Is the shop an expensive shop?

(2) Is it a quality shop? (3) Are the arrangements really artistic? (4) Is it an old-fashioned shop? (5) Is it considered a "late" shop with deliveries? (6) Is the florist really merchandising flowers? If the florist wonders if his answers are the same as his customers', he might try a little survey of his own to find out. Analyze the results and act on them. Set up a management program to improve the image of his store. Satisfying the desires of the consumers for accurate and timely information about floral products can help a retailer to attract consumers, and expand his business. Florists should encourage the use of flowers for home decorations, and other special occasions.

Understanding why people buy as they do is an important aspect in any retail business including the retail florist. Motivation research is a highly specialized part of market research being conducted in many areas. This affects all retail businesses. We need more of it in the florist industry so that we can effectively plan our selling and merchandising programs.

References

1. Anonymous. "The Garden Clubber, Friend or Foe?" *FTD News* (November 1966), p. 26.
2. New, E. H. and L. J. Tolle. "Studies Confirm It: The Carnation Is Among the Most Popular and Versatile Flower Type Sold by Retail Florists," *The Exchange*, Vol. 142, No. 8 (August 22, 1964), pp. 26-27, 41.

Chapter 19

TRADE PRACTICES; TRICKS OF THE TRADE

Trade Practices

There are several trade practices which should be considered by each florist. Just how they are handled depends on the location, type of shop, reputation, and desires of the owner.

1. **Open Sunday.** This policy will depend on the community and the type of store. Some shops in hotels, hospitals, and shopping centers may have to be open on Sunday. Most florists, however, should not have to be open on Sundays except at holiday times. A retail florist should educate the public that he is closed on Sundays, and try to get other florists in the area to agree to the same procedure.

2. **Renting containers.** Many florists will rent baskets and vases for funeral designs, and pick up the containers later from the funeral home or cemetery. Some florists feel it is a waste of time and money because the containers get broken, lost, may leak, and are sometimes impossible to recover. Whether the florist charges full price or a rental is up to him.

Some florists have a large selection of containers and decorative pieces for rent for many decorations besides funerals. M. Lange from Wilmette, Illinois, has been doing it profitably for over 15 years.

3. **Loaning palms.** It is a general practice for retail florists to loan palms, ferns, and cibotiums for weddings, funerals, and church or school decorations. It is hard on the fresh material so the florist must make a charge and prorate it over a six month's period, which is the expected life of the plants. Many florists are now using permanent (artificial) palms and ferns because they do not have a greenhouse or suitable facilities for caring for the live plants. These are expensive, but can be used over again many times.

4. **Slack times.** What does a florist do with his employees who are not busy during the slack times which occur in every shop? He should put them to work making bows, putting boxes together, inserting wax paper in the boxes, wiring and painting pine cones, making net puffs, checking supplies, and other small jobs that can be picked up at a moment's notice and put down when there is something else to do.

5. **Hospital practices.** Find out what the rules for receiving flowers are at the hospital and abide by them. In general, hospitals appreciate florists observing the following conditions: (1) Check carefully the correct name, floor, and room number of the patient before making delivery. (2) Make sure all female patients are addressed by their own first name (not their husbands), such as Mrs. Mary Smith, not Mrs. John Smith. (3) No loose flowers. All cut flowers must be arranged in containers that do not leak. (4) All orders should be delivered to the place or room designated by the hospital, or taken to the patient's room or floor if that is the policy. (5) All deliveries to be made between ――――A.M. and ―――― P.M. (6) No poisonous or irritating flowers or plants should be sent to the hospital. (7) Roses should be dethorned before delivery. (8) Make sure the patient is still in the hospital. (9) Check to be sure the patient can receive flowers. Usually patients are not allowed flowers in the intensive care unit.

6. **Renting items.** Many items can be rented profitably, according to various florists, including Bill Curtis of Phoebe Floral in Allentown, Pennsylvania. Items for rent include candlelabras, aisle runners, skirts of satin, compotes, canopys, fountains, plants, turntables, walk-through stands like hearts, apothecary jars, trees and tree stands (up to 50 pounds), and many other items. The secret of success in the renting of items lies in telling the customers and potential customers that these materials are available in the florist's shop. A standard rental price is posted so that there is no guessing, and everyone charges the same price for each item. A rule-of-thumb for most non-perishable rental items at Phoebe Floral is to charge 20 per cent of the original cost, plus the cost of cleaning and polishing to get the items ready for the next rental. Bill Curtis said that 25 per cent of one wedding order of over $800 was charged just for rental equipment. Most rental items are kept in a special room upstairs and are not open to public exposure until the special party or wedding.

7. **Floral contributions.** A retail florist is constantly getting re-

quests from various charity and local affairs for flowers or center-pieces. The advertising value from these is considered "nil," so the florist is usually just donating the flowers. This can eat into his profits. It would be better just to make a cash donation and deduct it on his income tax. Some florists have found the following form to be of help in eliminating these demands (Table 19-1).

Table 19-1. Printed Form to Be Used for Requests for Floral
Contributions.

REQUEST FOR FLORAL CONTRIBUTIONS

Organization _____ When Organized? _____

Address of Organization _____

President _____ Phone No. _____

    Address _____

Secretary _____ Phone No. _____

    Address _____

Type of Organization: CHARITABLE, NON-PROFIT, INCORPORATED,

                       UNINCORPORATED, OTHER _____

Purpose of Organization: _____

Event for Which Flowers Requested: _____

    Date _____ Time _____ Place _____

Type of Flowers Requested _____

Cost per Person Attending Event _____

Other Donations: Advertising Donated by _____

                  Printing Donated by _____

                  Entertainment Donated by _____

                  Dessert Donated by _____

Requested by _____ Title _____

Ask the person to fill this out and see what happens. Most people do not want to be bothered taking the time to fill out the form, and some are really embarrassed to put down that no one else is donating anything, and they finally realize that there is no reason why flowers should be donated.

8. **Do-it-yourself.** Some florists are providing a Garden Club Counter, Do-It-Yourself, or Knick-Knack Bar which is stocked with

ribbon, wire, floratape, chenille stems, pin holders, clay, spray paint, styrofoam, foam materials, and other items for the do-it-yourself flower arranger. Everything is priced and most customers help themselves. A 2 to 1 markup is usually sufficient for these items.

9. **Shop hours.** Shop hours are longer in some shops than others. They must be decided by the florist himself depending upon his type of business. If the hours are long, they should be staggered. If the florist shop has a garden center then the hours will be long, and the florist will likely have to pay overtime. If the annual gross volume of sales for the shop is over a half a million dollars, then the florist will have a real payroll problem due to the new Wages and Hours Laws.

These are a few of the practices which differ in each shop, and must be decided upon by the owner after careful consideration of each item. There are many more practices which space does not permit discussing.

Trade Papers and Organizations

A retail florist, to be successful, must keep up on new trends, developments, business suggestions, and other ideas which will help him keep up-to-date in this modern florist world of today. To do this he should subscribe regularly to at least one of the weekly trade papers and more than one if he can afford it. It is just like subscribing to his local newspaper. A florist wouldn't think of not receiving the daily paper in his own home town. At present there are four national weekly trade papers for retail florists, as follows: *The Florists' Review, Florist and Nursery Exchange, Southern Florist and Nurseryman,* and *Flower News.*

If the retail florist belongs to one of the telephone or wire service organizations, then he will automatically receive the monthly publication put out by that organization. At the moment there are three main national organizations for the transmittal of floral orders. A florist will only get the magazine if he is a member of that organization, but he can belong to more than one if he so chooses. The three organizations are: Florists' Transworld Delivery Association, TELEFLORA, Inc., and Florafax Association.

A progressive florist should also join his local, state, and national trade associations. The local may be an Allied or a local group of florists such as the Philadelphia Allied, New York Florist Club, Florists' Association of Greater Chicago, or any of hundreds like these. The state organizations may be one such as the Pennsylvania Retail Florists, Michigan State Florists Association, Ohio Florists' Association, or any of the other state organizations. The national organization is the Society of American Florists which represents all segments of the florist industry on the national level. Its headquarters are in Washington, D.C. Support of these organizations is an investment in the future of the florist industry in America.

Tricks of the Trade

1. **Keep daily orders separate.** Here is a good way to keep the daily orders in good shape in an orderly fashion for the designers. Use a regular 36 inch piece of 2 inch styrofoam with nails about 4 inches long pushed through from the back of the styrofoam. Use them in pairs so that the orders can be placed on them, and grouped for delivery. In this way the orders can be filled by the designers according to time, and then by sections of the city. The owner-manager can keep an eye on the orders, and plan his deliveries accordingly. Green styrofoam should be used for white order sheets, and white styrofoam for colored order sheets. The sheets will stand out much better that way (Figure 19-1).

Figure 19-1. Styrofoam block with nails to keep orders separate at the control center.

2. **Designer's clip.** To make sure that the designer does not lose an order sheet, or that it doesn't blow off the table into the trash, hang a clip above the work table to which is attached the order for the design that the designer is filling. A nail or hook can also be used.

3. **Preservatives.** Flower preservatives are being used extensively by many retail florists. Most of them put some preservative in every arrangement that goes out of the shop including funeral vases

and baskets. (If the funeral viewing is only one day, this won't be necessary.) Florists should also put a preservative in the water to impregnate the various foams on the market, such as: Oasis, Hydro-foam, Jiffy, Sno-Pak, Niagra, Fill Fast Foam, and others. Preservative should also be put in each can or vase of flowers in the storage and display refrigerators as soon as the flowers come from the market. The continued use of a preservative from grower to consumer has been proven beneficial (see Chapter 37).

4. **Doily.** A good idea for furthering public relations and good will with the customer, is by sending along a paper doily with each floral arrangement and pot plant to protect the furniture in the home. The doily may be plain if the florist wishes, or it may have his name on it for advertising. It is well worth the cost of less than two cents apiece. It is also a good idea for hospital and funeral vases.

5. **Pick-up notice.** A mimeographed sheet with standard items listed, is a quick and easy way to remind the driver to pick up certain items following various decorating jobs. Fill in the address and date, and check the items to be brought back to the shop. Have a place for the driver to initial it when he has completed the job.

6. **Nozzles.** Mist nozzles at each design table are a time-saver as well as added insurance that the flowers will last as long as possible. The initial expense of installation is well worth it. An overhead water line is installed along the ceiling for the full length of the workroom, with a hose and a nozzle hanging down from the ceiling beside each designer. The designer can easily fill his container without having to go to the sink, and can also mist the arrangement when it is finished and ready for wrapping.

7. **Wire holder.** An inexpensive holder for floral wire is a six-pack of empty soda bottles. On one side put 16, 18, and 20 gauge wire for heavy work; put 24, 30, and 34 gauge wires on the other side for the lighter work.

8. **Styrofoam cover.** A new and effective way to cover the styrofoam base used for many floral designs is to use sponge rubber. It comes in many colors, is inexpensive, stretches tightly and neatly over the styrofoam, and is thin enough to be easily punctured by most flower stems.

9. **Backboards.** Special effects can be achieved very easily on designs for special occasions. Make up a series of styrofoam backboards with different items attached, such as a check book for a bank opening, a picture of the latest rock music group for teenagers,

something from the kitchen for Mother's Day, and other items. When the order comes in, make up a neutral arrangement of flowers, attach the appropriate background, and it is all set to be delivered.

10. **Cymbidiums.** To increase the life-span of cymbidiums, put one drop of water down each one's throat.

11. **Plastic rings.** Don't throw away the plastic rings from rolls of florists' tape. Trimmed with a flower or two, they become attractive napkin rings or can be used in anniversary designs.

12. **Turntable.** Clever designers use a turntable when making designs that are small enough to sit on it steadily. This is an easy and excellent way to check the back of the arrangement. Whether the design is two-sided or not, the arrangement should always look finished from all sides.

13. **Basic door swag.** Sell a basic door swag for Christmas with a set of reasonably priced trims that can be changed with the seasons. Try snowy branches and red ribbon and balls for Christmas, daisies for spring, strawflowers for summer, and Indian corn for fall.

14. **Novelties.** Some retail florists incorporate a small inexpensive novelty in each design piece that goes out from their shop, with the exception of funeral pieces. This helps to attract attention, and creates a favorable impression for the shop, since this added touch will be different from any competitor. The novelty can be artificial, dried, flower, fruit, or animal.

15. **Styrofoam fastener.** There are several new materials on the market which are excellent for fastening styrofoam to the container, and objects to the styrofoam. They are stickier than clay and are called Permagum, Cling, and other trade names. These materials are excellent for anchoring driftwood in an arrangement. Medisco preservative is also an excellent glue for anchoring styrofoam in permanent arrangements.

16. **Bleach.** Clean containers in the refrigerator will help make the cut flowers last longer. Some florists use a small amount of bleach in the water to keep the water, stems, and containers clean. It cuts down on the disagreeable odor which develops when flowers are in the water more than just a few days.

17. **Styrofoam protector.** If a piece of styrofoam is used as the base for a floral design instead of pottery or some other container, it may scratch the furniture in the customer's home. A piece of flocked paper attached to the bottom of the styrofoam will give adequate protection, and more customer satisfaction.

18. **Candle or spray for mums.** A candle or a can of mum spray wax is good to use to repair the damage of a shattered chrysanthe-

mum. It is advisable for the truck driver to have one handy in his delivery truck at all times.

19. **Dish gardens.** Adding a few flowers in water tubes to a dish garden will make it look much more attractive with very little cost. Just a few pompons will do it, and will help to give the store a better reputation because of this added touch.

20. **Wrap arrangements.** Many florists are wrapping all artistic designs and floral arrangements in clear plastic. It protects them during delivery, and the arrangements can be seen and admired by many people when they are delivered. It is a good way to advertise the product, and helps to keep the flowers in a good fresh condition. It is essential in the north in winter.

21. **Time deliveries.** An excellent way to be sure that time deliveries are delivered on time and not lost in the rush of doing business, is to place a bright red or orange sticker on the order. The manager and the truck driver will both be able to see it, and can check the time of delivery very easily. This is particularly helpful during the rush at a holiday.

22. **Cut pot covers fast.** To cut aluminum foil fast and uniformly for use as a pot cover, make a board with a groove in it running the length of the foil roll. Attach a roller to the end of the board for the foil. Each time the foil is pulled across the board, run a wallpaper cutter down the groove, thus cutting the foil neatly, evenly, and quickly.

23. **Color petal tips.** To color only the tips of carnation petals, spray a round spot of paint of the desired color onto a piece of aluminum foil. Then take the head of the carnation and roll it gently over the spot of paint, and the petal tips will be tinted.

24. **Portable tables.** Portable design tables are used in some shops where space is at a premium. They are set up for a holiday, and then stored away the rest of the year. The tables can also be used for added display space when needed.

25. **Foliage.** Trim your foliage into unusual shapes to give the same old greens a new look.

26. **Wedding photos.** Most retail florists keep a book of pictures of wedding designs to show to a prospective customer. Many also have pictures and photos of the wedding work that they have done in the past. The photos may be in color or black and white. Some have two shots of each bouquet. One is a close-up of the wedding bouquet, and the other is a photo showing how it looks when being carried by the bride, or an attendant.

27. **Do-it-yourself.** Many people are interested in doing things

themselves these days. It has become quite a fad. If there is space in the shop, a florist might consider installing a do-it-yourself table for his customers. It can be a serve-yourself counter. It is a good-will builder, and will increase the gross sales if the florist does not let it get out of hand, and interfere with the management and operation of the shop. Pin holders, clay, wire, floratape, ribbon, chicken wire, foam materials, and chenille stems are just a few of the items that can be sold here.

28. **Ribbon on boxes.** Tie the boxes of cut flowers and corsages with brightly colored corsage ribbon, rather than string or scotch tape, to make the package look more attractive. It attracts attention to the order. It is more expensive, but it may be worth it for its advertising value. This depends on the customers and the type of shop operated by the retail florist.

29. **Stone chips.** An interesting and practical way to handle the floor of the display window, or even the display beds in the middle of the store is with the use of stone chips. They are attractive, require very little maintenance, and eliminate the worry and mess from spilled water. A watertight liner with a drain might be provided if the florist believes it is necessary.

30. **Customer's special occasions.** Keep a record of birthdays, anniversaries, and other important dates for regular customers if a florist wants to bring in more business. Use a card file, and keep it up-to-date. A note or phone call will remind the sender of the date, and suggest that he or she send a similar flower order this year. Be sure to remove the names of deceased people immediately from the file. This file can be operated by a handicapped person in the florist's neighborhood.

31. **Answering service.** Retail florists can use a telephone answering service for evenings and Sundays if they feel it will benefit their business. It can even be used during the day at holidays with the arrangement that the service answers it only after the third or fourth ring. The service personnel must know how to receive telephone orders from the various wire service organization members. Some florists like this service, and some do not. Some feel the answering service is too impersonal. If a retail florist uses one of these services, it is a good idea to have the operators visit the shop periodically to see what is being sold, and to learn about new ideas of operation.

32. **Pay phone.** The installation of a pay phone in a shop can be an asset. It cuts down on the use of the business phone by employees and customers. It is excellent for sending out FTD, Tele-

Figure 19-2. Stone chips in the floor of sales area. (Courtesy, Silverblatt's Flowers, Pittsburgh, Pa.)

flora, or Florafax orders without tying up the regular phone. Be sure to have plenty of small change handy. And, of course, the shop gets a small monetary return from the telephone company each month.

33. **Open refrigerators.** An open refrigerator, similar to the ones used in supermarkets, can be used in certain florist shops very successfully. The customers can see into the refrigerator very easily, and it is especially good for storing made-up corsages at holiday times if they are kept in order. It can also be used for vases of cut flowers for cash-and-carry specials. The specials can be tied in bunches, placed in water, and are ready to be sold, and can be wrapped easily. One drawback to this type of refrigerator is the space it requires in the shop. Used refrigerators can be picked up inexpensively when a supermarket remodels, or a small grocer goes out of business.

34. **Drive-in window.** If the florist has the space and can provide a drive-in window opening onto his parking lot it is an excellent idea. This is very helpful and a time-saver both for the florist and the customers, particularly for will-call orders. For dances and holi-

days, educate the customers to call for their corsages at the drive-in window.

35. **Guarantee.** A Des Moines, Iowa, florist guarantees every flower order and asks customers to phone at once if the flowers do not come up to expectation. However, no complaint is honored after 24 hours.

36. **Gypsophila.** When fresh gypsophila is hard to obtain, dried gypsophila can be made more pliable for use by placing it in a refrigerator for 24 hours. If placed in hot water, the dried pods will burst and give the gypsophila a fuller, fluffier look.

Whether the preceding tricks of the trade will be suited to a shop or not must be determined by the florist or manager himself. However, it may be worth-while trying most of them to see if they will improve the volume of business in the shop.

There are hundreds of other tricks of the trade besides these few listed here.

References

1. Curtis, William. "Rental Merchandise Comes to the Aid of the Party," *Teleflora Spirit* (October 1970), pp. 30, 31.
2. Gordon, D. A. "Flowers for Rent," *Florists' Review*, Vol. 136, No. 3520 (May 13, 1965), pp. 13-14, 54.

Chapter 20

PLEASE OMIT

Many funeral notices today carry the words "Please Omit Flowers" or "In Lieu of Flowers, Contributions may be made to . . ." It is a practice which has caused a loss of business for florists in certain cities for 50 years or more. It is gaining in popularity in many areas. The Exchange reported in 1964, that in the *New York Times* the number of Please Omits was up 77 per cent from 1940. Every 100 obits, according to their statistics, contained nearly 17 Please Omit notices. Compare that number to 11 in 1952 and nine in 1940. Those figures mean a greater than 54 per cent increase in the last 24 years. The difficult part is that for many florists, the funeral flowers make up from 50 to 80 per cent of their business. Thus, if people stop sending flowers to funerals, it can be a real hardship for these florists. It is also a practice which is very hard to combat by the florist industry. The Society of American Florists has a committee called the Florists Information Committee which helps florists in various cities to talk to funeral directors, ministers, and newspaper publishers to try to discourage the use of these negative phrases. *The florist industry does not object to solicitations of money for contributions, as long as they do not mention flowers. This way there is no discrimination of an industry, and friends are free to send flowers, or make a contribution whichever they choose.*

A funeral without flowers is very drab, dreary, and cold. Flowers add beauty to the casket setting and the funeral service. Flowers help to soften the grief caused by the death of a loved one. The funeral directors know this and are opposed to a funeral without flowers. Usually the family of the deceased realizes this also, and so there will almost always be family flowers and other pieces at a Please Omit Funeral. This is embarrassing for friends who have not sent flowers.

There are people, of course, who do not want flowers at a funeral, and this is their prerogative. However, in many cases of Please

Omit, the family has been persuaded by some well-meaning friend or relative to ask that donations be given to some church, hospital, or charity in lieu of flowers. Various organizations such as the American Heart Fund, American Cancer Society, and others have told the Society of American Florists that they receive very few contributions in lieu of flowers from the funerals that make the suggestion. *These societies themselves do not solicit donations in place of flowers.* It has been proven that many people just don't bother sending either money or flowers to a Please Omit funeral.

Surveys show that the problem is worse in some cities than others, and worse now than 15 years ago in many areas. It is no worse in some areas.

Many newspapers do not print the words "Please Omit Flowers" unless it is in a paid obituary.

What's Behind Please Omit?

A survey by FTDA in 1962 gave the following conclusions concerning Please Omit: (1) It is fairly deep rooted in present-day society, and promises to grow in strength. (2) The chief proponents of Please Omit are members of the Protestant clergy, with excess floral usage as their main target. (3) Funeral directors were absolved from blame. (4) There is a changing attitude towards death. (5) There is a rise of religious influence at the time of death, and also an enhanced status of religious leaders. (6) It is closely tied in with our changing society.

Public Acceptance

The public is accepting "Please Omit Flowers" because it is part of the changing pattern of today's living. There is a changing attitude towards funeral procedures as revealed in the following results of a recent survey: A growing desire for simplicity in funerals; the trend toward church funerals in preference to those in funeral homes; protests against the high cost of funerals (Jessica Mitford in her book "The American Way of Death"); feelings of waste associated with funeral flowers which are sometimes in excess, and this coupled with the post-funeral destruction of the pieces; a feeling that the money could have been put to better use; and the attitude that excess floral tributes are symbols of conspicuous spending and thus in poor taste.

An indication of future Please Omit behavior is evident in the findings of a survey that 67 per cent of those who have inserted Please Omit notices in the paper indicated that they would do so again.

Role of the Florist

People have traditionally expressed their respect for the dead, and sympathy for the bereaved, by sending flowers. The custom is long standing, and though on the wane in some areas, will be with us for many years to come. There are three points to be kept in mind concerning funeral flowers. First, the role of the florist is that of merely serving the people who wish to send flowers to the funeral. It is the people who come to the florist. Secondly, the flowers represent sympathy extended to the bereaved. Thirdly, it is not true that flowers are sent to the dead, who cannot see nor appreciate them. They are sent in memory of the dead, and to help buoy up the spirits of the living as a token of respect for the deceased. They are an expression of friendship towards both the living and the dead. They show an understanding sympathy that is so hard for many people to express in words.

Why Please Omit Is Wrong

1. The obituary is a public announcement of the death, with the date, and time of the funeral service. It is not considered good taste to openly anticipate an expression of sympathy.

2. A "Please Omit" or "In Lieu of" request causes embarrassment to friends. Some ignore the request and send flowers anyway. Thus, it is embarrassing to those who heeded the request, and then find flowers at the funeral when they attend the service.

3. Capitalizing on the sympathy of friends to raise money for a special cause is distasteful to many people.

4. Most people do not contribute to the cause, which is generally not helped financially.

5. Many people resent being told how to express their sympathy, and how to spend their money.

Combatting the Please Omit Problem

There are many ways that retail florists can try to combat the Please Omit problem.

1. One of the most important ways is in the handling of floral designs by the retail florists themselves. This means that florists should: (a) use flowers that conform to high standards of quality and use fresh flowers; (b) not use awkward, bulky, easily spilled floral arrangements; (c) be sure the arrangements have originality and good artistic design; (d) make sure they are properly wrapped, and contain proper identification; (e) make sure the card is properly filled out; (f) use a previously used container *only* if it is in good condition; and (g) deliver flowers on time. Many funeral directors are providing several small tables and stands in the funeral home for floral arrangements in attractive containers. Make sure that these arrangements are artistic and above average in design, and they will help to combat the criticism of flowers at funerals.

2. Florists can talk to funeral directors, ministers, and the newspapers, and ask for a member of the Florists Information Committee of the Society of American Florists to explain the situation to these local people. Most businessmen are very understanding and will not deliberately try to ruin an industry.

3. Include funeral flowers in the florist's advertising. The Society of American Florists has suggested many phrases to go with funeral flower ads which will not be offensive to the general public, nor to the customers.

4. Adopt a positive sales approach, setting forth the purpose of funeral flowers, and the things that flowers do for the bereaved and for the relatives and friends.

5. Follow the recommendations of the Florists Information Committee.

6. Suggest sending a sympathy bouquet of flowers or a plant to the home after the funeral service. These should be artistic arrangements in good taste, and must not look like a funeral vase or basket. These flowers, and the message with it, are greatly appreciated by the family during the week following the funeral. This suggestion to the customer will result in reducing the loss of business due to Please Omit and yet is very acceptable to the recipient, and is considered in good taste.

7. Work cooperatively with the funeral directors. The following are tips to florists on maintaining the good will of funeral directors from the Allied Florists of Greater Philadelphia as reported by W. Camerisch: "(a) Enclosure cards—print or type name of sender on front. Print or type name, address, relationship, if any, on the back of the card. (b) Sprays—wire the ends of styrofoam bars so they can be easily hung on easels or stands. (c) Casket

sprays—they should be at least 2″ x 6″ x 36″ to allow for proper placing on the rack. (d) Papier-mâché containers—use a large size for large arrangements. However, be careful that such containers are not top-heavy. Do not put too much water in the container. (e) Preservatives—use no preservative or chemical in the water unless the manufacturer guarantees the material will not damage rugs. (f) Vermiculite—cover Vermiculite with a foam material. (g) Deliveries—weekdays before 5 P.M. Family work should be delivered before 3 P.M.; Sundays and holidays between 10 A.M. and 3 P.M. (These times are for the Philadelphia area.) (h) Baskets—don't use leaky baskets. If you do use a reclaimed basket that is still good, be absolutely certain the paint is dry. Also see that the baskets have a large enough base so as not to tip over easily. (i) Metal picks—please omit or carefully place in the sprays, any or all metal barbed picks used to secure flowers in floral pieces. (j) Spilled water—tell drivers before they carry baskets into the funeral homes to check to make sure that the base is dry, because water might have been spilled enroute. (k) Entrances—be sure drivers deliver flowers through the door designated for florists and flowers. (l) Hemlock—do not use it in sprays."

Funeral directors are also trying to cooperate with retail florists. The following are tips to funeral directors on maintaining the good will of florists from the Funeral Directors' Association of Philadelphia reported by W. H. Carter: (a) Always handle flowers with love and care. Flowers are the symbols—the messengers of love—for those who live on. Funeral home staffs should always refrain from dumping, hauling, crushing, and tightly packing flowers into flower wagons or cars. People who witness this are sensitive about the callous disregard for flowers. Improper handling can wreck the very beautiful service the funeral director strives so earnestly to achieve. (b) Mark flower delivery entrances clearly. Signs at some funeral homes are often washed out, beaten up, and unsightly; and some even have directional arrows twisted or reversed. (c) Consult your florist before you advise a family on the price of any flowers, or request a certain type or color of flower. Weather and season vary the availability of some flowers during the year. (d) If water level is not excessive, the arrangement should not be emptied, since the water is used to keep the flowers fresh, and to present the best showing for you. It also adds to the stability of the arrangement. (e) Flowers should be placed so that the arrangement is in full view, and not half hidden by other flowers. (f) Flowers should be handled properly and promptly upon delivery. (g)

Special consideration should be given to the removal of flowers after the service, regardless of whether the family or friends are present. A mutual understanding on the use and handling of flowers is necessary between retail florists and funeral directors.

8. Special phrase cards suggested for death announcements include the following: (a) Memorials preferred. (b) Contributions may be sent to (name of charity). (c) Memorials may be made to the charity of your choice.

9. The final, and maybe the most important, point is for florists to recognize that Please Omit is here to stay and that they should concentrate on selling flowers for other occasions. Many florists are doing that now and report that funeral flowers are only 35 per cent of their gross sales rather than the 75 to 80 per cent that they were 10 years ago. *Let's sell flowers to the living!* Try to build up the sale of flowers for gifts, birthdays, anniversaries, and for home decorations. We should try to get the American people to use flowers in their homes every week of the year. *This is the business of the future,* and the place where the progressive florists of today are concentrating their best efforts, rather than spending time fighting "Please Omit"; except as noted in suggestion #1 under combatting Please Omit. Efforts should be spent towards the following two lines of endeavor: combatting Please Omit and developing new areas for flower sales.

References

1. Anonymous, "Handle 'P. O.' Intelligently," *FTD News* (July 1966), pp. 22-25.
2. Anonymous. "Please Omit Up by More Than 77 Per Cent Since 1940," *The Exchange,* Vol. 142, No. 3 (July 18, 1964), pp. 26-27.

Chapter 21

DIVERSIFICATION

All florists today find that they must diversify in order to stay in business. Some will handle just the usual sidelines, while others are branching out in all directions and handling many items. Diversification increases sales. Let's look at some of the logical as well as objectionable sidelines that might be considered by the average florist.

A retail florist should have a perpetual inventory of all stock and accessories. An up-to-date complete record should be kept on all items. There are many accessories which are used with flowers, and they are almost too numerous to mention. However, there are a dozen or so logical sidelines which a retail florist may handle in his shop. It is up to the individual retail florist to decide which of these he should handle, and particularly which ones will make money for him. Several factors will help him decide on these sidelines; such as type of store, location, size of store, and type of customers patronizing his florist shop.

Logical Sidelines

1. **Pottery.** This is the best and most logical sideline for a retail florist to handle in his shop. He will use pottery containers every day in his designing, and a good supply is necessary for sale to his customers. Hospital arrangements must be in containers as well as many funeral designs. Many customers will also purchase a container for flowers sent as a gift for birthday, anniversary, or other occasion. A good supply of plain, simple, and inexpensive containers is necessary. Don't buy too many fancy pieces, although a few for display and sale are good. Many novelty containers will be needed. Be sure to have a variety of colors, sizes, and styles, but only put one or two on display at a time unless they are to be merchandised. Keep the rest in storage. Compotes and other specialty items are good, if the florist has the type of customers who will buy them.

Animals and grotesque figures will only have a limited sale, so don't stock too heavily on them. There are many pottery items which can be sold as a good sideline to the flowers in a retail florist shop.

2. **Glassware.** Glassware is another logical sideline for the florist. It is a "natural" because, like pottery, there are many glass containers and compotes suitable for holding flowers. The type of glass the florist handles will depend on his business. He should have some inexpensive clear and opaque glass containers along with some milk glass. If he wishes to handle expensive Venetian glass or crystal, he must make sure that his customers are the type who will buy them. Novelty and colored glass may be handled in limited quantities. Experience is the best teacher in deciding what types of glass items to handle, and how many to stock.

3. **Candles.** This is another item which a retail florist should have on hand for his own designing, as well as for sale. Candles just naturally go with flowers, and can easily be sold along with a

Figure 21-1. An excellent display of candles. (Courtesy, Frederick's Flowers, Souderton, Pa.)

centerpiece or flowers for a party. The florist is the logical one to supply them for weddings, parties, and many other social functions. If the florist has the space, he should set up a nice display of all colors, types, and sizes of candles. There is no loss with these as long as they are kept away from the heat. Christmas candles are handled by every retail florist. If space is limited the rest of the year, the florist will handle just enough for his own use. But, if he has the room, this is a good sideline to handle. There is no need for his customer to go to the five-and-ten or a hardware store to buy candles to go with the flowers when she is entertaining. This is another service he can advertise as being available to his customers. The candles will sell themselves if displayed properly. Along with candles, a retail florist should stock a supply of inexpensive holders to use for large parties. These can be rented, and usually are not sold. More expensive candle holders can be handled for sale to the customers. Candelabras are also sold in retail florist shops, besides being used for weddings and other decorations, and in the window display.

4. **Brass and copper.** Whether a florist handles brass, copper, pewter, or other metal items will depend strictly on his customers and his own desires. These items are a logical sideline to the retail florist business, but only in a limited quantity. A florist can build up a good trade by handling these items. Buy cautiously at first to see how well they are going to sell.

5. **Planters and jardinieres.** It is absolutely necessary for a retail florist to handle planters and some jardinieres in his shop. It makes sense to promote planters. As to the type and number, this will be determined by his clientele. Planters may be in pottery, brass, copper, plastic, or other materials. Jardinieres may be pottery, wood, aluminum, or plastic. There are many different sizes, styles, and types, so it is up to the individual florist to decide how many and what types and kinds of materials he wishes to handle.

6. **Permanent materials.** Although many retail florists do not like the permanent (artificial, polyethylene) flowers and plants they have been forced into handling them. It has proven to be a good sideline. Many florists just sell the loose flowers while others sell the material made up in designs and arrangements. (It apparently has not interfered with the sale of fresh flowers as feared by some florists.) The pros and cons of this sideline are discussed in Chapter 39.

7. **Florist supplies.** If a retail florist has the space, a good sideline is that of handling florist supplies; particularly for garden club

Figure 21-2. Pennsylvania field stone walls and Vermont slate floor form
background for display of gift items. (Courtesy, Penny Hill Flowers,
Wilmington, Del.)

women and others who like to try their hand at flower arranging.
A separate bar or table should be set up with the materials properly
displayed and priced for easy sale. This can be called a "Garden
Club Corner," or "Do-It-Yourself Table." It can be self-service or not,
whichever the florist desires. He should make sure that everything
is priced. The supplies handled here would be florist wire, chicken
wire, pin holders, clay, styrofoam, foams, ribbon, aluminum foil,
floratape, chenille stems, net, spray paint, and other materials for a
do-it-yourself flower arranger. Many of these items, if well displayed,
will lead to impulse buying and an increase in the total volume of
sales, with no extra labor for the florist.

8. **Driftwood.** The handling of pieces of driftwood and manzanita branches is another logical sideline. The florist will need to
have some on hand for his own designing, and it is a good sales
item for customers who may want to use the material in their own
arrangements, or in their own decorating at home.

9. **Souvenirs and novelties.** If you are in a special area where

there are many visitors to the town, you may want to handle local novelty items and souvenirs. Many florists do not handle these items, preferring to leave them to the five-and-tens and variety stores. Others, however, are handling them as a come-on to bring in more customers to the store where they may also sell them plants and flowers. Whether this is a logical sideline or not is debatable among retail florists. If a florist can make money at it *without losing his florist trade*, it might be worth a try. One word of caution is for the florist to make sure he does not go overboard in handling these materials, so that he loses his identity as a retail florist.

10. **Greeting cards.** The small plain and occasion cards are provided free by the florist. However, another sideline in the florist shop is the handling of a regular line of greeting cards from 10¢ to 75¢ for customers to purchase to send either alone or along with flowers or a plant as a gift. Whether the florist handles this sideline or not will probably be determined by the size of his shop and his competition. To have a decent display, he will need to devote quite a bit of floor space to it, and must determine whether it is worthwhile or not. Another determining factor is the competition of stores nearby that are handling greeting cards. The florist may not sell enough cards to make it worth the effort. However, if he has lots of foot traffic by the store, he might sell enough to increase his net profit for the business. As with novelties, he should not have so many cards on display that it looks like a card shop rather than a florist shop.

11. **Christmas supplies and novelties.** This is a very logical sideline for all retail florists. Customers expect retail flower shops to handle Christmas supplies and many novelties. Ornaments, flocked and artificial trees, tinsel, styrofoam figures and novelties, Christmas ribbon, pine cones, spray paint, candles, and Christmas tree stands are just a few of the items which a retail florist will sell at Christmas. There are so many different novelty items, that the florist must choose carefully and buy wisely so that he only stocks what he can sell. It is best to have all Christmas items together in one spot or area. Some florists have them in a separate room while others turn the whole store into a Christmas showcase. Some florists feel these items should be separated from the main selling area. Many of the items will also be found in the five-and-tens so it may be a good idea and it may not. When Christmas is over, the florist either has to have a half-price sale to take care of the material left over, or else pack it away in storage for next year. It is best to buy wisely and moderately, and learn by experience. Items held

over for another year mean money tied up in inventory that the florist could use more profitably somewhere else. It is an excellent sideline, and many florists are competing very favorably with five-and-ten, variety, and hardware stores for the same items. Many of the sales are cash-and-carry and impulse sales by people who have come in to order flowers. Proper display and pricing is important. How deeply a retail florist wants to go into Christmas novelty items is strictly up to him. Try a few at first, and increase as business increases.

12. **Garden supplies.** This is a logical sideline for some retail florists but not for others. It requires a large amount of space and is especially good if the florist has a greenhouse. If he is in a small town where no one else handles these supplies, then he should stock them. The amount of supplies will be determined by available space. Some florists have enough area and business that they have opened a Garden Center in connection with their florist shop.

13. **Nursery stock.** This is a good sideline for certain florists which ties in with garden supplies. The main factor is space, coupled with competition. The sale of nursery stock is seasonal, usually only in the spring and early summer. This sideline as #12 may lead to the establishment of a Garden Center if the florist has the space, and believes he will make a profit on this business.

14. **Bedding plants.** Almost all retail florists handle bedding plants as a seasonal sideline. These include the annual flowers like petunias, marigolds, zinnias, snapdragons, pansies, and others as well as vegetable plants such as tomatoes, peppers, eggplant, etc. Geraniums are sold by all florists and are sometimes included in the group known as "bedding plants." Space is also a factor in deciding to handle bedding plants, although most florists will at least sell some of them. Bedding plants are sold from flats, pots, or market paks. The season for sale of these plants only lasts from four to six weeks, but the sales will increase the total volume of business for the year.

15. **Giftware.** Handling of giftware is one of the most natural sidelines for a retail florist. Flowers and giftware just go together. Giftware has become an established part of most retail florists' shops. Approximately $46,200,000 is spent yearly by retail florists for giftware items (including pottery and glassware). If handled properly, it represents a sizeable part of a florist's annual volume of sales. However, it must be handled by intelligent buying, promotion, and salesmanship, along with flowers. Gift items should be sold as added sales, not as a substitute for flower sales. The extent

to which a florist can invest in giftware depends upon the space and the money available for a profitable business. The items purchased should be different, in good taste, and be a good item to be merchandised and promoted. One of the biggest problems for florists who go to a gift show is deciding what to buy. Some shows have 600 to 1,100 exhibitors of gift items. The florist must select relatively few of these items which will fit into his flower business. Make sure the item has a definite relationship with flowers. Speed-a-Gift is an excellent way to sell flowers and gifts. Many are accessories that can be used with flowers. The following tips may help a florist to promote giftware: (a) Always look at a salesman's line. (b) Substantial orders make it possible to obtain gift lines exclusive to the florist's own area. (c) Change the appearance often of the giftware section by moving giftware lines around to different tables. (d) The buyer should acquaint store personnel (designers and salespeople) with the new lines, giving them information usable in design work and in sales presentation. (e) When the florist buys a gift item in large quantity, he should have a promotional idea in mind to move the material. (f) Use window displays—they sell! (g) Display giftware filled with fresh flowers and/or plants. (h) Stage a clean-up sale to dispose of slow movers once or twice a year when necessary. When it comes to selling giftware, there is no better setting than a flower shop.

16. **New products.** Every month there are new products appearing on the market for retail florists to use in their designing, display, and for sale. It is impossible to list them all or to keep up with new trends unless a florist goes to gift shows, trade fairs, sees the salesman's line, and reads the weekly florist trade papers. The following are a few (out of hundreds) of the new items offered to florists in the past few years to give some idea of the type of merchandise being discussed: adapters for miniature candles, ashtrays, brass stands for plants, flower carts, flowers in glass, fountains and waterfalls, handy trowels, madonnas, paperweights, plant food, planter lamps, planter poles, plastic bird feeders, salad bowl and servers, snack table set, sprayers, styrofoam, styrofoam adhesive, tiered plant stand, tints and dyes, trellis of aluminum or wood, television planters, wall candlelabra, wall plaques, and watering cans.

17. **Candy and fruit.** These were debatable items for many years for most retail florists. Now, however, many retail florists are finding candy and fruit to be very suitable for use in arrangements along with flowers. They make attractive gifts and should be considered as a good sideline in conjunction with flowers, not as competition. They are perishable, but florists all have refrigerators to use for their

Figure 21-3. Giftware items on display. (Courtesy, Silverblatt's Flowers, Pittsburgh, Pa.)

storage. Apples must be stored by themselves, not with flowers, because of ethylene injury.

18. **Wholesaling.** A new way that some retail florists are diversifying is by branching out into the wholesaling of flowers and florist supplies.

19. **Second shop.** Another way for a retail florist to diversify is by opening up a second shop. There are problems with this procedure, and it must be studied very carefully before the florist makes his move.

20. **Figurines.** Figurines are items that are used in and with many floral designs and seem to be quite suitable as well as profitable according to many florists.

Objectionable Sidelines

So far we have discussed the logical or natural sidelines. Now let's look at some of the objectionable sidelines which some florists handle, but most stay away from.

1. **Clothing and neckties.** These items are not considered profitable or practical by most retail florists who find they take up too much space with very little monetary return.

2. **Garden books and magazines.** This is not a profitable item, as it takes up too much display area and attracts people into the store who do not buy flowers, and spend too much time gossiping with friends and reading magazines. No Sale!

3. **Pets.** This is definitely an objectionable sideline for a retail florist. They create undesirable noise, odors, and atmosphere. Special facilities are needed as well as a large amount of space, with too much time having to be allotted to their care. (Yet, some florists handle canaries, parakeets, monkeys, rabbits, and dogs.)

4. **Antiques.** Although some antiques can be used for flowers, this is not considered a good sideline by many florists. The items take up too much space, and the florist will get too many viewers coming in to take up space and time without buying any flowers.

5. **Records.** This sideline is like some others in that the florist will get too many people in the shop who do not purchase flowers. There is no tie-in with flowers.

6. **Television and appliances.** Very objectionable and ridiculous. No tie-in with flowers at all, and yet the author has seen these in a retail florist shop.

7. **Wallpaper.** Another poor sideline with no tie-in with flowers.

8. **Linens and hats.** Another objectionable sideline with no tie-in. The shop will be filled with women not buying flowers.

9. **Cameras.** These will detract from flowers, and take up too much of the retail florist's time.

10. **Wigs.** Wigs are sold by a florist in Florida who says they are profitable. This seems to be getting pretty far afield from the florist business.

Most of the items discussed previously are objectionable; and some are even ridiculous. They are listed here because they have been seen in various florist shops at one time or another.

Stay away from sidelines unless they tie in with flowers and will increase the sales and profits of the store, and not at the expense of flower sales.

This discussion does not include all of the logical and objectionable sidelines, but most of the important ones. There will be more as time goes on, and many changes will be made in the years to come. Some objectionable ones now may become logical ones in the next few years.

Reference

1. Anonymous. "Flower Shop or Variety Store," *Florist* (August 1970), pp. 50-53.

Chapter 22

TELEPHONING AND WIRING FLOWERS

The practice of sending flower orders by telephone or wire has grown into an industry of millions of dollars in the past 60 years. This is the practice whereby a customer can go into a retail flower shop in any city, and have flowers delivered in another city by a second member florist. Flowers may be sent by this method anywhere in the world with the exception of the countries behind the Iron Curtain.

The procedure is quite simple in that the customer goes into his own local retail florist shop, if that shop is a member, and places the order. The customer pays for the flowers, the phone call or telegram, a small service charge, and the tax if any. The service charge, which is usually 50¢, is optional with the florist who takes the order, and who is called the sending florist. For most of these wire or phone orders, there is a minimum order which may be $5.00 or $6.00 depending upon the sending florist and the particular organization to which he belongs. A discount of 15 or 20 per cent (depending on the organization) is retained by the florist who takes the order if it is $6.00 or over. This is retained by the sending florist to help defray the costs of advertising and overhead. Most florists do not receive any discount for orders under $5.00, so it is optional with the sending florist whether he wishes to accept an order from a customer under $5.00. Many florists do accept orders under $5.00 as a *service* to their customers. Other florists use $6.00 as their minimum wire order. Each florist sets his own policy. The receiving florist, however, must accept all orders over $4.50 from a member florist, and must fill the order correctly and at full value. Most organizations handling the wire or phone orders will take out 5 per cent of the order for advertising and clearing-house operation expenses. Thus, the receiving florist receives approximately 75 per cent of the value of the order, but he is obligated by membership in the organization to send out the order with a full 100 per cent value of the flowers. Although he will not make the same profit on this order as on others, the receiving florist will not lose money; however, he will get a lower than normal markup on the flowers. This same receiving florist will, of course, make up some of this deficit on his own orders which he sends out as the sending florist, since he retains the 20 per cent of the order for all his outgoing orders. The total of the 20 per cent of his outgoing orders which he receives as the sending florist will add to his total gross sales, and if he sends out more than he receives, may in fact increase his net profit (see Chapter 6). As an example: A customer orders a $10.00 arrangement of roses and pays the florist $10.00 plus 50¢ service charge, plus $1.50 telephone charge, plus 30¢ tax. The florist taking the order keeps the 50¢ service charge and $2.00 (20 per cent discount). The $1.50 goes to the telephone company and the 30¢ to the government. $8.00 goes to the clearing house where 50¢ (5 per cent of $10.00) is retained. The receiving florist who fills the order receives $7.50 and sends out a $10.00 arrangement to the recipient. This varies slightly with the different organizations.

Each retail florist should obtain the following information from the customer for a phone or wire order:

1. Full name, address, and phone number of the customer sending the order. Even if it is a cash order, the florist should get this information so he can refund the money if the order cannot be delivered.

2. Full name and complete address, (phone number if it is an R.D. or unusual address) of the recipient of the order in the other city.

3. The nature of the occasion for which the flowers are ordered.

4. The exact order of cut flowers, plant, or arrangement. Also be sure to get a second choice in case the first choice cannot be filled by the receiving florist.

5. The price of the order.

6. The message for the card. Be sure there is always a card. If the customer does not want to send a card or message, try to convince him that he should send one even if he says that he is sure the recipient will know who sent the flowers. If the recipient *does not know* who sent the order, she may be very annoyed, and will blame the florist for the card being missing. So, for the florist's own protection, he should be sure that there is a message and

signature. This is another reason for point #1, so that the florist can check back to see who sent the order if it is questioned by the recipient.

7. The exact date the order is to be delivered.

All of this information, except for the name and address of the customer (#1), is sent to the receiving florist. This florist must be a member of the same organization. The information is sent by wire if the sending florist wishes the florist to receive it in writing for his record, and is often sent by a night letter if there is time. If the order is to be delivered 10 days or two weeks from the date of the order taken, then the order can be sent by mail, thus saving the customer the price of the telephone call or telegram. The majority (over 80 per cent) of the orders transmitted are by telephone (Table 22-1), because the one florist can talk directly to the other florist, and find out whether the flowers are in stock and available. If a substitution has to be made, he will know it right away. Most florists feel that the personal contact of a telephone call to the other florist is the best and, of course, the quickest method.

Table 22-1. FTD Profit and Expense Survey, Fiscal Year 1964-65. How FTD Orders Are Sent—by Shops Grouped as to Annual Dollar Volume.

	Under $30,000	$30,000 to $70,000	$70,000 to $125,000	Over $125,000
	Per Cent Distribution by Type of Transmission			
Telegraph	1.5	8.2	13.2	14.9
Telephone	94.7	88.1	80.9	81.3
Mail	3.8	3.7	5.9	3.8
All	100.0	100.0	100.0	100.0

Most of the organizations concerned with the business of transmitting orders operate in a similar manner with just a few changes in procedure. Essentially the orders are transmitted as described previously. A report of the orders is usually sent weekly to a central office or clearing house where every order is processed on computers, and each florist is sent a report monthly tabulating all of his incoming and outgoing orders. Each florist then is sent either a check (if the net dollar volume of his incoming orders exceeds his outgoing orders) or else he receives a bill (if the net dollar volume of his outgoing orders exceeds his incoming orders). These figures are based on the net amounts transacted, with all deductions figured on the transaction.

Each organization publishes a monthly magazine for its own members. The magazine includes advertisements, articles of interest to retail florists, and a complete up-to-date list of all its members. The retail members are listed by state, city, and in alphabetical order by shop name. The names of the shops in each town or city are rotated each month so that the same florist is not at the top of the list every month, unless he is the only member florist in that city. Each shop has a separate organizational number by which he is identified on all reports. Each order reported by each florist weekly must include the number of the sending florist and the receiving florist.

Some of the smaller retail florists in the United States do not belong to any transmittal organization, and thus transfer very few flower orders.

Retail florists may belong to one or more of the four principal flowers-by-wire or phone organizations operating in the United States today (1968).

National Organizations

1. Florists' Transworld Delivery Association is the oldest and largest of the organizations. It is a non-profit and member-owned organization and is the only such inter-city floral delivery service, according to John Bodette, Executive Vice President and Secretary.

The organization started locally in Milwaukee about 1892 and became nation-wide in 1910, when it was known as Florists' Telegraph Delivery Association. The name was changed in 1965 after an earlier survey showed that the majority of its orders were transmitted by phone rather than by telegraph. (See Table 22-1.)

Table 22-2 is an estimate of the percentage of total flower shop sales which are FTD orders in various gross volume sales categories. It shows that between 12 and 16.5 per cent of the total business by FTD retail flower shops comes from FTD orders.

FTD membership includes florists in Canada and other parts of North America and South America as well as the United States. FTDA is part of an international organization with its clearing house and headquarters in Detroit, Michigan. It is composed of 12,000 retail florists in the United States and Canada, teamed together with 24,000 other florists in 90 different countries. FTDA and two other organizations—Interflora British Unit and Fleurop—are affiliated in an inter-

national floral delivery network called Interflora, Inc. Total membership in Interflora is 35,000 retail florists.

FTDA is a non-profit cooperative association of its 12,000 members, with the clearing house in Detroit processing all FTD orders
monthly from the weekly reports from its members. The clearing
house charges 1½ per cent on the gross amount of all incoming orders
and ½ per cent on all outgoing orders for its operation. Three per cent
on the gross amount of incoming orders and 2 per cent on outgoing
orders is used for advertising and publicity.

The 20 per cent discount which is retained by the sending florist
(the one who took the order) is only on orders of $7.50 and above.
There is a 10 per cent commission on orders from $5.00 to $7.49, and
no commission on orders under $5.00. The individual member may
collect any amount of service fee depending upon his shop policy.
The magazine published monthly by FTDA is the *FTD News*.

Membership in FTDA is by application to the organization by
each individual florist, who is then investigated by an FTD committee.
The florist applying for membership is accepted only after careful
consideration, whereby he must satisfy a certain percentage of a long
list of qualifications. The committee in charge of applications (the
Membership Committee) is composed of member florists of the association who are responsible for enforcing the regulations that FTD
members impose on themselves to safeguard the public. The organization is operated efficiently by an executive vice president and secretary, plus a president and board of directors elected annually by its
members. FTDA is associated with Diners Club and other credit card
companies.

Table 22-2. Total FTD Portion of All Business, in Per Cent.

Under $30,000	$30,000 to $70,000	$70,000 to $125,000	Over $125,000
16.5	15.4	13.9	12.0

2. Another equally important network of florists who transmit
flower orders from one city to another or from one country to another
is TELEFLORA Delivery Service, Inc. TELEFLORA is the largest
independently owned flowers-by-wire clearing house in the world.
The company was started in Los Angeles in 1934 as a private corporation and was known as Telegraph Delivery Service, or TDS. In 1961,
a complete reorganization was accomplished, and today it is recog-

nized as a strong and aggressive company always identified as TELE-
FLORA. Unlike the Detroit-based association, TELEFLORA is a
privately owned, profit-motivated corporation.

By the end of 1971, almost 11,000 retail florists were subscribers
to the TELEFLORA clearing-house service. Its only president is
Charles G. Johnston, who supervised the reorganization of the old
Telegraph Delivery Service in 1961. Currently TELEFLORA is head-
quartered in its own building in El Segundo, California.

TELEFLORA functions in the same manner as FTDA. The sending florist accepts an order from a flower customer for long distance
delivery and refers to the *Teleflora Spirit* magazine and directory to
obtain the name of a retailer located in the city in which a delivery
is to be made. Because this sending florist created the sale he earns for
himself a sales commission. If the order is $6.00 or over, he receives
a 20 per cent commission. If the order is $5.00 to $5.99, he earns a 10
per cent commission. On all orders under $5.00 no commission is paid.

To accomplish accurate billing, TELEFLORA maintains its own
comprehensive electronic data processing center, which provides
TELEFLORA subscribers with a fully automated bookkeeping system
of long distance deliveries. The equipment utilized is Remington-Rand
Univac.

Once each month a TELEFLORA subscriber receives an accurate
record of all orders sent out and all orders delivered. Only the delivering florist reports to the clearing house. Payment is guaranteed by
TELEFLORA, regardless of the financial stability of the sending shop.
Once a TELEFLORIST has accepted and delivered a flower order,
he knows that TELEFLORA will reimburse him for that order.

Any retail florist who is accepted in his own community as a
reputable and qualified merchant may apply to the TELEFLORA
Service.

TELEFLORA charges each of its subscribers a $4.00 monthly
service fee and a $1.00 monthly subscription fee to *Spirit* magazine.
For each flower order that passes through the clearing house, both the
sending and delivering florist are charged a flat fee of 25¢ plus 1 per
cent of the gross amount of the order. The 1 per cent deduction is
placed in a marketing fund for advertising and public relations programs on the national level. At the present time TELEFLORA's major
advertising thrust relates to a comprehensive campaign of dealer aids,
all of which are personalized for the individual shops.

TELEFLORISTS regain their clearing-house fees by assessing the
customer a service charge that may vary anywhere from 50¢ to $2.00.

Although this service charge is optional it is estimated that more than 90 per cent of all TELEFLORISTS collect a service charge, the minimum of which is 50¢.

TELEFLORA is international in scope, working with affiliated clearing houses in the British Isles, Continental Europe, Australia and New Zealand, Central and South America, and the Orient. TELEFLORA is also a working associate of the Carte Blanche Credit Card Company, having enrolled all of its subscribers in this credit credential program.

3. The third wire service organization is Florafax International, Inc., located in Tulsa, Oklahoma. It is a privately owned organization. Kenneth F. Short began the company with only an idea in September of 1961 and watched it grow in five years to a membership of approximately 6,000 florists. Shortly after this, Florafax signed a reciprocal agreement with The United Flowers-by-Wire Service, Ltd., in Canada, thereby offering Florafax members the sending and receiving facilities of over 7,000 florists in the United States and Canada. In addition to this rapidly increasing North American membership, Florafax affiliates in scores of foreign countries are currently being added to the membership roster, making Florafax a truly world-wide oganization. In 1970 Florafax merged with Spotts International, Inc., in Minneapolis, Minnesota, to form Spotts Florafax Corporation, with Richard H. Hughes as president and chief executive officer. Present membership is in excess of 8,000.

Florafax is uniquely different from FTDA and TELEFLORA in that it offers its members "instant payment." Under this system the Florafax member receives an order, fills it, and writes himself a check on Florafax for 75 per cent of the order. Each member reports his incoming and outgoing orders to headquarters on a weekly basis and remits 85 per cent of his gross (outgoing) orders to headquarters.

The Florafax sending florist is entitled to 15 per cent of the order for his discount. The sending florist's reports and the receiving florist's checks meet and are matched in the clearing house, where a complete and up-to-date record is kept. Each Florafax member receives a complete accounting of his orders once a month.

Florafax members are provided monthly with the organization's official publication, *Florafacts,* which includes the nearly 500-page membership roster as well as news and feature magazine section.

4. The newest organization to enter this field is not a florist organization, but is Flowers-By-Western-Union. It started in California in 1964 and became national in 1966. It is owned and op-

erated completely by the Western Union Telegraph Company with
the cooperation of retail florists in various cities throughout the
country. Customers place their orders with any Western Union office rather than a retail florist shop. The flower orders, however,
are filled by member florists who receive 75 per cent of the order.
As of 1966, there were 2,500 retail florists in the United States participating in the program. The receiving florist is paid for the
order within two weeks.

In all of these organizations, payment is guaranteed to the
receiving florist by the organization headquarters.

In figuring the profit picture, a retail florist who belongs to one
or more of these organizations must list the wire order business
as volume at *net* or he will have the wrong picture for total sales
volume, and hence profit. Outgoing orders are listed at 20 per
cent and incoming orders filled are reduced by 20 per cent, or
whatever the percentage is for that organization. This is all part
of the accounting procedure and also will affect the percentages
of the gross volume that the florist lists for salaries, advertising, and
other items of expense. They will not be accurate unless the net
volume for wire orders is correct.

International Organizations

The three major organizations of FTDA, TELEFLORA, and Florafax are all international in scope. The FTDA international organization is known as Interflora, Inc. In order to bring all countries
and all florists to a common understanding of the price of an
order, they use the medium of exchange called a "fleurin." It is
worth a certain number of U.S. dollars, British pounds, French
francs, and so forth for each country. Thus, the orders are transmitted all over the world by fleurins, and each florist can translate this into his own monetary value. It has helped to greatly
relieve the confusion of the various monetary systems.

Another point of confusion has been cleared up by Interflora
relative to terminology. Official definitions to be used in all countries
have been described by Interflora for the following standard pieces:
"(1) Arrangement: Cut flowers arranged in a container (if plants
required, this must be specified). (2) Bouquet: One or a variety
of flowers on natural stems tied into an arranged bunch. (3) Corsage: Flowers arranged for a lady to wear. (4) Funeral Sheaf:
Flowers and foliage with stems tied to form a fan-shaped arrangement. (5) Funeral Spray: An elongated flat assembly of flowers

inserted into a foundation. (6) Wreath: Flowers and foliage arranged on a circular foundation. (7) Boutonniere: One flower for a gentleman's buttonhole."

The sending of flowers from one city to another is big business and increasing in volume every year. It is an important part of the retail florist's business and another important service to his customers. It is not a large money-maker, but it will help to increase his volume and also his net profit. For most florists, it is well worth the cost of membership.

Another organization that is international in scope which services U.S. florists is linked with Florafax Delivery, Inc. It is called United Flowers-by-Wire Service, Ltd., started in Toronto, Canada, in 1961. This organization (popularly known as "UFC") has over 1,600 shops in Canada, plus many subscribers in the U.S.A. It has broad overseas coverage and is Canada's largest wire group. Present rates to subscribe to UFC services are: enrollment, $33, 1½ per cent fee on gross amount of all incoming orders and 1 per cent on all outgoing orders, plus 25¢ on each outgoing order only. All subscribers pay $2.50 monthly dues and $8.00 for annual subscription to United Florists News.

UFC operates similar to its counterparts in the U.S.A. and provides many services and floral promotional pieces to its members.

References

1. *Florafax Memorandum* from headquarters, Leachville, Arkansas (1971).
2. *FTDA Memorandum* from headquarters, Detroit, Michigan (1971).
3. *Teleflora Memorandum* from headquarters, El Segundo, California (1971).
4. "U.F.C." *memorandum* from headquarters, Toronto, Canada (1972).

Chapter 23

PACKING; INSULATION; STORAGE; GRADES AND STANDARDS

The packing, shipping, and storage of cut flowers is a wholesale as well as a retail operation, and important from the standpoint of making sure the flowers reach the consumer in the fastest, best, and freshest condition possible.

Most cut flowers are packed in cardboard boxes lined with newspaper and kept fresh with ice in the box. Even in winter ice is used around rose stems. A wooden slat is often fastened across the box to keep the flowers stable in shipment, and then the box is tied with heavy twine. The boxes are fastened on the outside with heavy twine, rope, or metal wire. In place of the wooden slats inside the box, some wholesalers tie down the flowers securely in the box with wide twine. Most of our wholesale florists use one of these methods today, although several new boxes have been on the market since 1958 which will be discussed later in this chapter.

Winter Packing

Flowers freeze at different temperatures so they must be protected in winter. The U.S. Department of Agriculture has given us the following temperatures at which freezing causes damage to the flowers: roses 30° F., carnations 28° F., chrysanthemums 28° F., gladioli 28° F., gardenias 28° F., orchids 30° F., poinsettias 30° F., iris 30° F., daffodils 30° F., violets 28° F., and Easter lilies 27° F. Sheets of newspaper are used inside the box to keep the flowers from freezing. Research has shown the following lengths of time for which newspaper insulation will keep the flowers from freezing: 12 to 15 sheets of newspaper will hold for two hours above freezing if the outside temperature is 20° F.; 40

sheets of newspaper will hold for one-half hour above freezing if the outside temperature is 15° F.

Most shipments of flowers are not out in zero weather too long. Often they are in a boxcar, truck, storage shed, or plane.

In below freezing weather, it is advisable to spray the sheets of newspaper with water. As the water freezes, it gives off heat in what is called the "latent heat of water." Heat is absorbed from the water before it can freeze and this helps to keep the flowers in the box from freezing.

Some wholesalers use an insulating paper called Kimpack in place of sheets of newspaper. One sheet of Kimpack is about equal to 15 sheets of newspaper. It is expensive, but requires less labor in lining the box.

Summer Packing

In the summer it is best to try to keep the inside of the box below 65° F. The box is lined with 10 to 15 sheets of newspaper and should be set in the refrigerator for an hour before shipment. In hot weather it is necessary to use ice, dry ice, or a combination of the two in the box of cut flowers. After the box is packed with flowers, the ice is put in, either wrapped in newspaper or placed in a plastic bag, and tied to the box so it will not move around and injure the flowers. The amount of ice depends on the outside temperature and the method of shipment. Three to four pounds of crushed ice in a 36" x 16" x 8" box (standard) will reduce the temperature 15° F. for a period of 24 hours. The amount of ice is doubled when the temperature outside is above 90° F. One and one-half pounds of dry ice plus two pounds of ice can also be used in place of the four pounds of ice. This cuts down on the weight and bulk in the box. The dry ice must be kept in a plastic bag to keep the carbon dioxide from being given off too rapidly and causing damage to the flowers. Roses are packed with their stems in crushed ice most of the year to keep them fresh.

New Shipping Boxes

Several new boxes for shipping cut flowers have been designed. In 1958 a new method for shipping carnations was developed by the Colorado Agricultural Experiment Station to improve the packaging and shipping of carnations. The box eliminated newspaper, ice, and wooden boards. It saved up to 40 per cent of the shipping costs. The new containers are 36 and 48 inches long, and come in widths of 12, 16, and 20 inches. They are lined with a six-foot square piece of polyethylene film which makes an airtight seal that retains the moisture. Two cardboard inserts in the top and bottom of the box help to keep the flowers secure while in transit.

In 1963, Davis Brothers in Denver announced a new semi-automatic machine that eliminates twine. It uses pressure-sensitive filament tape and a semi-automatic taping machine to accomplish a neat, trim, and economical box reinforcing.

In 1964, Kenco of Dayton, Ohio, manufacturers of permanent flower arrangements, announced they could ship permanent arrangements to any retail florist in the United States. This was made possible by using a carton package designed by the Packaging Division of Olin Mathieson Chemical Corp. An inner pack in the carton made of a scored sheet of corrugated board holds the floral arrangements firmly in place.

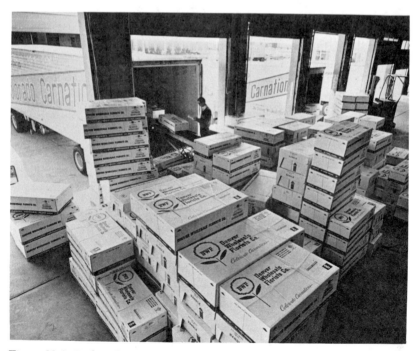

Figure 23-1. Packaged carnations ready for shipment. (Courtesy, Denver Wholesale Florists Co., Denver, Colo.)

Other methods of packing and shipping are being tested in various parts of the country.

Cold Storage

Cut flowers are stored in refrigerators to make them last longer. The lower the temperature the better, down to 35° F. The effects of temperature on the keeping quality of cut flowers are discussed in Chapter 37. Most cut flowers are stored with their stems in water in a refrigerator that is kept between 35° and 40° F. Orchids and gladioli should be stored above 40° F. The closer to 35° F. that the wholesaler and retailer can keep the flowers, the better they will be. Reducing the storage temperature from 50° F. to 35° F. will almost double the keeping life of the flower.

Flowers should be moved as quickly as possible from the grower to the consumer. Some wholesalers and retailers keep the flowers too long in the 35° F. storage and then, when the customer receives them, they go bad and do not last as long as they should. This procedure of keeping cut flowers in water in a refrigerator too long is called pickling, and should be avoided. Pickled flowers do not help the image of the florist industry, nor do they help retail-wholesale relationships.

Do not store fruits such as apples, bananas, or avocados in the same refrigerator with flowers, as the ethylene gas given off by the fruits will shorten the life of the flowers.

Dry Storage

A process developed at Cornell University can be used by the grower to hold cut flowers for a week or more without harming their keeping quality or length of life. This method can be used only by growers who have the facilities to hold flowers during a glut, or period of oversupply on the market, so they can sell them later at a better price. Or they may hold them for a holiday in case the flowers bloom a little too early. Again, they will get a better price. However, the procedure for dry storage requires special equipment and precise directions. The grower must follow directions, and not try to keep the flowers beyond the specified time or he will end up with poor quality material. In this method, flowers are not put in water, but are stored dry. As soon as the flowers are cut and graded they are packed in air-tight cans, boxes, or Leverpak drums. The containers are lined with polyethylene or wax paper but not newspaper. The boxes or drums are sealed so they are airtight and placed in a special storage refrigerator held at 31° F. with no more than one degree fluctuation in the refrigerator. A good circulating fan must be used. In this way, the flowers packed in the boxes or drums will be kept at a constant 31° F. temperature in a dry condition. When the flowers are removed from storage, the stems are cut and put in tall cans of hot water (100° to 110° F.). They are then placed in a 35° F. refrigerator and hardened for six to eight hours before shipping. If these directions are followed exactly, cut flowers will have as good quality and be as fresh as if they had just been cut from the plant, provided they are not kept in dry storage longer than the recommended times, which are as follows: roses, up to 18 days; carnations, three weeks; chrysanthemums, four weeks; snapdragons, two weeks; gardenias, two weeks; iris, three weeks; and tulips, four weeks. Orchids and gladioli cannot be held in dry storage. This process should only be used by growers with special facilities to hold the storage refrigerator at exactly 31° F.

Bud Cut Flowers

The packaging and shipping of bud cut carnations is becoming more common every day. More flowers can be shipped per day and the retailer gets them before they are fully open. Recently, standard mums were being bud cut and shipped. The retailer must use an opening solution to open the buds when they arrive.

Retail Packing

Packing of flowers in the retail shop is important to insure delivery of the flowers that look neat, and are in an undamaged condition. There are at least a dozen different sizes of boxes available from the supplier. The retail florist selects that one which is just large enough to hold all of the flowers in the order without crowding, and not so large that the flowers look lost and the box of flowers looks skimpy. The box is lined with wax or tissue paper which should extend over at least two sides so it can be folded over the flowers. The flowers are laid in very neatly in rows with each row moved slightly down in the box so that most of the flowers can be seen.

The stems of roses are often inserted in a small block of foam to keep them fresh. Greens may be placed in the box first, or put in last on top of the stems. The card is inserted in the bottom of the box on top of the stems and greens. The box is closed and wrapped with paper, or tied with string or ribbon. Florists differ in their handling of boxed cut flowers. If the boxes themselves are attractive and have the name of the shop on them, that is all that is necessary plus the string or ribbon. If the florist uses a plain box, then he may wrap it in paper first before tying.

Pot Plant Wrapping

Pot plants are almost always wrapped with a foil or crepe paper around the clay pot to make it more attractive to the customer. By dressing up the pot plants, the florist can improve the image of his shop. Some pot wraps are already cut to size to fit various pots, while others are on a long roll, and are cut by the florist. There are several different pot wrap materials on the market for the florist to use. If a jardeniere is sold with the plant, then no pot wrap is needed. Some florists will use a pot wrap around a foliage plant while others do not. However, all of them use a pot cover of some sort around all flowering pot plants. Plastic pots do not usually need a cover.

Some florists wrap the plants for delivery and others do not. They may be wrapped in plastic, cellophane, or the florist's own wrapping paper. They are then tied with string or stapled.

The art of putting on a pot wrap and then wrapping the plant for delivery can easily be learned with a little practice.

Many florists use paper sleeves which are drawn up around the plant to make wrapping very easy. Since poinsettia flowers are so fragile, each individual bloom is usually wrapped separately in wax paper with a rubber band around it, to hold it in place before the whole plant is wrapped.

Grades and Standards

The grading of flowers is a process which should be done by the grower before he ships the flowers to the market. Grades and standards are almost non-existent in the florist industry except for some gladioli, carnations, bulbs, and roses. The meaning of "grades" and "standards" is to set up a system of standards or media by which a commodity can be separated into various grades or classifications. It sets up a common language so that the grower, wholesaler, and retailer all know what one another is talking about. Roses have been graded for many years according to stem length, and pompons have been sold according to the weight of the bunch. But there is no one standardization for all the florists all over the country. It will be of tremendous value to retail florists when they can ask for a certain grade of cut flower, and know for sure the number of flowers, size of bloom, length of stem, and *quality* of the flowers they are getting.

The florist industry is the only industry selling perishable products that is not subject to some grade standard. Grades and standards will be set up by the U.S. Department of Agriculture *only* upon request of the industry. At the writing of this text, the Society of American Florists is conducting a survey and study of grades and standards for the florist industry. They have the following six objectives: (1) to devise and promote a system of grading for cut flowers which will adequately classify the material of the industry; (2) to choose a method for the evaluation of flower qualities which is positive, based on universally accepted scales of measurement—ounces, inches, numbers—, can be reduced to writing, and will remain inflexible from season to season; (3) to choose a nomenclature which shall not depreciate the merchandise in the eyes of the consumer; (4) to establish grade limits for the various cut flower crops; (5) to offer such a system to the trade for voluntary acceptance; and (6) to establish a continuing re-examination of the use of standard grades.

The Society of American Florists has already established the following points: (1) Four standard grades are sufficient for most crops. (2) The weight of a flower correlates very closely with quality, and this coupled with stem length and diameter of the flower, serves to sort flowers into different grades. (3) They have adopted the following grade classifications with corresponding colors to be used to designate the proper grade: Blue, top quality; Red, second; Green, third; Yellow, fourth; and White. They are proposing the using of colors rather than names which seem to differ in various parts of the country. Only minor defects are tolerable in the Blue, Red, Green, and Yellow grades. Any flowers which exceed the minimum tolerance are removed as not worthy of recognition by the Standard Grade "stamp of approval." Those not qualifying are relegated to the White grade, as in the case of split carnations and bullhead roses.

The producer of cut flowers who qualifies and uses the SAF Standard Grades is obligated to pledge adherence to the grade definitions to the best of his ability. How well he adheres will be judged by others in the industry. No enforcement agency is to be used, but economic attrition will separate those who persist in substandard procedures.

When grades and standards for cut flowers are adopted for the whole industry, it will be of benefit to growers, wholesalers, and retailers, and will tend to eliminate a lot of poor quality material from the market.

Proper handling of cut flowers from the producer to the consumer is essential to the success of the retail florist industry. With a highly perishable commodity like flowers, everyone in the industry must do his part to make sure the flowers, which may have been growing in the greenhouse for from 4 to 12 months, will reach the consumer in the best possible condition. High quality merchandise will help to promote flowers to the general public.

References

1. Anonymous. "New Taping Operation Saves Money," *Florists' Review*, Vol. 131, No. 3405 (February 28, 1963), pp. 15-16.
2. Anonymous. "Packaging: A Must," *Florists' Review*, Vol. 135, No. 3470 (May 28, 1964), p. 32.
3. Anonymous. "SAF Grades Emphasize Quality," *Florists' and Nursery Exchange*, Vol. 146, No. 13 (September 24, 1966), p. 11.

Chapter 24

DELIVERY

Services in many shapes and forms are a positive asset in the independent retailer's continuous battle with discounters and chain stores. In today's mass market economy, service is just about the only thing which the independent retailer has to distinguish himself from the mass market crowd.

Of course, service costs money, and this must be passed on to the consumer in one form or another. This indicates that the retail florist cannot afford to be overly generous on service without charging for it, if he wants to remain reasonably competitive with his non-florist competitors. However, retail florists have a tradition of service; one of the most important of which is *delivery*.

Here are some good reasons for offering delivery as a service to customers of retail florists: (1) If an order is phoned in, it usually must be delivered; and thus the florist is ready to suggest additional items of purchase over the phone to the customer, which can be delivered with no extra cost to the florist or to the customer. (2) The retail florist who delivers, encourages additional purchases that the customer might otherwise hesitate to carry home. (3) Good will created by delivering even small orders can lead the customer to give the store substantial business on other occasions, and may build up a sizeable account later on. (4) Delivery is something that customers just naturally expect, and take for granted, as they do the extension of credit.

Since the act of service is the very backbone of the retail florist's business today, and will be even more important to the industry in the future, the retail florist must consider the expenses involved in a service such as delivery. This is one phase of the process of selling flowers where most of the competition fades out of the picture, and the florist automatically sits in the driver's seat according to Bill Curtis, Allentown, Pennsylvania. We have to think of deliveries from two angles: the provider of the service—the florist; and the receiver of the service—the recipient.

It is a common procedure in all retail florist shops to concentrate on getting the order made up and out on delivery, and at this point many florists consider their job finished. However, the florist has the responsibility to see that each piece of merchandise reaches the recipient properly. Several factors should be considered by the florist, including the following: (1) Has the product been designed properly so that it will travel without being disarranged? Before the introduction of tape, clips, springs, and forms, we often found that bouquet and arrangements would lean or tip over; but now with all the new gadgets on the market there is no excuse for this. (2) Does the florist have the merchandise wrapped properly to withstand either heat or cold? Keep in mind that half the thrill of receiving a gift is in the unwrapping. Wrap not only for appearance sake, but because it will protect the flowers from becoming bruised or broken, as well as to give protection from the elements. (3) Is the package addressed properly, and can the customer read the card that is attached? Proper addressing will save the driver time in making his deliveries. A sloppy procedure could be very costly in time and money to the florist. (4) Do delivery equipment and the driver properly represent the florist as being a first class service business? The truck and the driver are often the only contact a customer or potential customer may have with the shop. (5) Is the delivery being made at the proper time? While none of the florists should encourage timed deliveries, more and more businessess that

Delivery Area	Rush Orders	DESIGNERS					Finished Orders
		A	B	C	D	E	
North							
East							
South							
West							
Will Call							

Figure 24-1. Wall construction with pigeon holes to keep orders separate for systematic designing and delivery of all orders.

are closely related to the florist business, are becoming conscious of the time that flowers are delivered. Hospitals and funeral homes usually have set hours for flower deliveries and these should be observed by all florists and their delivery men.

Each retail florist should have a cut-off time in his shop for deliveries beyond which no order should be taken for that day's delivery. Always explain this to the customer so he will know the order will be delivered tomorrow, and why it is impossible to deliver it today. This is a good and economical business practice.

Customer Viewpoint

The retail florist should consider deliveries from the standpoint of the customer. A poll of some of the better floral customers in one town showed the following complaints: (1) The delivery man handed the lady of the house a floral arrangement either filled with water, or no water at all. In the one case she ends up with a wet floor, and the other a wilted arrangement. In either case, a vase half filled with water plus a simple "Add Water" tag would have prevented an irate customer. (2) In another case, as an arrangement of chrysanthemums is handed to the customer, one of the flowers hits the door and shatters. If the driver is smart, he will have a candle or can of spray wax in the truck, and he can be of real service by repairing the damage on the spot (see Chapter 19). (3) Another complaint is about the florist who leaves flowers at the front door when no one is home, and if the family does not use the front door, they may not find the flowers for several days. Either place a tag on the back door or leave a tag on the front door, and return to the shop with the arrangement. He should call before delivering a second time. Some drivers leave a tag on the door, and leave the flowers at a neighbor's house. It often depends on how far the customer is from the shop. In any case a follow-up phone call is important to make sure the proper person receives the flowers.

Flowers should always be delivered to the front door even in an apartment house. They are in a category of their own and not to be classed with general deliveries. It is the one commodity which is an exception to the rule of "deliveries are to be made only in the rear." A good rule is to deliver flowers to the door that has the mailbox.

Delivery Problems

Downtown stores in medium-sized communities usually face more formidable delivery problems than other florists. The more widespread the customers are in an area, the greater the cost factor and more unwieldy this service may become. Many shops in downtown areas are likely to rely on cash-and-carry business. The neighborhood flower shop almost always runs its own delivery service. Such a service must accomplish several objectives at the same time: it must get the merchandise to the customer in the shortest possible time, it must do this with the greatest possible efficiency and accuracy, it must be able to handle the largest possible volume at the lowest possible cost, and it should eliminate mistakes and delays in delivery.

Costs

Full-time delivery men are an expensive part of the business, justified only by high volume. Part-time delivery men, who also do other jobs for the store, help to keep the costs low. Each florist must decide himself whether to own his vehicles outright or to lease the vehicles. Both systems are expensive, and must be considered as to the pros and cons for each situation. There are advantages and disadvantages to both, which relate directly to the size of the shop, volume, and size of the community. Cooperative delivery is practiced by various groups of retail florists particularly in the very large cities where it is uneconomical for each retail florist to try to deliver to all parts of the city, such as in Philadelphia, Los Angeles, Chicago, and New York. There are also delivery companies who will pick up floral orders in one central spot and deliver anywhere in the city for a certain price per piece. All of these systems must be weighed against each other as far as costs are concerned. In small towns, however, the cheapest way is probably for the retail florist to own his own truck and hire his own delivery man. Most retail florists in the United States use this system.

According to recent surveys, the florists estimate that deliveries cost them anywhere from 50¢ to $1.50 per piece. However, a few florists have reported costs up to as high as $2.00 per delivery. The size of the city has a direct relationship to the cost, as does the volume of business.

The best way to reduce delivery costs is to encourage will calls. Other florists will lease all their vehicles because it is cheaper for them, but this depends on a study of the entire delivery costs. Others lease because they don't have the time to worry about operation and maintenance.

The latest FTD Profit and Expense Survey of 1965 showed the trend of decreasing overall operating costs to sell and deliver, as the sales volume increased. Total delivery expense ranged from 4.3 to 6.1 per cent of total annual gross volume of sales as shown in Table 24-1.

Table 24-1. Selling and Delivery Expenses as a Percentage of the Gross Volume of Sales.

The Costs to Sell and Deliver, by Shops Grouped as to Annual Dollar Volume	Under $30,000	$30,000 to $70,000	$70,000 to $125,000	Over $125,000
As a Per Cent of Total Sales and Other Income				
SELLING EXPENSE				
Advertising and promotion	1.3	1.8	2.1	2.1
Travel and entertainment	.2	.3	.3	.3
Commission to agents	.2	.1	.3	.2
Commission FTD incoming	2.4	1.8	1.6	1.5
Clearing house deduction	.5	.4	.3	.3
TOTAL SELLING EXPENSE	4.6	4.4	4.6	4.4
DELIVERY EXPENSE				
Other than wages	3.2	2.8	2.0	2.3
Wrapping and boxes	1.1	1.4	.7	1.8
Express and cartage-in	.3	.7	.6	.5
Depreciation—vehicle only	1.3	1.2	1.0	.8
TOTAL DELIVERY EXPENSE	5.9	6.1	4.3	5.4
TOTAL SELLING AND DELIVERY EXPENSE	10.5	10.5	8.9	9.8

Free Delivery

A 1965 statistical report from a U.S. Department of Agriculture survey of 2,000 retail florists from all parts of the country showed that 97 per cent of the florists surveyed offered free delivery to their customers. It showed that 77 per cent of the sales were delivered free and that the delivery costs to all the florists averaged 67¢ per item. (A range of 50¢ to $1.50 was reported earlier.) This is considered an average expense for an average florist and, of course, must be absorbed somewhere in his operating costs as reflected in the price of the flowers as discussed in Chapter 14.

In the same survey, nearly all florists, regardless of size, offered free delivery. However, 72 per cent of these florists did have some restrictions on order size and/or distances for free delivery. There should be a minimum delivery set by each florist which may be $3.50, $4.00, or $5.00. Below this a charge should be made.

It was noted that larger florists tend more to apply delivery restrictions than do the smaller florists; nearly 85 per cent of the larger florists invoked these restrictions as against only 66 per cent of the smaller florists.

Only about 16 per cent of the florists used commercial delivery service for all, or part, of their deliveries. Those florists most often using this service were the larger florists (over $100,000 sales).

Air-conditioned vehicles were scarce among the florists. Only 13 per cent of the florists surveyed used them. However, there was an additional 18 per cent who favored their use and felt it would help to have them. This was particularly true of the larger florists.

Sixty-three per cent of the florists said they never pool deliveries. Thirty-one per cent said that they pool deliveries occasionally, and 6 per cent pool deliveries often. This is one place where many florists in both large and small communities could cut down on their delivery expenses.

Equipment

The equipment varies with the individual shop. Some retail florists find that a station wagon is adequate. Others use a small pickup van or regular florist's truck. Some florists, who do a lot of decorating, need a larger special truck which will be high enough inside to haul trellises, ferns, palms, cibotiums, and other items. Some florists only need one vehicle while others need several. Almost all florists hire other drivers with station wagons or trucks for the holidays.

An insulated truck is best in all areas. The northern trucks must be equipped with a good heater. Many florists would benefit by an air-conditioned truck, but as noted previously, only 13 per cent of the retailers in a recent survey said they used them.

The trucks should have racks and braces in the truck to hold vases, baskets, and sprays in place during delivery. There are many ideas for holding containers in the truck, from the use of sand bags, to the use of an iron stand with two or three springs that clip over the lip of the container and hold it steady. Each florist has his own method and gadgets to use.

The truck can be plain black, colored, multicolored, or even polka-dotted depending upon how much attention the florist wishes to attract with his truck. No matter what color or style a florist uses, he should take advantage of the advertising value of the truck. For very little cost, he can have his name, address, and phone number painted on it. Many florists also include the emblem for FTDA, TELEFLORA, or Florafax if they belong to one of those organizations. The lettering should be small and neatly done. A flower design is sometimes included to call the attention of people to the fact that it is a florist's truck. Uniformed delivery men might be considered by retail florists in the industry. However, it should be something very snappy, not sloppy! Adequate insurance on the truck is absolutely essential.

Delivery is one of the most important and the most costly services rendered by the retail florist to his customers. The florists' responsibility does not stop with the sale and the designing, but goes on until the item is delivered in a fresh and good condition. It is up to the manager or owner to select the orders according to delivery areas, and give them to the proper designers at the proper times. The manager must coordinate the designing with the delivery schedules. Delivery costs money so must be figured into the sale price of the item. The delivery man is as important an employee as the salesman and the designer. He is often the major link between the store and the customer. The reputation of the florist frequently hinges upon the delivery man. He is often responsible for the image of the store in the eyes of the consumer.

References

1. Anonymous. "Free Delivery and Credit," *FTD News* (February 1966), pp. 24-25.
2. Anonymous. "How to Build Customer Relations with Service," *The Exchange*, Vol. 141, No. 15 (April 11, 1964), pp. 28-29.
3. Anonymous. "New Survey Reveals Average Profits, Expenses," *FTD News* (April 1966), pp. 18-20.
4. Butler, Thomas M. "Vehicle Leasing Buys Peace of Mind," *Florist* (May 1970), pp. 38, 39.

Chapter 25

ACCOUNTING; BOOKKEEPING;
KEEPING RECORDS

Accounting

Accounting practices of retail florists vary a great deal. A variety of methods have developed within the individual shop, and no doubt have been improved from time to time as the business has grown, or as it has been acquired from one generation to another. New shops have adopted a number of the basic rules and thus their own accounting procedure has continued with a build-up around the traditional markup policy discussed in Chapter 14.

In every flower shop, regardless of the size, bookkeeping is the main artery of the business, according to Herb Mitchell. No one can manage a flower shop successfully without advanced planning, and when you don't know what's going on when it's happening, it is impossible to look ahead and plan intelligently. Many florists say that it is foolish to worry about bookkeeping and accounting. They feel they can hire trained accountants to do this work for them. However, unless the florist understands what the accounting figures really mean, he is not in a position to manage intelligently. No one but the florist himself is in a position to understand and interpret the accounting figures of the business. The accountant can tell the florist how much he has made or lost, but the florist himself must understand the figures to be able to improve his operation.

Many small retail florists do the bookkeeping themselves, so they should know the fundamentals involved in accounting, bookkeeping, and keeping records.

Simple Sales Analysis

An intelligent manager should make a sales report and sales analysis daily. In small operations especially, it is easy to let all the

Table 25-1. Daily Sales Journal for June 1.

Amt. of Reg. Sales	Amt. of Incoming Wire Sales	Perishable Mdse.	Inventory Mdse.	Outgoing Wire Orders	Phone Charges	Labor
$ 5.00		$ 3.75	$ 1.00	$ 6.00	$1.00	$ .25
7.50						.50
10.00		8.00	1.50			.50
4.00		4.00				
	$15.00	12.25	2.00			.75
25.00		19.00	5.00			1.00
3.00			3.00			
20.00		17.00	2.00			1.00
		8.00	1.50			.50
12.50	10.00			10.00	2.00	.50
87.00	25.00	72.00	16.00	16.00	3.00	5.00

Adjustment for outgoing wire orders (80%) is $12.80.
Adjustment for incoming wire orders (20%) is $5.00 and phone $3.00.
Adjusted daily rates: $72.00 $16.00 $-1.80 $3.00 $5.00
Daily sales report: TOTAL NET SALES: $91.20 ($87.00 + $25.00 — $17.80 — $3.00 equals $91.20)
(The total of the first two columns should always equal the total of the last 5 right-hand columns.)

bookkeeping go until the end of the month. This is a mistake, as the accounting operation should be done on a daily basis. In the average florist's shop, a sales report and a sales analysis can be prepared in less than an hour, and it is well worth the time it takes. There are only two records the florist needs to keep in order to have a satisfactory sales record according to Herb Mitchell. The first is a daily sales journal (Table 25-1), and the second is a monthly summary (Table 25-2), or re-cap sheet.

The purpose of a daily sales report is to give the florist a form on which to make a simple sales analysis, as well as to give him a report of net sales for the day. The purpose of a monthly summary sheet is to keep account of his net sales on a daily, weekly, and monthly basis. These can be easily compared with last year's figures to see how this year's sales compare. The two illustrations presented here show how these forms accomplish the job. The incoming and outgoing wire sales order plus telephone charges must be considered, and adjusted so that the florist will get a true picture of his net sales.

The main goal in all retail florist shops is to make money. Keeping books and studying records is sometimes dry and difficult work, but it must be done in all businesses. The retail florist business deals with a perishable commodity. Flowers cost money, and the markup has to cover the loss of flowers if a florist does not buy according to his daily sales. The most important accounting practice is the budget record of purchases related to daily sales. The secret of making a comparison of these two factors is doing it by percentages. Following this method, a florist can control his gross profit, and see almost daily his possible net profit for the month; and he can thus allocate his average monthly overhead expenses on a daily basis.

Record Keeping

Record keeping is one of the most necessary phases of business management, yet too few retail florists place the proper emphasis on it. Without records, a business operates with no organized direction. Records should be kept for legal reasons as well, and to get the business back in operation following a disaster.

The three reasons why a florist needs good records are as follows: (1) for determining his true income, (2) for reducing his tax liability and avoiding penalties, and (3) for better management of the business. The following check points should be kept in mind by all retail florists who wish to be successful: (1) consider the

Table 25-2. Monthly Summary of Net Sales for June.

Date	Total Net Sales	Perishable Items	Inventory Sales	Wire Order Sales	Phone Charges	Labor
June 1	$91.20	$72.00	$16.00	$-1.80	$3.00	$5.00
June 2						
June 3						
June 4						
——						
——						
June 30						

basic points on keeping effective books, (2) check to see if the records are really useful, (3) make sure the florist understands the statute of limitations, (4) be sure he has proper storage for his records, (5) he must make sure his accounting practices are kept up-to-date, (6) he should always report pre-paid income under the proper circumstances, (7) depreciation must be handled properly, (8) accurate tax-withholding records must be kept, and (9) the florist has to watch out for unusual expenses, such as entertainment, personal bills, and business losses.

The system of keeping records should be so designed that it gives the florist the results of his operations as clearly, and as quickly, as possible. These records should give him a financial statement every month including a profit and loss (P&L) statement (Table 25-3) and a balance sheet (Table 25-4). A P&L statement shows very quickly for any time period, covering any operation, the position of the business at that time. The following P&L statement is a sample which shows how much money the business earned or lost in that month. The real management dimension comes into effect, however, when the florist takes this statement and compares it to what his business did in the same period last year, and what his business accomplished in comparison to what it should have done; that is, what was planned and budgeted for the business.

A look at Table 25-3 shows that profits were down in 1960 even though sales exceeded 1959, and those budgeted for 1960. This shows that something was wrong and, therefore, the rest of the figures should be analyzed. The figures show that the cost of merchandise was up and out of line, and that delivery, payroll, and other expenses were higher than budgeted. Something was wrong with the management; either the figures were not budgeted properly or the operation was not managed properly. If expenses could not be cut, the only solution here is to increase prices, and to be more careful in buying to reduce the cost of merchandise. If the prices are in line, then check the expenses. This illustration shows the importance of the P&L statement for the successful management of the retail flower shop.

The two most frequently used financial statements are the profit and loss statement and the balance sheet. They should be used together to give a true picture of the business. However, the P&L statement is probably read and studied more often than the balance sheet. The accuracy of one depends on the accuracy of the other and time must be taken in making them out. As mentioned previously, the P&L statement serves to tell how well (or poorly) the

Table 25-3. Profit and Loss Statement for January 1959 and 1960.

Item	1960 Budget	1960 Actual	1959 Actual	Increase or Decrease %	% of Total Budget	% of Total 1960	% of Total 1959
Net sales	12,000	12,300	11,500	+7.0	100.0	100.0	100.0
Cost of goods sold	4,400	4,900	4,150	+6.5	36.6	39.9	36.1
Gross profit	7,600	7,400	7,350	+ .5	63.4	60.1	63.9
EXPENSES							
Delivery	720	750	710	+ .4	6.0	6.1	6.2
Payroll (adm.)	1,200	1,200	1,200		10.0	9.8	10.4
Other payroll	1,800	1,900	1,600	+2.6	15.0	15.4	13.9
Expenses	3,000	3,150	2,750	+3.5	25.0	25.6	23.9
Financial	200	200	200		1.7	1.6	1.7
Totals	6,920	7,200	6,460	+6.5	57.7	58.5	56.1
Net operating profit	680	200	890	-7.0	5.7	1.6	7.8

Table 25-4. Balance Sheet for 1966 for John Smith, Florist.

Balance Sheet, December 31, 1966

Assets			
Current Assets:			
Cash		$ 5,000	
Accounts Receivable	$ 3,500		
Less: Allowance for			
Bad Debts	500	3,000	
Merchandise Inventory		7,000	
Total Current Assets			$15,000
Fixed Assets:			
Furniture & Fixtures	$ 2,500		
Less: Allowance for			
Depreciation	1,100	1,400	
Building	$40,000		
Less: Allowance for			
Depreciation	10,000	30,000	
Land		20,000	
Total Fixed Assets			51,400
Deferred Charges:			
Prepaid Insurance		$ 250	
Office Supplies Inventory		150	
Total Deferred Charges			$ 400
			$66,800

Liabilities and Proprietorship		
Current Liabilities:		
Accounts Payable	$ 3,500	
Wages Payable	200	
Interest Payable	400	
Property Taxes Payable	350	
Accrued Liabilities	300	
Total Current Liabilities		$ 4,750
Fixed Liabilities:		
Mortgage Payable	$13,500	
Deferred Credits to Income:		
Advance Rentals	50	
Total Liabilities		$18,300
Proprietorship:		
John Smith-Capital,		
December 31, 1965	$45,000	
Add: Net Income for		
1966	6,500	
	$51,500	
Deduct: Withdrawals in 1966	3,000	
John Smith-Capital, December 31, 1966		$48,500
		$66,800

firm and its management have performed in the past. Since the time involved and the actions recorded are fixed and unchangeable, the information derived is of use only with respect to plans for the future. The usefulness and applicability of any financial statement is dependent upon its accuracy. The accuracy must be thought of in terms of reasonableness of judgment as well as in an arithmetic sense.

The balance sheet (Table 25-4) must give an accurate account of the present value of the property owned by the firm. It must show the assets and liabilities, and often indicates the net worth of the business. The biggest errors in the preparation of the balance sheets occur in connection with the inventories and the major fixed assets. In order for the balance sheet to be of maximum benefit in making management decisions, these items should be accurately reported. The balance sheet must balance, hence the need for accuracy. If the inventory increases during the year, this must be reported. Don't assume that it is always the same. If the building increases in value over the years, this must be included. If the assets are wrong, the balance sheet will give a false picture of the business.

Cost Analysis

Many florists use a simple cost analysis system so that each month they can easily check on all the items of cost and expense. This can be compared very easily with the last month or the same month last year. Often florists do not realize their expected profit, and the monthly statement may show them why. Various columns on a single ledger sheet should be used for certain items so that comparison is very easy. If one expense is out of line, it should be corrected for the following month. Table 25-5 is a sample cost analysis sheet.

Simplified Accounting

The simplified accounting system recommended for most retail florists is called the double entry system of bookkeeping. With this system, the records show property received and exchanged, cost of conducting the business, and the profits of the business. It is based upon the principle that each transaction involves an exchange of equal value, and the record must show the value of property or

Table 25-5. Cost Analysis, May 1966.

Flowers and Greens	Supplies, Boxes, Wire, Pins, Ribbon, etc.	Advertising Printing Postage	Delivery Garage Gas, etc.	Salaries	Rent Util. Taxes	Misc. Exp.
$ 75.00	$10.50	$35.50	$12.50	$100.00	$200.00	$1.75
106.00	6.50	20.75	3.50	75.00	5.00	2.50
45.75	11.20	15.00	4.75	125.00	4.50	5.00
79.00	9.45	1.00	25.00	50.00		.50
$305.75	$37.65	$72.25	$45.75	$350.00	$209.50	$9.75

services received and exchanged in each transaction. The double entry method requires a record of property and services both.

The following explanation of terms refers to the double entry method only:

1. **Bookkeeping**—the record of business transactions in the proper sequence and properly arranged in a blank book.

2. **Business transactions**—an exchange of goods or services by which the business is affected.

3. **An account**—record of all transactions with any one person or with any particular kind of property, services, revenue, or expense.

4. **Debits and credits**—all accounts are affected in two ways: one opposite to the other; plus and minus.

5. **Classification of accounts**—all accounts must be properly classified, and this is the most important feature of accounting and bookkeeping.

6. **Asset accounts**—this is the value of property belonging to the business. Current assets are property bought for resale. Fixed assets are value of property bought to be used in the business, but not for resale.

7. **Liabilities**—obligations owed by the business are in three classes: (a) verbal promises (trade creditors), (b) written promises (notes and mortgages payable), and (c) money owed to stockholders.

8. **Current liabilities**—these include accounts payable, notes payable, installment purchases, taxes, etc.

9. **Fixed liabilities**—these represent the value of long time obligations such as real estate mortgages.

10. **Accrued expense**—outstanding obligations at the end of the year; earned payroll, rent due, taxes, etc.

11. **Income accounts**—shows profit derived from sale of merchandise or services: sales, income from rent, commissions, and miscellaneous income.

12. **Operating accounts**—expense accounts which may be selling or administrative.

Figure 25-1 shows a copy of the Florists' Transworld Delivery Association Daily Summary of Business from their Uniform Accounting System. This form should be filled in daily so that the manager can tell at a glance the amount of sales, cash received, accounts receivable, and expenses for the day. It gives a good picture of the business for the day, to help the manager figure out how well the shop is doing on a day-to-day basis.

DAILY SUMMARY OF BUSINESS

FTDA UNIFORM ACCOUNTING SYSTEM

DEBIT OR CREDIT ACCT. NO.	CASH RECEIVED		DEBIT OR CREDIT ACCT. NO.	CASH DISBURSED	
CR 301	Sales, Taxable		DR 102	Deposited in Bank	
CR 302	Sales, Exempt		DR 121	Purchases of Merchandise	
CR 216	F.T.D. Outgoing (Gross)		DR 261	Owners Withdrawal	
CR 221	Sales Tax		DR 23	Maintenance & Repairs	
CR 306	Relay or Service Charges		DR 31	Advertising	
CR 52	Telephone & Telegraph		DR 41	Delivery	
CR 111	Received on Account See Other Side For Names & Amounts		DR 51	Postage, Office Supplies	
CR			DR		
CR			DR		
CR			DR		
CR 63	Cash Over		DR 63	Cash Short	
DR 101	Total Cash Received		CR 101	Total Cash Disbursed	
	Add Cash At Beginning of Day			Add Cash At Close of Day	
	These Totals Must Balance				
	CHARGE SALES			**ACCOUNTS RECEIVABLE CONTROL**	
CR 301	Sales, Taxable			Due From Accounts At Start of Day	
CR 302	Sales, Exempt			Add: Total Charges Today	
CR 216	F.T.D. Outgoing (Gross)				
CR 221	Sales Tax			Less: Received on Account Today	
CR 306	Relay or Service Charges			Due From Accounts At Close of Day	
CR 52	Telephone & Telegraph				
DR 111	Total Charges			**CASH IN BANK CONTROL**	
				Balance in Bank At Start of Day	
CR 303	F.T.D. Incoming (Gross)			Add: Deposit Today (As Above)	
DR 106	F.T.D. Receivable				
				Less: Checks Issued Today (See Record)	
				Balance in Bank At Close of Day	
				Other Credits (Add)	
				Other Charges (Deduct)	
				Total Cash in Bank At Close of Day	

Form 321

PREPARED BY_____ DATE _____

Figure 25-1. Daily summary of Business Form 321 from FTDA Uniform Accounting System.

Cash Register

Some florists are using newer methods for their records. Many florists are using their cash register for their bookkeeping, such as Brill's in Ardmore, Pennsylvania. They use the National Cash Register system which does a total bookkeeping job for them. It not only keeps track of cash receipts, but handles the charge sales as well, and produces reports that give a shop picture of the state of the business. The tape in the register is printed in a special optical type font, legible to both human and electronic eyes. Every detail of each sales transaction, as well as other bookkeeping entries, are recorded on the cash register's internal audit tape. Each month the register tape is sent to an NCR data processing center. With this system, the shop gets daily analyses as well as monthly ones. Daily summaries come directly from the cash register tape, and show such things as total of cash and charge sales for the day, the amount of sales tax collected, how much the shop took in from promotional specials, the value of incoming and outgoing wire service orders, and the total service charges collected. The following are the reports which the NCR data processing center prepares for the retail florist at the end of the month: (1) cost inventory management report, (2) sales summary analysis, (3) sales and tax report, (4) income statement, (5) balance sheet, (6) accounts receivable aging analysis, and (7) statements for each customer. The shop simply mails the statements to the customers without having to type them each month.

Another system offered to retail florists by certain banks is the Mellon Bank System used by Silverblatt's Flowers and others in Pittsburgh, Pennsylvania.

The Mellon Bank Billing System has been developed to emphasize simplicity, and to impose only minimum demands on the retail shop itself. When the service is installed, the florist receives an IBM 1001 Data Transmission Terminal and a complete file of pre-punched cards, one for each customer. The transmitting unit is linked directly to the Datacenter over existing telephone lines. The florist has no more typing of statements, copying ledgers, and no stuffing, sealing, or stamping of statements. The customers receive professional-looking itemized statements promptly, and the florist receives a prompt payment which is opened by Mellon Bank employees who automatically credit payment to the customer's account and deposit the money in the florist's free Mellon Bank checking account. Each day the florist's office employee dials the telephone number of the receiving key punch unit in the Mellon Datacenter and, when ready, inserts the customer's cards into the IBM transmission unit. The florist's account number and customer identifying number are automatically transmitted. The employee transmits the amount of the charge or payment, and the designation of purchased items by prearranged code. The florist daily receives the following reports: (1) transaction journal, (2) trial balance journal, (3) a summary of all daily activity including charges, payments, adjustments, month-to-date and year-to-date receipts, (4) deposit tickets for money automatically credited to florist's account, and (5)

IBM cards for new customers. The florist receives the following accumulative reports monthly: (1) an aged trial balance report showing delinquencies in 30, 60, and 90 day categories, (2) a listing of all new customers and closed accounts, and (3) a recap of sales to include number and dollar amounts in each category. Mellon Bank prepares and mails a detailed statement to each customer with a duplicate copy sent to the florist. Banks in other areas of the country are offering the same type of system to florists.

Florists Transworld Delivery Association has set up a billing system for its members which includes many advantages to the individual retail florist. An FTD representative shows the florist how to assemble the names of all active accounts and FTD prepares a small plastic customer card for each name. The florist receives two machines: an encoder and a visible index file. FTD also sends the plastic customer cards, a master customer list, master customer list binder, four or five-part sales slips, three-part payment slips, and additional new customer forms. An FTD representative shows the florist how the system operates.

The advantages of the FTD Complete Billing Service to the florist are as follows: (1) it does the entire job including stamping and mailing the statements; (2) it does away with ledgers and ledger-keeping routine; (3) it provides the florist with a regular monthly list of all accounts 30, 60, or 90 days overdue; (4) it provides the florist with a monthly statement of who his active accounts are, and how much they buy; (5) it gives the total charge sales month by month; (6) it makes it unnecessary for the florist to prepare and submit an FTD Report of Orders Filled; and (7) it gives the florist an automatic way to follow up with direct mail in the statements. The system handles all facets of the business, not just FTD orders alone.

The keeping of records and a system of accurate accounting and bookkeeping is one of the most important aspects of the retail florist business. The manager must have accurate reports to use in keeping track of the business and its profits to be able to accurately plan for future business.

Whether a florist uses one of the record keeping or billing services offered to retail florists or not depends on each individual florist and his type of business. Each florist must figure his costs and time involved in keeping books, sending statements, and other transactions and compare this to the cost of one of the newer systems. Accountants have told retail florists that if a florist sends out less than 400 statements monthly, then it is more economical to do it himself.

The bookkeeping and accounting can be done by the manager, a bookkeeper and accountant, or by a machine through any of several processing outfits. Whatever method is used, accuracy is the keynote along with a constant analysis of the records. The size of the shop and total volume of business will help to determine which system the florist should use.

References

1. Anonymous. "His Bookkeeper Is a Cash Register," *FTD News* (July 1966), pp. 24-25.
2. Beitler, John. *FTD Complete Billing Service.* Memo from Headquarters (November 1966).

Chapter 26

CREDIT AND COLLECTIONS

Credit

No sale is complete until the money has been collected. It is essential for a retail florist to develop a good credit and collection policy, and stick to it. The accounts receivable can make or break him. The florist should remember that he is loaning money at no interest, and even banks don't do that!

The charge account is customary in the credit field today, and the florist must go along with it. In simple language, a charge account presupposes that statements are sent by the merchant every month for the purchases made during the previous 30 days, and that payment of the entire amount is expected within 10 to 30 days after receipt of the bill. Many statements contain a note to this effect. Many retail florists who belong to various wire service organizations accept certain national credit cards as well as some local bank credit cards. The expected increase in business must exceed the cost of the system.

The most important reason for the extension of consumer credit is that it affords retailers a fairly constant volume of business that could not be obtained if they were operating on a strictly cash basis. There are very few cash florists. Ninety-five per cent of the retail florists surveyed recently indicated they offer credit to their customers. Their losses for bad debts are only 1 per cent of their gross sales.

Here are some of the principal advantages of credit selling: (1) it creates more store traffic, (2) it brings in more sales, (3) it increases unit sales, (4) it results in greater customer loyalty, (5) the florist's competitive position is better, (6) income is greater, and (7) profits are better. A retail florist can't develop a successful credit policy overnight, however. It must be well planned and promoted.

A U.S. Department of Agriculture survey showed that florists' credit policies are probably the most liberal of all the businesses in the United States. Moreover, only 12 per cent of the florists add a service charge to accounts considered past due.

There are many reasons for extending credit including the following: (1) It develops confidence between the customer and the store personnel. (2) It is a builder of sales volume. (3) The charge customer generally buys quality goods because the price is not as great a factor when the article is charged as it is when cash is paid for the article. (4) The use of credit apparently develops closer relationships between the management and the customer.

There are also reasons why the public uses credit, particularly regular charge accounts. For instance, expansion in the use of the telephone has made it simple to order by telephone, and such orders must be charged to the customer ordering; and secondly, more permanent records are kept of charge transactions than cash transactions. Thus, it is necessary for retail florists to extend credit. But not haphazardly! He should make sure that he has a business-like system. Certain questions should be asked in any interview or application for credit: (1) Who is the customer and what does she (or her husband) do? (2) Why is the customer applying for credit? (3) Will she pay her bill on time? (4) Who recommended this shop to her? (5) What references can she give? Use the following procedure in checking on whether to extend credit or not: Get the full name and address of the applicant, name of husband and his business address, occupation of the husband, two credit references including a bank reference, and telephone number of the applicant.

One florist has instituted a system whereby he gets many customers to pay in one week. He has set up a billing system using a three-copy order pad. The original is white, and the copies are yellow and pink. On the day the order is filled, the pink copy is mailed to the customer as an acknowledgment of the order. The other two copies are filed. Many of his customers pay within a week of receiving the pink copy, and thus he has cash coming in every week. If a customer does not pay by the first of the following month, the yellow copy is mailed to him. This saves the time of making out a separate statement. When only the white copy is left, and payment has not been received, the florist telephones the customer. This is just one system. Many florists have adopted variations of this procedure.

Some florists are now using a system called "cyclic billing" which means billing according to the letters of the alphabet. It spreads the billing out over the 30-day period, so that it doesn't have to be done all at once. It also brings cash into the store every week. Some customers do not like this system so it must be explained to them. It is not worth-while for a small florist. Accountants tell us that a retailer should have at least 10,000 accounts for it to be worth-while. Therefore, it is not applicable to the majority of the retail florists in this country.

Centralized billing and several other billing systems used by many retail florists were discussed in Chapter 25.

Delinquent Accounts

In the collection of deliquent accounts there is a basic formula: Remind—Request—Insist—Act.

1. Don't be afraid to ask for the money. Remember, it belongs to the florist, and he just loaned it to the customer.

2. Never allow accounts to grow cold.

3. Set up a definite policy and stick to it.

4. Don't write nasty or libelous letters.

5. Personal visits are often better than telephone calls or letters.

6. Delinquent accounts will avoid the shop so try to get them paid.

7. If customers do not pay, the florist may have to borrow money at 6 per cent to pay his own bills.

8. The best way to handle the overdue account is to avoid it. The second way is to have an efficient billing and collection process.

Collection Policy

Set up a definite collection policy similar to the following: (1) Mail the statements promptly on the same date each month, preferably before the first. Many florists close their accounts on the 25th, so that the customer has the statement when he receives his pay check on the 30th. (2) The second statement should be mailed prior to the first of the following month. Some florists send it on the 15th. (3) Add a 1 per cent service charge after 30 days. (4) Send a follow-up letter on the 15th of the next month. Don't give the customer time to forget it. (5) A second follow-up letter is sent on the 1st of the next month. (6) Make a telephone call on the 15th. This is most important. Be courteous, and find out why it hasn't

been paid. Suggest the customer stop in and pay at least part of it.
(7) Send a final letter stating that drastic action will be taken.
(8) Turn it over to a collection agency after six months overdue.
(9) Write it off as a bad debt after one year.

One florist has adopted a policy of sending three notices for
past due accounts receivable. The first notice reads as follows:
"PLEASE AND THANK YOU are brief and to the point. So
won't you PLEASE send us your remittance for $. THANK
YOU!" The second notice is as follows: "NOTICE. We are most
willing to extend favors as far as possible, but your indebtedness
is past due. In sending you this reminder for payment, we are
asking nothing more of you than our creditors demand of us. Please
give this your immediate attention. $ past due." The third
notice reads: "FINAL APPEAL. Repeated statements and courteous
treatment have failed to bring in your remittance of $, long

---

DEMAND FOR PAYMENT OF DEBT

_____

_____   Creditor

_____

_____   vs.

_____   Debtor

_____

TO THE DEBTOR

NOTICE!   The above named CREDITOR makes demand on you

for payment of the sum of $_____ with interest at the rate of

_____ per cent per annum.

NOW THEREFORE, unless said amount is paid to the creditor

at his place of business in the city of _____ ,

County of _____ , State of _____ ,

within _____ days from the date hereof; or you make provision

for satisfactory adjustment thereof, legal action will be necessary,

incurring COSTS and EXPENSES in addition to amount of said

claim, as well as the embarrassment of this action.

Dated at _____ , this ___ day of _____ A. D. 19__

FINAL NOTICE

overdue. Settlement must be made within 10 days from the above date to avoid claim being placed with our attorney."

Some florists use a drastic looking Final Notice, printing it so it looks like an official legal document. It does bring results for some florists (see insert on page 272).

To be sure that collection letters will collect, the following advice is given from the American Collectors Association, Inc.:

1. Send at least two statements to the customer before a letter.

2. Mail the first collection letter not more than 10 days after the last statement has gone unanswered.

3. Do not use more than one collection letter in urban areas, and not more than two in rural areas. If the customer has not paid his bill there is a reason for it. A telephone call may find this out for the florist.

4. Write the letters to appeal to the customer.

5. Use the "you" approach rather than the "we" approach.

6. Use motivating factors. Appeal to his sense of honesty, security, etc.

7. These letters must be complete, and should tell him the date, amount of the bill, what the order was, and where to send the money.

8. There are four C's which should be met if your letter is going to be effective at collecting: courteous, clear, concise, and correct.

Color

Since color is an attention-getter, use it in the envelopes and second statements to attract attention. Many florists will use a plain envelope or a window envelope so that people might think it is a check, and will not know whom it is from; so they at least won't throw it away before opening it.

If a person complains about poor flowers and refuses to pay, try to straighten it out and get a satisfied customer. If he is a chronic complainer, let him go elsewhere for his credit and merchandise. The florist will be further ahead in the long run.

Bad Debts

Bad debts should be less than ½ of 1 per cent of the volume of sales. They should be written off annually. Remember unless a bad debt is written off in the year it is ascertained to be worthless, it may be turned down by the federal income tax office. The statute of limitations differs in each state. Don't let an account go too long, or the customer will say that he doesn't have to pay; although morally he should. The U.S. Department of Commerce tells us that $1 is worth 90¢ after two months, 67¢ after six months, 45¢ after a year, 23¢ after two years, and 1¢ after five years. Therefore, it hardly pays to try to collect it after one year.

Black Lists and Collection Agencies

One solution to the problem of bad accounts is the use of a black list. This can be very effective in small communities where all the florists cooperate with one another. Any person owing a florist over six months is placed on this list. Once this becomes known, many customers will pay. It protects fellow florists from a bad risk. However, to be effective and in fairness to the customer, the list must be accurate and kept up-to-date. Many florists are definitely against the black list.

Collection agencies are used by some florists and abhorred by others. Most florists are reluctant to turn over their bad accounts to an agency. However, some florists will send out an "official looking" demand for payment of debt. The florist himself will have to decide how drastic his action must be to keep his bad debts at a minimum.

The following factors should be checked by each florist to discover if he is granting credit efficiently, and to discover any weakness in the system: (1) Is he selecting new customers carefully, and through a definite credit investigation? (2) Is he making sure that each applicant and present customer clearly understands his credit terms? (3) Is he controlling the credit limits that he set for his various customers? (4) Is he sending statements promptly? (5) He should check up on himself and make sure he is handling his credit-granting function efficiently. (6) He must be sure the collecting mechanism is well organized and efficient.

Screening Phone Orders

The problem of screening phone orders from strangers is one which each individual retail florist must decide for himself. The policies adopted by retail florists across the country are many and varied. They go all the way from a retail florist in Portland, Oregon, who, a few years ago, advertised: "If you've got a phone, you've got a charge account at . . . . . florists," to a florist in New York City who says over the phone: "It is not our policy to accept orders from unknown persons." These are the two extremes and many florists are in-between. Podesta-Baldocchi in San Francisco reported several years ago that they would accept all phone orders up to $10.00. Then they would check the address immediately. If there seemed to be any doubt, they would bill the sender right away. In fact, many florists told me that they always bill a new account immediately as a means of establishing a credit rating for the customer. Most florists will ask the person on the phone for his home address, business address, phone number, and credit references. Some florists will ask who recommended him to the customer, and often this is sufficient. Some florists use the system requiring the new customer to stop in and pay cash for the first order before it is sent out. Some florists make their decision based solely on the section of the city. Undoubtedly the size of the city will have a lot to do with the policy adopted. If a florist does accept orders from unknowns over the phone, he should be sure to check them if they sound phoney. I was in a florist shop recently in a large city when a phone order was received from a new account, for a basket to be sent to another individual at the same address. The manager was suspicious and called the address, and found it was an automobile agency with no one there by the names of either individual mentioned on the order. Obviously, it was a prank, which could have been costly to the florist in materials, time, and delivery.

Often a phoney will hang up when questioned for a bank reference, how the shop was recommended, or when asked why he wants to charge the order. If it is a legitimate customer, he will have the answers to these questions and be glad to tell the florist.

No matter what system he follows, the retail florist should be sure to explain the policy to each new customer.

Reduce Charges

One retail florist that I know has been able to reduce the number of charges in his store. He uses a simple plain pad for orders he takes from people who are not regular charge customers. He tells these people the amount of the order, and most of them will pay cash. This reduces his billing expenses and gives him more cash for operating his business. Of course, he uses the regular charge ordering pads for his regular customers.

ABC's of Credit and Collection

A. Set up a definite credit policy and stick to it—probably 25 per cent of sales for new shops on up to 70 per cent for established shops.

B. Obtain general information such as name, address, phone number, business address, and one or two references.

C. Screen phone orders from strangers.

D. Join your local retail merchant's credit association.

E. Send statements to new phone order accounts immediately.

F. Close accounts on the same date each month. The 25th is considered best by many retail florists.

G. Send statements promptly each month. Most customers appreciate prompt billing.

H. Follow up unpaid accounts quickly and at regular intervals.

I. Send the second statement before the 1st of the following month.

J. Send a follow-up letter on the 15th.

K. The next letter goes out on the 1st of the next month.

L. A telephone call is made on the 15th.

M. A final letter or notice is sent on the 1st of the next month.

N. Add 1 per cent service charge after 30 days.

O. Check collection letters with your attorneys. Don't be liable for a lawsuit. Good collection letters should make friends, not enemies.

P. Since color is an attention-getter, send out the reminder statements in a different color from the regular statement.

Q. As a last resort turn the account over to a collection bureau.

R. Write off all bad debts annually. Don't let them accumulate.

S. Keep the bad debts below ½ of 1 per cent of the gross volume of sales.

T. Be methodical and keep the business healthy.

Credit Standing

How about the retail florists' own credit rating? This is also a very important part of the subject of credit. Many florists get into real trouble by not keeping their own credit rating in good order. It is good business because it will help the profits if the florist can get discounts in his buying as was discussed in Chapter 13. He should always take advantage of cash discounts if he can. If he needs a special favor or something in a hurry from a wholesale or supplier, his chances are much better if he has a good credit rating.

There are also times when the florist may want to borrow money from the bank. It may be to start in business, to buy another business, to buy more equipment, to remodel and modernize, or to expand his present business. A bank will rate the florist's credit standing according to the five C's: (1) character—dependability and reputation, (2) capacity—his achievement as a businessman, (3) capital—can he provide 50 per cent of it himself, (4) collateral —this will help to get a loan, and (5) conditions—the influence of business trends in general, and the tightness or easiness of credit at the moment.

To improve the credit picture remember that a banker analyzes the financial statement to determine the loan. He assesses a florist's economic health by the following ratios: (1) **Current ratio.** Current assets divided by current liabilities. It should be at least 2 to 1. (2) **Quick assets to current debt.** Cash, receivables, and other ready cash items divided by current debt; 1 to 1 is the best rule of thumb. (3) **Debt to capital.** Money owed to creditors compared to owner's money in the business. The lower the ratio the better. (4) **Fixed assets to capital.** Real estate, buildings, and fixtures divided by net assets. The ratio should be kept as low as possible. (5) **Inventory to working capital.** Shows per cent of working capital tied up in inventory. An abnormally high ratio will result in a shortage of cash to meet other expenses.

These factors will not only help the florist to determine his chances of a bank loan, but will give him a good picture of his business as a whole.

Credit, which is commonly known as "man's confidence in man" is a vital and necessary part of the entire business world including the retail florist business. Handled properly it can help to enlarge the gross volume of business with the end result of a better profit for his investment.

References

1. Anonymous. "Free Delivery and Credit—Expensive Customer Services," *FTD News* (February 1966), pp. 68-69.
2. Butler, Thomas M. "New Ways to Handle Overdue Accounts," *Florist* (October 1969), pp. 47-49.
3. Havas, N. *Profile of the Retail Florist Industry.* U.S. Department of Agriculture Marketing Research Report #741 (1964), 27 pp.

DESIGN IN FLOWER ARRANGING

Chapter 27

HISTORY AND PRINCIPLES OF
FLOWER ARRANGEMENT

The reputation of the retail florist and the backbone of the industry rests with the floral designs produced by each florist. Anyone can put a bunch of flowers in a Mason jar, but it takes a trained artist to arrange those flowers in an appropriate container so that they form an attractive design.

Flower arrangement is the art of arranging flowers and/or plant material in a container in a pleasing manner. It is a picture in which living lines and colors are the artist's medium. The purpose of flower arrangement is to create something that is pleasing to the eye.

Floral design by the florist is something more than just the art of flower arrangement. It also includes the science of putting together materials which, when used with flowers, create an artistic design far beyond an ordinary flower arrangement. Thus, the retail florist builds his reputation on artistic designs, wedding designs, and funeral arrangements. Floral design includes imagination and originality to make the florist's artistic designs different from those of his competitor.

History

The history of flower arrangement goes back many centuries to the two different civilizations of the Orient and Europe.

The Oriental history of flower arrangements comes to us from the Chinese and the Japanese. It was the Japanese who refined it into a special art which is uniquely based on religion. It was primarily a worship, or prayer, to the gods and goddesses. The emphasis of Japanese flower arrangement is on line design using mainly twigs and branches with few flowers. Each bud, branch, and flower should be seen. The line designs are primarily based on a three line arrangement consisting of heaven, man, and earth. Heaven is the tallest and most vertical line, earth is the lowest and is horizontal, and man is in between, usually 20 to 30 degrees from the vertical line of heaven. Heaven is always the longest line.

There are many variations to the Japanese arrangements which represent different types of prayers and messages, but all conform to the three lines or planes no matter how many pieces of plant material are used. The materials may number 3, 5, 7, 9, or 11 branches, all in just three planes. The stems are usually held together for 2 to 4 inches above the rim of the container to give the effect that it is one piece of plant material growing out of the container. Some of the arrangements are formal or classical while others are called informal, free-style, or naturalistic. They all, however, are line designs based on heaven, man, and earth, and stressing twigs and branches with just a few flowers.

European flower arrangements date back many centuries, and have always been based on mass and color. The arrangements have changed during the centuries and have come to be called Period Arrangements. These include the Greek Classical, Medieval, Renaissance, Flemish, Italian, French, Colonial, Georgian, and Victorian, and refer to various eras in Western or European history. They differed in the various eras in types of containers, types of flowers, use of accessories, use of fruit, and the type and size of the design. However, even though they changed as civilization changed and were appropriate to each era, still they were mainly arrangements based on large quantities of flowers with many colors.

Modern

Modern American flower arrangements are a combination of the Japanese and the European. They have the characteristics of both types; so today we call them line-mass arrangements stressing color. They are characterized further by originality, simplicity, and depth, which make them different from other arrangements around the world. The mass is often quite small like a focal point, and not the enormous mass of the European.

A modern American flower arrangement is a planned composition whereas a bunch of flowers is not.

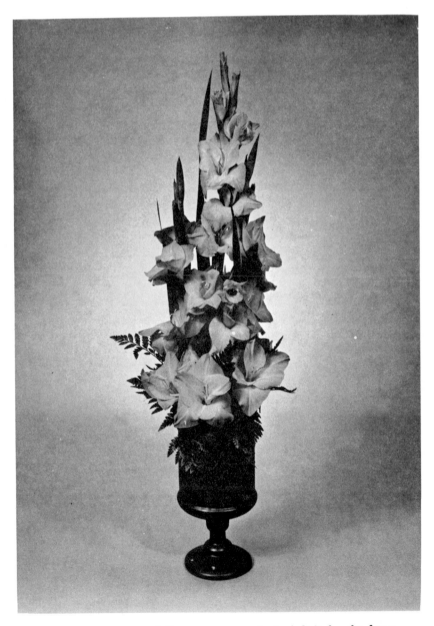

Figure 27-1. A vertical flower arrangement of gladioli for the home.

Principles

Flower arrangements are based on the following nine specific principles:

1. **Design.** Design is the overall shape or form of the composition. It is the planned relationship between flowers, foliage, container, and the surroundings. It is influenced by various elements and rules.

The elements of good design include line, form, pattern, texture, and color. *Line* means that under every good design there is a skeleton or framework which is the underlying linear pattern that holds the whole composition together. All arrangements start with a linear piece of plant material such as a leaf, twig, flower, or branch. *Form* refers to the geometric form or line design which is the outline of the flower arrangement. Today there are 13 forms or line designs which any flower arrangement may possess. These are the basic line designs which a florist achieves when he practices his artistry. He must select the line design that he is going to use before he starts to work. These 13 will be discussed and illustrated later in the chapter. *Pattern* is a silhouette against a space, and may be linear or mass, or a combination of the two. It is made up of voids and solids. Voids are just as important as solids. A void is open to the outer atomsphere and not to be confused with holes which are very poor in floral design. A void is used in an L-shaped arrangement to change the design of a normal asymmetrical triangle, and use less flowers. The void or space adds to the design. *Texture* is the structural quality or feel of the materials used. They may be fine or coarse. Texture is applied to flowers, foliages, and the container. It is always best to combine materials which have a similar texture. Never put orchids in Mexican pottery, or zinnias in fine Venetian crystal. *Color* is such an important item it will be discussed in detail later on in this chapter.

There are certain rules of design which must be followed if the designer is to make an artistic arrangement which has good design and composition: (a) Proper height and width of a flower arrangement are necessary. The general rule to use on most designs (except horizontal) is that a flower arrangement should be 1½ to 2 times the height of the vase or the length of a bowl or tray. This height is measured from the rim of the container to the top of the tallest flower The tallest flower should also be the longest. The width of the arrangement is less than twice the height, except in a horizontal arrangement. This becomes obvious when we consider that the tallest flower is also the longest flower in the arrangement. The width can be just slightly less than twice the height or it can be a great deal less, depending upon how wide or narrow the arrangement may be. A low horizontal arrangement such as a centerpiece is the exception to these two rules. (b) Good design usually includes only one, two, or three colors. Four different colors, not counting green, is the absolute maximum unless you are making an old-fashioned bouquet, or Period Arrangement. (c) Two or three different types of flowers are the optimum. Four would be the maximum for most designs. (d) Buds and small flowers should be at the top and outer edges of the arrangement with larger flowers to the bottom and towards the center. (e) Light colors are usually at the top of the arrangement with darker colors at the base. This helps to give the arrangement better balance. (f) There should be a ratio of approximately three light flowers to every dark one if they are the same size. (g) When less than 12 flowers are used, it is best to use an uneven number. These rules will help the florist to achieve good design in his floral arrangements.

Symmetrical   Asymmetrical

Figure 27-2. Two types of balance: symmetrical and asymmetrical.

2. **Balance.** Balance is stability. It is the relationship of the component parts so that they create the impression of being stable. The arrangement should not look like it will fall over to the right, left, front, or back. Balance gives a visual weight to the arrangement, and makes it more pleasing to the eye. Visual weight is determined by the size of the plant material, distance from the axis, and tonal value of the plant material. There are two types of balance: symmetrical and asymmetrical. Symmetrical balance is formal balance where the two sides of the center line are the same,

and equal in weight. An equilateral triangle with all sides equal is a good example. Asymmetrical balance is informal and one in which the two sides of the center axis are entirely different, but equal in visual weight so they will appear stable. This is illustrated by a seesaw where the heavier person is in close, and the thin one is out at the end. And so with flowers. The type of balance must be decided upon before the designer begins an arrangement, since it determines exactly where the first flower is to be placed (Figure 27-2).

3. **Scale.** Scale is the size relationship of the component parts of an arrangement. The size of the flowers should be reasonably related to each other, although they don't need to be all exactly the same size. That would lead to monotony. For instance, Easter lilies with violets would be out of scale; whereas roses and snapdragons would be acceptable. Scale is also important in the relationship of the floral design to the table or to the space where it is to be used. Proportion is the overall size in relation to the space it is to fill, and is important so that the whole picture will be complete.

4. **Harmony.** This means that all of the component parts of the arrangement are in tune with each other. This applies to color as well as to the textures of the materials used. They must all blend together.

5. **Focal point.** Most flower arrangements (like a painting) have a focal point or center of interest. This is needed to keep the eye from wandering aimlessly all over the arrangement. The focal point is just above the rim of the container, and at the base of the tallest flower, leaf, or candle. It is usually the largest flower, darkest flower, or a cluster of many dark flowers. It usually extends out a little in front to give depth to the arrangement, and is on line with the rim of the container.

6. **Accent.** Accent is accomplished through contrast and is used for emphasis. The focal point is the greatest accent point, but there can be several other accent areas in an arrangement. Sharp contrasts may occur through color, size, form, or texture of materials used.

7. **Rhythm.** The feeling of motion or swing in an arrangement is called rhythm. It is the placement of various parts so that the eye is carried through the arrangement with a feeling of smooth motion. It often leads the eye to the focal point. It is an easy path along which the eye may travel through the arrangement of lines, forms, colors, and light or dark areas.

8. **Repetition.** This is the repeating of one or more elements in the arrangement to add more interest to the design. It may mean repeating a flower such as a rose, a color like red, an object like a pine cone, a large ti leaf, or other items several times throughout the arrangement. Some arrangements do not have repetition as we use the term here. One dozen red roses in a bowl has no separate repetition unless we think of it as 100 per cent repetition of red roses. Repetition is mainly done to add interest, and provide contrast.

9. **Unity.** Unity means a oneness of the parts of the design. The whole composition must be a complete unit, and not look like several groups of flowers put together with no design to them. All white snapdragons at the top and all red roses at the bottom would look like two unrelated parts of the arrangement, and lack unity unless there was an integration and repetition of each flower in the arrangement. An arrangement must have unity to be a whole composition with good design.

Color

Color is the most important characteristic of flowers. Everyone is conscious of color and it affects us emotionally. When customers exclaim over a floral arrangement it is often due to the color or colors used. Red is the favorite color of women, while men favor blue. Violet is the next most popular color. Then come green and orange, with yellow the least liked of all colors, even though it is bright and cheerful. In this text we will use the term "color" to refer to the primary, secondary, and tertiary colors of the spectrum as well as the tints, tones, and shades of various hues. Color is translucent in flowers, while color in pigment is opaque, so we have two different color mediums with which to work when arranging flowers in a container. Often a true red flower will not match the true red in the container. Hue, the pure color itself found in the spectrum, is seldom found in flowers. More often in flowers we find the tertiary colors as well as tints, tones, and shades of one hue. The three primary colors are red, yellow, and blue. The three secondary colors are orange, green, and violet. The tertiary colors are combinations of primary and secondary colors such as red-violet, yellow-green, and green-blue. A tint is a hue plus white, and is lighter than the true hue. It gives a psychological effect of being uplifting. Tones are hues plus gray, are duller than the pure hue, and give a soothing effect. A shade is a hue plus black. It is darker than the true color, and gives a depressing effect. Other psychological effects from colors are spiritual from violets and purples, coldness from blue and green, and warmth from red, orange, and yellow.

Color harmony is the characteristic that we are looking for in a flower arrangement because this is the combination of colors which is pleasing to the eye. There are six main color harmonies of interest to floral designers. They are understood more easily through the use of a color wheel which makes color harmony more understandable than a straight line spectrum of colors. (1) Monochromatic harmony is a harmony using tints, tones, and shades of the same hue. There is a whole scale of just one hue from light to dark and from bright to dull which gives interest to any arrangement. It can be a combination of two, three, or four colors. (2) Analogous harmony refers to two or three colors that are adjacent to each other on the color wheel. They may include primary, secondary, or tertiary colors; such as yellow, yellow-orange, and orange. (3) There are four types of complementary harmony using colors opposite to each other on the wheel. The first and most important is the direct complement. This harmony includes just two colors only, that are directly opposite to each other on the wheel such as yellow and purple, or red and green. This combination is the most popular one used in flower arranging today and gives the greatest contrast. The colors must be used in unequal amounts to be effective. (4) Split complement is a harmony made up of exactly three colors. It includes one color plus the two colors on each side (adjacent) of its direct complement. An example would be orange with blue-green and blue-violet. (5) Triad is a color harmony which is also made up of three colors only, that are equidistant from each other on the color wheel, such as red, blue, and yellow. A red and yellow combination is not pleasing to most people unless tempered with some blue or blue-green. (6) A tetrad is often called a double or paired complement. It includes four colors that are equidistant from each other on the color wheel and is made up of two direct complements that are at right angles to each other. It is not often used in flower arrangements because it uses four colors which is considered too many for most designs. Orange, yellow-green, blue, and red-violet would be an example.

Color is a definite part of the design and must not be spotty. Group the flowers of one color together in one or two different areas in working out the design. There must be contrast, and repetition, as well as a blending together of various colors to achieve the best design which is not spotty.

Many colors, such as blues and violets, are lost under artificial light particularly if seen from a distance. Artificial light usually casts shadows which change the intensity of some colors. Fluorescent lights have a different effect on color than incandescent lamps and must be considered by the florist in display and decoration. This is particularly true in churches, clubs, halls, and meeting rooms.

We have discussed briefly the history of flower arrangement and the principles of good design. The rules and principles should be used as guidelines only, and not considered unbreakable under any circumstances. Once an artist has learned how to design, he may break some of the rules and still have a perfect design. It may be much higher than twice the height of the container, but if it still has balance and scale it is acceptable. All of the principles are not applicable to all flower arrangements as has been pointed out. The best way for a person to learn floral design is to go by the rules and principles at first and then get lots of practice. That is why we recommend that a future florist attend a design school and work for a florist to get the experience that he needs to become a good designer. The reputation and success of the florist rests with his artistic design work, including his originality and imagination, which will make his designs different from those of his competitor.

Chapter 28

CONTAINERS; ACCESSORIES;
STEPS IN CONSTRUCTION

Containers

The primary purpose of the container is to hold flowers, foliage, and water. The florist has innumerable containers from which to choose for sale in his shop, and for use with his designs. Experience and practice will usually dictate the type of container to use as well as the occasion. The price of the arrangement is also an important factor. We are not going into specifics in this text on the variety of shapes, sizes, and styles because there are too many and they change every year. However, there are a few general rules to follow in selecting the proper container for a flower arrangement. The main criterion for selecting the proper container is *suitability*. This means that the container must be suitable from several standpoints including the proper size so it will hold the flowers, is in scale with the flowers used, and will make an arrangement to fit the price; proper design so that we can make the arrangement to fit the occasion; the proper texture so that it blends with the flowers; and, of course, the proper color. The color of the container is very important. It may duplicate the color of the flowers or it may be the direct complement of the color of the flowers. Green and black containers are excellent for almost any design. White is very good, but the arrangement should include some white flowers to cut down on the contrast. The container should enhance the flowers, not dominate the arrangement. Plain and simple containers are best for most arrangements. However, an ornate container may be used if the customer picks it out, or brings it in to the store to be used. The florist should know his customer's likes and dislikes before sending out an arrangement in something other than a plain and simple container. Sturdy containers should be used for heavy flowers like gladioli, chrysanthemums, and stock, while fragile containers are used for delicate flowers. Silver bowls are very effective for anniversaries and formal decorations. Pewter, copper, and brass are all good for certain flowers and special occasions, but they are not used in the same quantity as are pottery and glass. Plastic containers and papier-mâché are very inexpensive and used for many arrangements where the customer does not want to spend much money on a container.

If a base or stand is used under the container it is considered as part of the container. Thus, when the designer measures the container to get the correct height of the arrangement, the base is measured also. Not too many of these are used in the retail flower shop except in special arrangements.

Accessories

An accessory is any object included in the composition, but detached from the plant material in the container, and supplemental to the theme. It may be a candle, pine cone, book, picture, fruit, or any of a number of figures and figurines. It can be a flower if it is a complete flower like a rose. However, a rose petal or a snapdragon floret is not an accessory. These do not add to the composition and give the illusion that the flowers are old and falling. Styrofoam novelties are used as accessories for many special occasions and party decorations. An accessory must be appropriate and fit the arrangement in scale and color harmony. If an arrangement is complete without an accessory, leave it out. If the arrangement is symmetrical then the accessories must be too; such as two candles, one at each end of a symmetrical centerpiece. If the arrangement is asymmetrical, then the accessory or accessories must be arranged in an asymmetrical design. The symmetry of the accessories must conform to the symmetry of the floral design in order to have proper design for the whole composition. The accessory or accessories for an asymmetrical arrangement will usually be just on one side of the arrangement. The three tests for adding an accessory are: (1) Does it contribute to the design? (2) Does it supplement the theme? (3) Does it harmonize in color, size, and texture?

Mechanical Aids

There are many different holding devices for florists to use to make the flowers stay in place in the containers. These are often

Figure 28-1. Foam material taped into a black tray container.

called mechanical aids and are absolutely necessary for good designing. The type used will depend on the container, type of arrangement, and the personal preference of the designer. We will briefly list the main ones used by retail florists today. (1) Chicken wire or wire mesh is one of the most common materials used in tall pottery containers, paper-mâché, and baskets. (2) Pin holders are used in the low bowl and tray type containers, and must be attached securely with floral clay. (3) Foam materials (Figure 28-1) which absorb water, such as Oasis, Hydrofoam, Jiffy, Quickee, Fill Fast, Niagara, and others are used in tray containers, tall containers, and sometimes on the top of baskets, pottery, and papier-mâché containers. They can be used also as the foundation for wreaths and sprays. (4) Shredded styrofoam (Tufflite) is a good holding device in any type of a tall container. It does not absorb water, but holds the flowers in place very well while allowing plenty of room for water in the container. (5) Regular styrofoam is used as a base and holder for many arrangements which do not need water. Or, if moisture is needed for a few flowers, a piece of foam material can be used in a small plastic cup or wrapped in foil, and placed in a small hole dug out of the styrofoam. (6) Regular greens such as laurel, cedar, hemlock, and others are used by florists in papier-mâchés and baskets as a mechanical aid to hold the flowers in place. The aid will be determined by the individual florist and the type of container used.

Steps in Construction

Before starting to construct an arrangement there are three things to decide. These will be determined by the type of arrangement, placement, occasion, and the ideas of the designer. First, the designer must know if the arrangement is to be one-sided or an all-around arrangement (one which is attractive from all sides). If this is not known, then the florist must make the decision. Secondly, he must decide if it is to be symmetrical or asymmetrical so that he will know how and where to place the first flower. Third, he must decide what type of line design or geometric form to follow. (There are 13 line designs discussed in Chapter 29.) Those three things must be decided before the designer can be-

Figure 28-2. Steps in constructing a flower arrangement: One-sided, asymmetrical triangle.

gin. It is impossible to start with an asymmetrical design and end up with one which is symmetrical unless the designer starts over.

There are seven main steps to follow in constructing an arrangement whether it be in pottery, glass, metal, papier-mâché, or a basket (Figure 28-2).

1. After selecting the proper container and seeing that it is clean, put in whichever mechanical aid is going to be used and add water. Never start a flower arrangement without water in the container.

2. Establish the main line of the arrangement by putting in the tallest flower first. It should be 1½ to 2 times the height of the vase or width of a bowl or tray, as measured from the rim of the container to the top of the tallest flower.

3. Add the secondary lines for the width. Two flowers will be used for a one-sided arrangement, and four flowers for an all-around arrangement. In the one-sided arrangement, the two flowers will be horizontal if the arrangement is symmetrical; while one will be vertical and one horizontal if the arrangement is asymmetrical. In an all-around arrangement the four flowers will all be horizontal (one to each point of the compass) if the arrangement is symmetrical; while one flower will be vertical and three horizontal if the arrangement is asymmetrical.

4. If a focal point or center of interest is to be used it may be added now or after step 5. One large flower, a dark flower, or a cluster of flowers is placed at the base of the tallest flower and in line with the rim of the container. There is just one focal point in a one-sided arrangement, while there will be two or three in an all-around arrangement, if any are used at all. Many all-around arrangements do not have a focal point.

5. Fill in the arrangement with flowers of various stem lengths for interest, with some towards the front and some towards the back for depth. Don't crowd in too many flowers. None of the flowers should extend beyond the imaginary border formed by the height and width flowers. This step may be interchanged with #4 depending upon the habit of the designer.

6. Look it over and add or take away flowers and/or foliage. Either add another flower to complete the design or else remove one. Remember, not to exceed the number needed to make a profit on the design. Snip out excess foliage or add more if needed.

7. The final step is to let it alone. Once the designer is finished with it, he should not try to change it. A good designer will be satisfied with it when it is first completed, so let it alone.

Figure 28-3. Three flowers form the length and height of a horizontal arrangement.

Figure 28-4. A completed horizontal flower arrangement frequently used for a table centerpiece.

There are always exceptions to the rules and steps in construction, and a low horizontal arrangement such as a centerpiece is constructed in a different manner and will now be discussed. For a horizontal arrangement place in the two longest flowers to give the proper length of the arrangement (Figure 28-3).
These two flowers will be horizontal and resting on the rim of
the container. Add two more horizontal flowers to give the width
of the arrangement. Put in the vertical center flower to give the
height which usually will not exceed 12 to 15 inches for a table
centerpiece. Put in four slightly horizontal flowers in the four corners. Add the rest of the flowers making sure that they do not
extend out beyond the lines of the framework formed by the
length, width, and center flowers. The horizontal arrangement will
be roughly a long, low pyramidal form (Figure 28-4).

Faults

There are certain faults that the designer should recognize and
avoid if he is to achieve a perfect design. They are the following:
(1) straight line—flowers forming a straight line, (2) cross stem-
ming—stems of flowers crossing each other above the rim of the
container, (3) sandwiching—two or three flowers sandwiched or
crowded one on top of another, (4) flower stepping—flowers arranged in equal steps along the margin of the design, (5) equal
ranging—all flowers mathematically equidistant from each other,
(6) parallelism—all flowers facing in exactly the same direction,
(7) massing—too many flowers jammed into the container, (8) too
many colors, (9) too many flower types, (10) lack of depth or
third dimension, (11) hidden flowers, (12) unfinished base. The
arrangement should always be finished around the base with flowers, greens, or ribbon.

These faults should all be avoided in good design.

If the principles, rules, and steps in constructing an arrangement are followed, the design should be above average in attractiveness. Experience is the best teacher and the ultimate goal
is to achieve a perfect composition. Each florist will have his own
methods for design, and will rely on his own experience. The
better the designs, the better the reputation of the shop.

Knowing these principles and procedures is what makes the
florist a professional; and, consequently, he must charge accordingly.

Chapter 29

LINE DESIGNS

There are essentially 13 line designs or geometric forms which flower arrangements may take. However, most of our retail floral designs fall into one of eight line designs so we will discuss these first. The vast majority of designs from a retail florist shop are in the form of some sort of triangular design. These are the most popular, pleasing, and easy to accomplish.

Florists' Designs

(Figures 29-1 to 29-10)

1. **Symmetrical triangle or pyramid.** This is the most popular design for vase arrangements as well as many funeral vases, papier-mâchés, and baskets. The three sides are equal, or else the two sides are equal with a different length base, and the triangle is completely filled in with flowers and greens.

2. **Asymmetrical triangle.** This is an off-sided triangle where the two sides of the center axis are entirely different. The one side is short and more vertical, while the other is longer and more horizontal. The line of the design can extend either to the right or left. It is completely filled in.

3. **Right-angled triangle.** This is an asymmetrical triangle that is L-shaped. It employs a void as part of the design. It is an asymmetrical triangle not filled in. It is pleasing in design and uses less flowers, thus is more economical from a cost standpoint.

4. **Open triangle.** This is one of the newer forms of triangles which is an American interpretation of the Japanese Moribana. This can be either symmetrical or asymmetrical with the triangle not filled in, and the two sides of the triangle angled slightly towards the front rather than in a straight line as is found in the

conventional triangle. It also uses less flowers and is of economic importance to the florist.

5. **Horizontal.** The horizontal arrangement is typified by the regular centerpiece for the dining room table. It is symmetrical and an all-around design. It is long and low in the shape of a very low triangle or pyramid, or possibly an upside-down crescent. It can be used in a low container for a centerpiece, or designed in a wide container on a pedestal or stand.

6. **Vertical.** This is a tall vertical arrangement that is quite narrow and has tall slender lines to the design. It is very effective in a narrow wall space. If it gets too wide at the base it will become a pyramid.

7. **Hogarth.** The Hogarth or S-curve is one of the most attractive of all the types of flower arrangements. It is very popular with garden club women, but not as much with retail florists. The flowers must all be wired to get the lower part of the S, and it takes longer to make this type of a design. Many designers like to try it and use it when they have the time to work on it.

8. **Crescent.** The crescent shaped flower arrangement is a half-moon type of design. It is an asymmetric arrangement with one side higher than the other. It must be a wide crescent, and not a U or V shape. It is very useful for coffee table arrangements where the viewer is looking down on the arrangement.

Secondary Designs

(not used as often by retail florists)

1. **Round.** This is a mass type of flower arrangement whereby the flowers are all put together with an outline that is a full circle.

2. **Oval.** This is the same as the round design except some flowers hang over the rim of the container down in front to form an oval rather than a circle. It is also a mass type of arrangement.

3. **Spiral.** This type of flower arrangement is called a spiral or figure-9. It is formed by parts of two crescents forming the figure-9, but with an opening in the top of the arrangement. It is hardly ever seen in flower arranging today.

4. **Zigzag.** The use of plain branches and twigs may lead to a zigzag pattern of design. It is an asymmetric type of arrangement and only used on certain occasions. Hawthorne branches often give

Figure 29-1.
A symmetrical triangle or pyramid.

Figure 29-2.
An asymmetrical triangle.

Figure 29-3.
An L-shaped, or right-angled triangle.

Figure 29-4.
An open triangle.

Figure 29-5.
A horizontal arrangement.

Figure 29-6.
A vertical arrangement.

Figure 29-7.
A Hogarth or S-curve.

Figure 29-8.
A crescent arrangement.

Figure 29-9.
A round arrangement.

Figure 29-10.
An oval arrangement.

this effect. Some florists use this type of design to make a gum-drop tree or life-saver tree for a child.

5. **Diagonal.** This type of design is an asymmetric form with the flowers and foliage placed in the container to form a diagonal line across the container. It usually reaches from twice the height of the container down to the table top. It is not often used because the straight line is not too pleasing to the eye. With two slight curves it becomes a Hogarth which is more pleasing. Or by bending the straight line at the rim of the container it becomes a shallow right angle or L-shape.

These then are the 13 line designs or geometric forms from which the florist can choose the proper one. Two geometric forms which are displeasing to the eye and are to be avoided are the square and the rectangle. Almost all good designs come out to points rather than straight lines or sides. This is true of the eye level pattern as well as the outline of a centerpiece or horizontal arrangement. Squared sides are not pleasing.

Most of our retail florists use the triangles, vertical, and horizontal designs for most of their work.

When planning the design to be used in flower arrangements, it is well to keep in mind the various flowers which will be useful to achieve different forms, and which are typical of the various elements of design. Line flowers that are useful for height and width, and give the proper line to the arrangement are gladioli, snapdragon,

Figure 29-11. An asymmetrical triangle arrangement of snapdragons and iris in a pedestal container.

stock, standard chrysanthemums, larkspur, and delphinium. Mass flowers which are used for a focal point, contrast, and interest are roses, carnations, chrysanthemums, daisies, and asters. Form flowers which are useful because of their unusual form or shape are orchids, calla lilies, gloriosa lilies, anthuriums, bird-of-paradise, red hot poker, poinsettia, and Easter lilies. Filler flowers which are useful to fill in between the other flowers in place of greens are baby's breath (gypsophila), feverfew, statice, sweet peas, small pompon chrysanthemums, and cornflowers. These are just a few of the many flowers available in each group.

Anyone can learn to arrange flowers in a container. The successful florist, however, is the one who makes more eye appealing artistic designs so that people will come to his shop because of his superior designs rather than going to some other shop. This helps to build his reputation and helps to get more customers into his shop. It ties in very closely with the successful management of a retail florist shop along with pleasant, courteous service. When a retail florist develops this ability he is giving something extra, and he can charge accordingly for this professional service. Originality is the key word.

Chapter 30

HOME DECORATIONS; TABLE ARRANGEMENTS

Home Decorations

Flowers for home decorations are becoming more and more popular all of the time, but the florists have only started to develop this market. As mentioned in a previous chapter, people will buy more flowers for the home more often, if the flowers are readily available at the right price. This is the type of business which the florist should be cultivating; not only the cash-and-carry for the home, but also designs from the florist for decorating the home for special occasions.

The retail florist should advertise and promote flowers for home decorations, particularly for parties, dinner guests, and special occasions. He should follow this with good salesmanship when the customer comes into the shop. He must find out what the occasion is, where the flowers are to be used, the color scheme of the home, and the décor for the party, and then make suggestions for really beautifying the home with flowers. It is essential for the florist to obtain as much information as he can concerning the decorations for the home. The possibilities are unlimited as far as the florist is concerned. The main limiting factor may be the amount of money the customer wishes to spend. A good florist, however, should know how to do a good job with the funds available, or else persuade the customer to spend more so that it will be a good decorating job and one which will please the customer and guests.

Uses in the Home

There are many places where flowers can be used in the home, and it is up to the retail florist to suggest these to the customer. Most people are aware of the beauty in flowers in a centerpiece

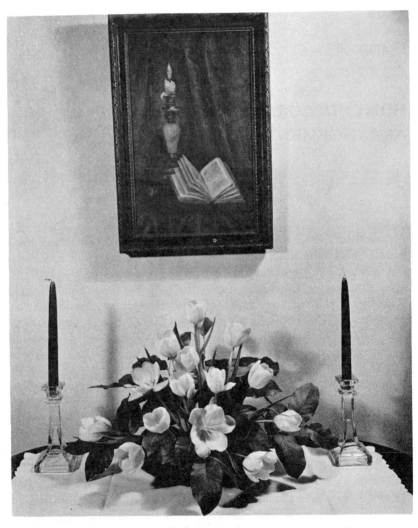

Figure 30-1. A symmetrical buffet table arrangement plus two candle accessories
which tie in with the candle in the painting.

on the table but don't realize that they can be used elsewhere to
brighten the home. The following are some of the places where
flowers and plants can be used effectively in the home: (1) A dining
room table centerpiece is the most common place for flowers in the
home. (2) The buffet table can be used for special occasions. The
placement of the table will determine the type of arrangement to be
used. (3) The coffee or cocktail table is an excellent place for a flower

arrangement in the living room. (4) End tables can be used for matching arrangements. (5) The luncheon table is a good place for using just a few flowers. (These table-type arrangements will be discussed in detail later in this chapter). (6) The television set can be used for flowers although the arrangement should be small, and may not last too long due to the heat given off from the set. The florist might suggest a permanent arrangement for this spot to be replaced by fresh flowers on special occasions. (7) The hallway is a good place for flowers to greet people as they enter the home. They can be placed on a table or stand if available, or even on the floor. This is an excellent place for a large foliage plant, the size to be determined by the space available. (8) People often place flowers on the mantel over the fireplace, or on the hearth. Several suggestions are in order for the hearth, such as an arrangement of large flowers like gladioli, a vase of greens such as laurel, rhododendron, or pine, a flowering pot plant, or a nice attractive foliage plant such as a philodendron, ficus, or schefflera. (9) The powder room is another place where a small flower arrangement can be used to brighten the room, both for the family and for friends. (10) A small fresh flower arrangement in the bedroom is an added touch for overnight guests which tells them that the hostess is glad to have them in her home. (11) A landing on the stairway is a good place for a foliage plant. (12) Flowers or a plant can also be used to brighten a dark corner of the living room. The retail florist can make many suggestions for flowers and plants in the home if he is aggressive, and he can make extra sales if he is a good salesman.

The florist should find out from the customer just where the flowers are going to be used and for what occasion. Flower arrangements for a party, birthday, or anniversary can be quite different from flowers for the everyday decoration of the home. If the customer is sending flowers to someone else, try to find out the occasion and where the flowers are most likely to be used. It is also helpful for the florist if he knows something about the color scheme and décor of the home to which the flowers are going. Often this isn't known, but wherever possible this is a help to the florist. An arrangement with the proper colors will not only enhance the room but also the arrangement itself.

Flowers can be sent to men and children as well as to women. Men appreciate an arrangement for the den or office if it is not a dainty arrangement. Make a masculine arrangement using loud, bright colors such as bright red gladioli, red and white carnations, or red roses in a bold design. Including some men's accessories will

Figure 30-2. An artistic design for the home.

add interest to the arrangement and make it more acceptable, such as a pipe, cigars, sports magazine, card, fishing equipment, and other items. These arrangements are also acceptable to men on Father's Day, birthday, or if they are sick. Children enjoy receiving a flower arrangement if it includes some accessories that they can use while they are sick or confined to the home. A florist should have things available to use in these arrangements such as candy, crayons, comic books, cards, games, puzzles, books, magazines, and small toys, or else be able to get them quickly and easily for the design. The flowers used will be loud, bold colors for boys and pastels for the girls. The colors should tie in with the accessories. The container can even be a tiny wagon or some other item which the child can play with when the flowers are gone. An imitation flower soda is a big hit with many sick children. Teenage girls also appreciate flowers, either in an arrangement, or in a corsage for the school dance. Retail florists should cultivate the teenagers and college students to get them into the habit of purchasing flowers, so that they will continue to do so the rest of their lives.

Table Arrangements

There are essentially five types of table arrangements for the home and each of them has different characteristics and must be designed differently to fit the proper table. The retail florist really has to know the placing of the arrangement to be able to design the proper type of design (Figure 30-3). Often a florist does not know where it is to be used, so many florists will send out a table centerpiece for most of the average home table arrangement orders. There are many important points to keep in mind for various table decorations.

1. **Dining room table centerpiece.** The centerpiece should be an all-around arrangement attractive from all four sides. The average one is symmetrical and placed right in the middle of the table. However, in special cases it may be an asymmetrical design placed off-center on the table. It must, in general, take the shape of the table: round for a round or square table and oblong for an oval or rectangular table. The size must be in scale with the table. It must be low enough to see over (12 to 15 inches) or thin enough to see through, so that it does not interfere with the diners. The colors and textures must fit with the appointments of the table. (Marigolds are not used with crystal, or the best china and silver.) The arrangement should not interfere with the diners while they are

eating, such as hanging over the water glass or into the salad. There will probably not be a focal point, but if one is used then there must be two.

2. **Buffet table.** There are several choices for a flower arrangement for a buffet table. If the table is along the wall, the arrangement should be one-sided. It can be as large as the table, room, and price will permit. It can be any height and width. It will be symmetrical if placed in the center of the table and asymmetrical if placed at one end. In placing the asymmetrical arrangement be sure the line of the design flows to the center of the table which means the high side of the asymmetrical arrangement will be the side closest to the edge of the table. If the table is in the center of the room, then the arrangement must be all-around and attractive from all sides. A symmetrical arrangement can be placed in the center of the table or at one end if turned sideways on the table. An asymmetrical arrangement is placed at one end of the table with the line of the design flowing towards the center of the table.

3. **Coffee table.** Scale is the most important point for a coffee table arrangement. The size must be in scale with the size of the table. The arrangement is usually low to fit the table and should

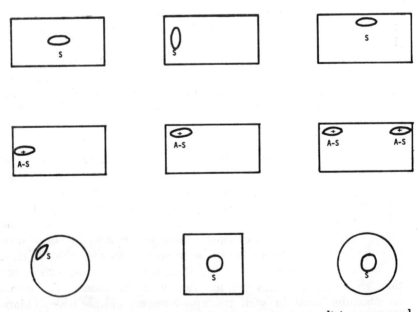

Figure 30-3. Various placements of flower arrangements on dining room and buffet tables for different occasions. (S: symmetrical; A-S: asymmetrical; → direction of the line of the design)

be attractive from all angles since 90 per cent of the coffee tables in our homes today are out in the center of the room. It may be symmetrical or asymmetrical depending upon the placement of it on the table, and should, in general, take the shape of the table.

Figure 30-4. A symmetrical arrangement for the center of a coffee table.

4. **End tables.** Here is an excellent place for two matching arrangements if there are two end tables in the room. The flower arrangements should be small so they are in scale with the table and will not interfere with a lamp or other object used on the table. They are usually one-sided arrangements but may be all-around depending upon the set-up of the furniture. They can both be symmetrical and identical, or else they can be asymmetrical with one the mirror image of the other. The line of the design of both of them will flow towards the furniture in between the two tables. If there is only one end table, the arrangement can be either symmetrical or asymmetrical to fit in with the arrangement of the furniture in the room.

5. **Luncheon table.** If the customer is having a formal luncheon or bridge luncheon suggest some flowers to her. If she has several bridge tables, the florist can provide a small arrangement for each one. It may be just one or three flowers, or a few pompons in a tiny container for each table. If it is a large formal luncheon then the arrangement will be larger and similar to a buffet table arrangement or a table centerpiece. The florist might also suggest a single flower for each lady to wear at the luncheon. These always look festive on the table when the guests arrive.

These are general suggestions for various table arrangements, but not the only ones. The florist may make many suggestions which will appeal to the customer, or the customer may have definite ideas of her own for various table decorations. Unusual artistic designs are often used, showing real originality and the imagination of the designer. Home decorations are a good place for the florist to portray his designing ability.

Club Banquets

Table arrangements for banquets require skill in designing because of the limited facilities usually found at various clubs, halls, and churches. A good deal of advance information must be received from the customer so the retail florist can do a good job. The number of people should be known as well as the number and size of the tables. The arrangement of the tables is essential because the tables can be individual, requiring an arrangement on each one; or they may be set up in some geometric pattern such as T, U, E, H, L, or ⊫. If there is a speaker's table it should have the largest arrangement. The number of centerpieces is determined by the number of people, size of the tables, and how much money is available for the job. If people are sitting on only one side of the tables, the arrangements can be wider than normal. Most clubs and churches use very narrow tables with people sitting on both sides of them, which does not leave much room for the flowers. Be sure to find out the width of the tables. If the centerpieces can only be six inches in width, it takes a clever designer with just the right flowers to stay within bounds. If the florist knows the number of people but not the exact length of the tables he can roughly estimate 1½ feet per person if they will be sitting close together or 2 feet per person if they are sitting more comfortably. The florist must decide on the number of centerpieces for the banquet. Three smaller pieces may be better than one large one on a very long table. If there are many individual tables, and the money available will not pay for a centerpiece on each one, suggest a bud vase for each table with one flower and some greens; plus extra greens around the base of the vase.

Containers

In decorating for the home or for banquets the florist may use the customer's containers or his own. There are many inexpensive containers of pottery, glass, and plastic on the market. A supply of these should be kept on hand for sale or rental whichever the case may be. Often a florist will rent the containers and pick them up later. Inexpensive glass or plastic containers can be figured in the price of the decorations, and then the arrangements left with the hostess. Be sure the containers do not leak, and do not use wire around papier-mâché to hold in the chicken wire. It may get wet and rusty and leave a spot on the tablecloth. If a florist uses the customer's good silver bowl, he must be sure to protect it by lining it with cotton or plastic. If he uses a pin holder in it, he must be sure to use a guaranteed non-tarnishing clay to anchor the holder.

The use of a few greens around the base of the flower arrangement will help to partially hide the container and give it a finished appearance. This is particularly needed for papier-mâché, plastic, and other inexpensive containers which do not add anything to the beauty of the design. A silver bowl would not require anything to hide or detract from its beauty.

Planters

Indoor planters are now an integral part of home decorations and should be planned and filled by the retail florist, rather than by someone less familiar with plants and their proper growing conditions. These contain mostly foliage plants although seasonal flowering pot plants can be added. Foliage plants and their uses and growth are discussed in Chapter 35.

Mantel Arrangements

Flower arrangements for the mantel can be used to decorate the home not only at Christmas, but whenever the customer is entertaining or decorating for a special occasion. The arrangement can be any width or height if it fits the scale of the fireplace and the room. It is one-sided and can be symmetrical or asymmetrical depending upon where it is placed. In designing the arrangement, the florist should remember that the arrangement should be held in the air to see how it looks. Mantel arrangements are always seen either at eye-level or from below eye-level. A flower arrangement may be beautiful when seen from above, but lose much of its artistic design when placed up on a mantel. If two arrangements are used on the mantel they should be asymmetrical mirror images of each other. The florist should know how to properly place them. The high sides of the arrangements will be towards the outer edge of the chimney with the low sides towards the center if the focal point on the mantel is low like a clock, bowl, figurine, or mantel scene such as is often found at Christmas. However, if the focal point is a large picture, mirror, or statue then the two arrangements will be reversed with the low sides to the outside and the high sides framing and pointing towards the focal point (Figure 30-5).

Figure 30-5. Two different settings for mirror image flower arrangements on the mantel based on the size and type of the center of interest.

Flowers for home decorations, gifts, special occasions, and banquets are the ones the florists should be promoting today. It takes advertising, promotion, salesmanship, and good design to accomplish this along with all the ideas of merchandising. This is the market that many florists are concentrating on to help combat the loss in funeral flowers taking place in our present-day society as discussed in Chapter 20 on Please Omit.

The preceding discussion shows how important it is for the florist to do a real selling job. By asking a few questions he can ascertain the type of party the hostess is going to have and then sell accordingly. The availability for rental of items like candelabras, bud vases, or punch bowls can be stressed at this time and will result in extra sales. Promoting flowers for home decorations is developing into big business today.

Chapter 31

CHURCH AND HOSPITAL FLOWERS

Churches

Flower arrangements for churches offer florists many opportunities to publicize flowers, and to improve their own reputation. There are several points that a florist must keep in mind when arranging flowers for churches. (1) Special rules and regulations of a particular church must be followed. (2) The arrangement should be large enough to be seen from the back of the church. (3) It should be bold and distinct, not feathery; but it should not be so large and outstanding that it detracts from the church service. (4) It should serve to enhance the service, not dominate it. (5) The flower arrangement must not impede the church service in any way. (6) No part of the flower arrangement (including the greens) should stick out in front of the cross. (7) The flower arrangement should be provided with a background of greens so that the flowers will show off to the best advantage. Often the natural background for the flowers in the church is not the most desirable. Yellow flowers are lost in front of the gold pipes of the organ. (8) The arrangement should have a definite design to it that ties in with the décor of the church. (9) In placing the arrangement, care should be taken to avoid spilling water which may damage the carpet or furniture. (10) Flowers should be placed so they can be seen by all, but will not obstruct the view of any of the members of the congregation.

Style of Churches

There are various architectural styles of churches in this country, and there are many which conform to no real period or style. Along the East Coast· most of the church architecture has been influenced by Sir Christopher Wren, the great English builder, whose architecture is typical of the Georgian period. Farther south the churches are influenced by the Greek temple revival style. These two types of churches have much white in them with columns, pillars, paneling, and many windows. Many of these are not too large, so the flower arrangements can be in graceful vases with many types of flowers which can easily be seen by the small congregation. There will be plenty of light and an absence of shadow, so the colors will show up well. In the Southwest the adobe, stone, or crude masonry churches prevail. They are neutral in color with small windows and dim interiors. Bright strong colors in pottery containers are appropriate. The Midwest churches follow the Gothic style of architecture from Western Europe with tall slender windows and peaked arches topped with a high spire. The light is soft and diffused through stained glass windows which adds to the beauty of the flowers used. Strong colors are better than pastels, and blues and purples should not be used. The arrangement must be large and bold to stand out in these churches. A type of church found all over the United States is based on the old Roman Forum with an auditorium-like interior. It is almost square with the distance from the pulpit to the rear of the church, the same as from one side to the other. It is the hardest of all in which to achieve a pleasing effect with flowers, and the one most in need of it. Many churches have special stands for the flowers, while others place their flowers on the platform or altar. The placement of the flowers so as not to impede the service or obstruct the view of the people in the congregation may not always be the best from the standpoint of the design of the arrangement. Here is where the florist should do his best to make the arrangement as artistic and pleasing as possible.

Containers

The containers in churches are an important part of the design and often the greatest drawback to the designer. For some reason or other, the vast majority of vases in our churches today are tall, narrow, upright containers with very little flare at the top. They often are made of brass, and very beautiful, but the most difficult of any container in which to design flowers. Some have a tall narrow cylindrical insert only 2 or 3 inches in diameter. Many of these creations really tax the ingenuity of the designer. Often in Protestant churches they are in pairs and it is difficult to design two matching arrangements for the same church. The style of the vase should conform to the style of architecture of the church. It should have a firm base and should be suitable in size to the size of the church. The vase should be wide-mouthed with a flaring lip. This gives the designer more chance to provide the best artistic design possible. If the florist uses his own container it should be brass or pottery. Papier-mâché is too "cheap" looking and has no place in a church. It is hard to discuss vases of very modern design because so few churches can use them. However, vases can be contemporary in design, and very attractive and still be practical to the florist. Brass, aluminum, stainless steel, chromium, and opaque glass can all be used if they are designed with a wide or flared opening and a sturdy base. A florist in a congregation that is building a new church would be wise to consult with the architect and the minister, to discuss the type of containers and their placement as contemplated for the new church. He will avoid headaches later on. His experience and knowledge is of value, and will be appreciated by most architects and clergymen.

Designs

The design of the flower arrangement should be the one most suitable for the church. The one used more often than any other in our churches today is that of the symmetrical triangle or pyramid. Depending on the placement, an asymmetrical triangle can be used. Both of these are mass arrangements and show up well in most of our churches. In modern churches, florists should try using the open triangle, right-angled triangle, vertical, and Hogarth curve. If they are well designed, they will be appropriate and not look out of place. It's time that retail florists put some new designs into our churches, and get away from the old type massed pyramidal arrangements every Sunday.

The colors which are suitable for the church will depend on the type of church, color of the interior, and amount of light present. If the church is painted white inside and there is plenty of light, any color will do. However, blues and purples do not show up at night, in subdued light, nor in a very large church. Blues and greens are good to use in summer, while reds, oranges, and yellows are best in the winter because of their psychological effects on people.

The final analysis of flowers used by the retail florists for churches will depend on the flowers available to the florist and the amount of money allocated for the arrangement. Many churches budget a certain amount to be spent each Sunday. Others vary this from week to week. Many times individual customers will pay for the flowers on a particular Sunday, and the florist should charge what is necessary to make the best showing to make the customer satisfied with the flowers.

Special Holidays

Florists must plan ahead to have flowers and plants available for churches for special occasions and holidays. (1) Easter is the holiday when the Easter lily and palms are used in most churches. These are traditional, although some churches are changing to pot plants of spring flowers like hyacinths, tulips, and narcissi. (2) Christmas is typified by poinsettias, cyclamen, and red and white flowers; plus Christmas greens and candles. Christmas wreaths and swags are also used in some churches including an Advent wreath. (3) Mother's Day is another holiday when flowers are used in the church. Red and white, pink and white, or all white flower arrangements are appropriate. Pot plants that are acceptable would include lilies, cyclamen, azaleas, and hydrangeas. (4) Palm Sunday is typified by using palms and palm branches. (5) Many churches have services on Thanksgiving and the flower arrangements should emphasize the bountiful harvest and horn-of-plenty. Fall colored leaves are appropriate as are pompon chrysanthemums, sheaves of grain, seed pods, and bunches of grapes. Bittersweet is often used to add color to the arrangement.

Religious Symbolism

Flowers have come to play an important part in the religious life of America. The use of flowers in church-connected activities has long been established. Most florists have a repertoire of suitable arrangements of each of these occasions: wedding, baptism, confirmation, and funeral. The use of flowers in worship services, though perhaps equally well established, had until a few years ago no comparable collection of designs. Professor L. J. Tolle of Michigan State University studied the liturgical days of the church calendar, and has designed a symbolically correct arrangement for every season of the Latin church year. The Christian symbolism of flowers is of two types. First, there are individual species of flowers which have become associated with Christian ideas or events such as: the rose as the symbol of messianic promise, the lily of the Resurrection, the iris of the Trinity, the almond as symbolic of a miracle, etc. Second, flowers and plant life have a general significance which is relevant to the churchly arts. St. Paul saw the seed or bulb as an allegory of the Resurrection. Christ used the lilies of the field to teach His Disciples to trust in God. There are many other examples. Mr. Tolle has designed 17 arrangements for the following church calendar: Advent, Christmas, Epiphany, Ash Wednesday, Lent, Palm Sunday, Maundy Thursday, Good Friday, Easter, Ascension Day, Pentecost, Trinity Season, Feast of the Assumption, Reformation Day, All Saints Day, Thanksgiving, and Sabbath Day. The details are in articles written by Professor Tolle. The articles are available through the Society of American Florists, and titled as follows: "Flowers for the Sabbath," "Flowers in Presbyterian Worship," "Flowers in Catholic Worship," and "Flowers in Methodist Worship."

Sales Opportunity

Churches offer a wide opportunity for sales and service, as more and more enterprising florists are discovering. Irving Allen, Chairman, Florist Information Committee of the Society of American Florists, points out that the uses of flowers and plants in churches are many and varied. They provide an excellent source of sales, particularly when a church contracts with a florist to handle all its floral work. Since the floral pieces are seen by the entire congregation, they are an important means through which florists can attract new customers.

An extra bonus from church work is improved relations with the clergymen. The florists who are on good terms with the clergymen they serve, are in an excellent position to know about and head off any "in lieu of" threats.

Florists should consider this list to see which of these services could be introduced into their local churches:

1. Altar flowers—Most churches have flowers on the altar each Sunday. Many maintain a Flower Calendar, and members sign up for a Sunday on which they furnish the memorial flowers or flowers marking an anniversary.

2. Flowers or plants for shut-ins and hospitalized people. Often the altar flowers are delivered to these people following the Sunday service. In addition, some churches order special arrangements for members who are ill.

3. Wedding flowers.

4. Funeral flowers.

5. Flowers for bereaved members and their families are often

included in the church budget. Flowers are sometimes wired to parents of deceased members.

6. Special arrangements for church holidays, such as Christmas, Lent, and Easter.

7. Boutonnieres for ushers.

8. A single flower to identify new members on the Sunday they join.

9. Floral arrangements for church suppers, teas, and other social events.

10. Plants and flowers are often used throughout the church building to decorate corridors, console tables, and the sanctuary foyer. Flowers and plants add warmth and a note of welcome.

11. An arrangement or corsage for new mothers.

12. A single flower on the altar to commemorate each new birth in the congregation.

13. A planter or screen of foliage in front of the choir loft.

14. A single flower presented to parents who present a child for baptism.

15. A plant or flowers may be sent to new members. One church accompanies each order with a card saying, "Water this plant regularly and it will grow. Attend church regularly and both you and the church will grow."

16. A plant or cut flowers presented to participants of every-member canvass.

17. Decoration of the platform is being used by more and more Christian Science churches. Planters on the platform and steps leading to it afford florists an opportunity to design and maintain the plants. This idea has been used extensively in the South and has spread to many other areas.

18. Some florists welcome new ministers to the community with a plant or flowers.

The church field is tremendous for the retail florist, but he must educate himself on individual denomination customs as well as to familiarize himself with the church calendar. Successful florists have found that by acquiring several books on these subjects their shops have become more authoritative on the subject. One florist reported in 1966 that he added four new churches in the fall and he now does 24 every Saturday. The cheapest that he does is $4.00 per week and he has one that is $35.00 each week. His overall church volume last year was over $28,000 including holiday work.

The sales opportunities for church flowers is without limit, and is another market to be developed in the retail florist business in the face of the decreasing funeral flower business.

Hospital Flowers

The hospital flower business is one of the mainstays of many retail flower shops. This is particularly true in the summer and fall and during the long winter months after the Christmas holidays.

Many hospitals throughout the country regard floral arrangements as a nuisance, although doctors and nurses alike realize the benefit of flowers to the morale of the patients. When the floral arrangements are huge space-consuming baskets of flowers, then they are a nuisance. It is up to the retail florists to put more thought and effort into hospital flower arrangements. The florist must sell the customer on the use of prestige flowers in an expensive arrangement in order to build up the order but hold down the size. Few hospital rooms have sufficient space for large bouquets, and, even when they have, most hospitals lack the personnel to care for flowers properly. As a result, the blooms quickly droop and fade, and patients, visitors, and hospital personnel are all left with a poor impression of florists and their hospital arrangements.

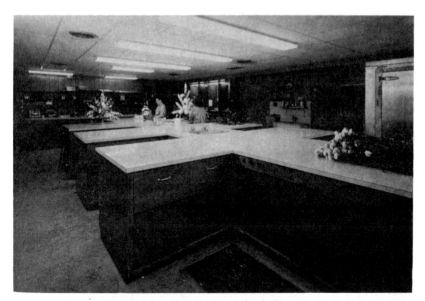

Figure 31-1. A well-planned workroom for making all types of designs, including the hospital arrangements shown. (Courtesy, Frederick's Flowers, Souderton, Pa.)

To prevent hospitals from joining the ranks of those who would omit flowers altogether it is up to the individual florist to improve the image of flowers by sending only compact, minimum-maintenance flower arrangements to the hospital. Some of this will require education of the customers. The florist may be acquainted with the situation in the hospitals, but it will not do much good if he does not convey this information to the customer when he or she is ordering hospital flowers. Once the customer learns the situation and the facts concerning the problems with hospital arrangements, he will often agree to a small, minimum-maintenance flower arrangement, dish garden, or pot plant.

The florist can also help the relationship with hospital personnel by observing the regulations of the hospital concerning flowers for the hospital. Some of these rules were given in Chapter 19. If every florist would find out these rules from his own hospital and abide by them, it would strengthen the position of florists with the hospital.

Many florists are displaying floral arrangements in the lobby of the hospital as a second shop to take advantage of hospital sales. If only a display box is used, then the women from the gift shop may handle the sales.

Effects of Flowers

A florist trade journal reported in 1965 an article about the bad effects of flowers in a hospital room. It was written by a doctor and hinted that the oxygen-consuming floral arrangements had a damaging effect on the hospital patients. Drs. Boodley and Fox at Cornell University conducted a study in a small room with 10 dozen roses and found that the roses only used up 1¼ per cent of the oxygen in the room space in one day, and the total carbon dioxide consumed was less than ½ of the oxygen consumed. This was in an airtight room, which situation does not prevail in our hospitals. The door is opened many times during the day. Their conclusions showed that *flowers do not endanger the oxygen supply of a hospital patient.* This so-called damaging effect is only a myth in some hospitals and has no truth at all.

Florist Designs

Many retail florists should turn over a new leaf when it comes to hospital designs. Since rooms are small and display space is limited, large flower arrangements are a nuisance, besides being in poor taste and inappropriate to the situation. Small arrangements not only fit better but are more appropriate. Florists may raise the objection that small arrangements will mean selling down their product. Certainly this is not the case. Instead of a large, spreading mixed bouquet, try using two or three cymbidiums or cypripedium orchids with a few sprays of Baker fern and a branch of Manzanita in a good quality small container that the recipient can keep as a remembrance or a few choice chrysanthemums in a slender cylinder vase with a figurine to add interest, and all fastened to a piece of styrofoam.

The retail florist has unlimited possibilities to use styrofoam novelties cut out and designed to fit each patient. Children's toys, books, crayons, and many other items can be used to add interest to the arrangement. A man will appreciate an arrangement which includes some masculine object as has been mentioned previously. Flower arrangements for men should give the impression of strength and masculinity through use of strong colors and sturdy accessories, which get across the message of cheer without being coy or flimsy. A dish garden or pot plant is very acceptable to most patients, and will last much longer than a flower arrangement. Some florists insert a few flowers in a plastic water tube and add it to the dish garden. Others add a few flowers to the water-holding center of a bromeliad (pitcher) plant. A few flowers in a water tube with a little ribbon can even be placed on the tray or night stand so that the patient can see the flowers more easily. These can be replenished every few days if the patient is bed-ridden for a long period of time. A pot plant should be accompanied with a care tag to tell the patient and friends how to take care of it, and when to water it. Most nurses will not have time to care for it. If the flower arrangement is in one of the foams, an "add water daily" tag should be included with the arrangement.

The florist must also avoid sending poisonous plants like primrose, or flowers with pollen or a strong fragrance. Many people love hyacinths, but would find them overpowering in a hospital room. If fruit is added to the arrangement, the florist should consider the harmful effects to flowers of ethylene gas given off from ripening fruits such as apples, pears, and bananas. Carnations will close up, snapdragons drop their florets and roses turn blue and lose their petals if the concentration of ethylene gas is too heavy.

The superintendent of the hospital and the grey lady staff can be worth their "weight in gold" to the local florist. Their help and understanding should be cultivated. At all costs the florist must have them on his side, so that the greatest benefit possible will be obtained for his flowers.

Always remember that the florist is not only a designer and salesman, but also an educator. He should inform his customers about the best selection of flowers and plants to send to the hospital and tell him how he can best serve them. The customer will appreciate this consideration and return it with increased business for that florist.

References

1. Allen, I. *Churches Offer Wide Sales Opportunity.* Society of American Florists' Memo (1964), 3 pp.
2. Fox, R. "Flowers in Hospitals," *The Exchange,* Vol. 143, No. 8 (February 20, 1965), pp. 20-21.

Chapter 32

FUNERAL FLOWERS

The sending of flowers to funerals to express sympathy has been practiced for many decades in this country. While the use of flowers has been curtailed in some areas due to Please Omit (Chapter 20), it will undoubtedly continue to play a large part in the retail florist business for many years to come. It ranges from 80 per cent of the business for some florists down to 30 per cent of the business for other florists.

The handling of flowers for funerals, and the relatives of the deceased is where another one of the services comes in that the retail florist can offer the customer. He is a consultant as to what flowers are available, what types of arrangements are most appropriate, and how they should be handled.

The florist must be able to handle the order for flowers in a sympathetic manner. He must show an interest and understanding of the situation as well as having patience with the person ordering the flowers.

Family Flowers

When the relatives of the deceased come into the shop to discuss the family flowers for the funeral it should be discussed in private if possible, and often a florist uses his office or consultation room for this, so the customer may sit down. The florist must tactfully get information on the deceased before making suggestions. The age and sex of the deceased are necessary as well as the relationship of the survivors. The florist must talk to the relatives and find out what they have in mind, and then make suggestions of what would be most appropriate and suitable. The florist must know if the casket is to be open, closed, or a half-casket. If the deceased is female, the color of her dress may be important. There are several types of designs recommended for the family flowers.

They may be a double spray, single spray, blanket, scarf, garland, or sheaf for the top of the casket. It may be a floral rosary in the casket lid or a cross. It may be one large vase of flowers at one end of the casket, or two vases of flowers with one at each end of the casket. Some customers will request a floral pillow or other emblem. Sometimes a corsage is placed inside the casket on the pillow or in the hand. There are many possibilities for family flowers and often they will be dictated by the deceased, the relatives, or the customs of the community. The flowers may be ordered by phone, and the same sympathetic understanding and patience must be practiced by the florist. If a spray is used on the casket, it should be on a rubber-footed frame to protect the casket. Nothing must be used which will mar the casket itself. Flowers are sometimes ordered by the family through the funeral director and usually it is a specific order. This is one reason why it is advisable to work cooperatively with the funeral director so that he will not take orders for flowers which are unavailable, nor take an order whose price is too low to make a presentable showing. *The funeral director should let the family and florist decide on the flowers,* but many of them do it themselves as a part of their service. Some florists give a percentage to the funeral director for all flower orders he sends them. This is unethical, and a *very poor business practice,* besides being one that can be financially disastrous. Some florists give a 10 to 20 per cent discount when their own net profit for the year is only 6 per cent. It doesn't make good business sense. *The funeral directors are not florists and have no legitimate reason for taking flower orders,* or expecting a commission on them. Florists must work with the funeral directors and vice versa. (See Chapter 20 on tips to florists and tips to funeral directors.)

Other Funeral Orders

The florist should treat anyone coming in to order funeral flowers with the same interest and understanding as he would the relatives of the deceased. He must handle the order properly, and recommend something that is appropriate. He should find out the sex and age of the deceased, and the relationship of the customer. The cost for funeral flowers usually comes up early in the conversation. Most florists have a minimum which is only mentioned when specifically asked for by the customer. Many times a retail florist will quote a range of three prices to the customer so he can make his own choice without asking for something cheaper.

The florist, however, if he is a good salesman, can upsell the order. He should know the customer or try to find out something about the customer, so he will know what that person is in the habit of spending. Often the salesman can get $20 instead of $15 for the order by upselling and telling the customer how much better the $20 piece will be. Don't just say it's bigger, but use descriptive adjectives to describe it. If an executive from a large company calls or comes in and is quoted $7 he will be insulted and may go somewhere else. Thirty to 50 dollars may be more what he had in mind to spend. The florist must ask questions and listen to the customer to determine the price he should quote. If a person is representing a group of neighbors or associates they may have collected a certain amount of money and the florist will then be limited to that figure. If they don't have a set figure, again don't quote such a low price that it will produce an arrangement that is much too small to represent a group of people.

The florist should be sure to get all of the accurate information, particularly the time and place of the funeral. This plus the name and sex of the individual is most important for telephone orders to a funeral in another city. Don't depend on the other member florist to know the details of the funeral unless the customer does not know himself, and asks to have the other florist find out the information for the order. A phone call should produce the desired results.

There are also many types of designs which may be chosen for funeral flowers from friends, relatives, or associates. The majority of funeral pieces in the country today are either sprays, vases, or baskets (including papier-mâché containers). However, many funeral homes have small tables and stands so that artistic vase arrangements can be used. There are many emblems and designs which are popular in certain sections of the country. These include crosses, pillows, gates ajar, broken column, broken wheel, vacant chair, harps, wreaths, and many others. Some florists haven't made one of these in a year, while others make them every week. Many areas of the country are getting away from some of the more elaborate emblems. If the deceased were a member of a club, lodge, or trade association, there are emblems used for the funeral sent by that organization. These are still used in most sections of the country and include Eastern Star, Odd Fellows Lodge, Masons, Knights of Columbus, and many others. The florist must keep these frames on hand if he is in an area where they may be used. The techniques of some of these designs will be discussed in Chapter 33.

Funeral flowers should be delivered in good condition and on time. The tag must be accurately written with all of the correct information. Often the signature card is kept by the family. Many florists put a brief description of the flower arrangement on the back of the card. This is just another little service offered by the florist whereby the family can write a more personal thank-you to the sender of the flowers. It is nice to be able to mention a spray of yellow roses, a basket of white and lavender chrysanthemums, or a vase of pink carnations rather than just thanking someone for the flowers they sent. The card is usually placed in an envelope or cellophane bag, and should be securely fastened to the floral piece. If there is a bow of ribbon on the arrangement, the card may be pinned, or paper clipped to it. Don't use a staple as it is too hard to remove. If there is no ribbon, the florist may use a paper clip and attach it to the leaves, or use a wire, ribbon, or string to fasten it to a piece of the foliage or one of the stronger stemmed flowers. Each florist has his own method, but the main thing is to have it securely fastened. The card should be legibly written, preferably in a woman's handwriting, or may be typed possibly in script, which is attractive, appropriate, and easy to read. There should be no mistakes on the card, and the family must be able to read the person's name easily and accurately. It is embarrassing for the family to thank the wrong person for the flowers, or to not thank someone at all for some flowers. Usually the florist is blamed if an error occurs.

The retail florist can do a lot to curtail the growing problem of "Please Omit" and "In Lieu of Flowers" by using good judgment in his handling of funeral flower orders. More artistic designs of attractive floral pieces rather than large massed arrangements in too lavish a display will help to avert criticism of funeral flowers.

It is up to the florist to be sympathetic, interested, and understanding in handling people ordering flowers for funerals; as well as to suggest and execute designs which will be best suited and most appropriate for that particular funeral. A florist with a good imagination and originality can send out many pieces to the same funeral without having them all look the same. The customers will appreciate it, and so will the family of the deceased. All florists should do their best to make funeral designs more attractive and more appropriate, and handle all funeral orders properly. It is not in good taste for a florist to say "thank you" for a funeral order.

Chapter 33

DESIGN TECHNIQUES; CORSAGES

Design techniques are primarily learned at design schools, design courses in our colleges and universities, and by experience in retail florist shops. Here are some basic ideas that will be helpful to the young person interested in becoming a retail florist.

Wiring

The wires which most retail florists have on hand run from #18 (heaviest) to #32 (thinnest). They come in the following sizes: 18, 19, 20, 21, 22, 23, 24, 26, 28, 30, and 32. The length which most florists' use is 18 inches long. However, some of the wire is cut in 12-inch lengths, and this is preferred by florists for certain design work. Wire also comes in spools and is used in making wreaths and sprays. The wire is used to strengthen the stem on many flowers so they will not bend or break and will help to hold the flower head in the proper position. Wire is used to wire flowers in corsages, which replaces the natural stem. Every flower and most foliage in a wedding bouquet is wired. Wires are used on most flowers in funeral work to give added support to the stem. Wires are used on flowers in vase arrangements for the home only when it is absolutely necessary. Wires are unsightly and considered objectionable in the home. Sometimes the flower has a very weak stem and requires a wire for support, if it is to be used in a vase arrangement. This should be kept to a minimum by using good quality flowers. The wires used in funeral vases, baskets, sprays, and wreaths are used at the discretion of the designer to make sure the pieces arrive at the funeral in the best possible shape and design. Some florists wire all flowers in funeral work to give the best protection. Other florists wire very little. It is mainly a question of habit. Most florists wire the flower stems which need it, and which they feel are necessary to keep breakage to a minimum during delivery.

Figure 33-1. Piercing method for wiring flowers such as roses and carnations.

Figure 33-2. The clutchwire method for wiring flowers such as gladiolus florets, or putting an extra wire on a flower.

Figure 33-3. The hook method for wiring any daisy-type flower.

Figure 33-4. The hairpin method for wiring funnel-shaped flowers like lilies and stephanotis.

Figure 33-5. The straight wire method for wiring flowers like roses and snapdragons which still have their stems attached to the flower.

There are many ways to wire flowers and it depends on the
flower type and the use of the flower. A rose is wired one way
for a corsage and a different way for a funeral spray or in a vase
arrangement. Various methods are shown in Figures 33-1, 33-2, 33-3,
33-4, and 33-5. The piercing method is used on roses and carnations for corsages, wedding bouquets, and funeral sprays. The
clutchwire method is used on individual gladioli florets and funnel-
shaped flowers for corsages and wedding bouquets. The hookwire
is used on any daisy, aster, or pompon-type flower for corsages,
wedding bouquets, funeral work, or vase arrangements. The flower
heads are removed for corsages and wedding bouquets, but the
stems are left on for other designs with the wire twisted around
the stem to give it needed support. The hairpin method is used on
lilies, daylilies, funnel-shaped flowers, or any daisy-type flowers for
any of the designs. The straight wire is used on flowers when
the stem remains attached to the flower for funeral work and
for vase arrangements. This is used on roses, carnations, chrysanthemums, daffodils, iris, gladioli, and many other flowers. Spike
flowers are usually wired with the hook-straight wire with a small
hook either pushed into the stem or twisted around the lowest
floret of snapdragons and stock. Some flower stems are hollow inside so the wire can be pushed up inside, gives good support, and
is invisible. Unfortunately this method can only be used on relatively

few flowers such as calla lilies, daffodils, thick-stemmed snapdragons, majestic daisies, and a few others. The size or number of wire used for flowers cannot be given here because it depends on the use of the flower, size of the flower, size of the stem, and thickness of the stem. It must be learned by feel and experience. Some flowers like lilies-of-the-valley, pansies, stock florets, and hyacinths are quite difficult to wire. Patience and practice are necessary to learn how to wire these.

Ribbon

Ribbon comes in different colors, styles, materials, and widths. Most of the corsage ribbon is narrow and comes in sizes 2, 3, 5, and 9. Funeral and Christmas ribbon comes mainly in two standard widths: #40 (approximately 2¾ inches wide) and #120 (approximately 4½ inches wide). There are other sizes but these are the ones commonly used by florists today. There are several ways to tie a bow of ribbon. One method is shown in the following sketches. It can be used on corsages, wedding bouquets, funeral sprays, funeral wreaths, Christmas wreaths, and Christmas door swags. With a little practice, it is very easy to learn to make an attractive bow. The size of the bow will depend on the amount of ribbon used. One and one-half yards of material will make an average sized bow. The procedure for tying a bow is as follows:

1. Hang the ribbon over your left thumb with the long side in front, and about 2 inches behind the thumb as shown in Figure 33-6.

2. With your right hand take the long side of the ribbon and loop it under and around the left thumb squeezing the ribbon between the left thumb and forefinger as in Figure 33-7.

3. Grasp the ribbon with the right hand about 3 inches from the crushed part and make a loop in the air, bringing the ribbon to the spot between the left thumb and forefinger, and crushing it between the two as in Figure 33-8. The ribbon must always be looped under so that the ribbon will fit between the left thumb and forefinger. Never leave the ribbon flat, but squeeze it after each loop. Looping over instead of under will make bow tying more difficult.

4. Go down the ribbon 3 inches and loop it under, squeezing it between the left thumb and forefinger. Thus, the first two loops as shown in Figure 33-9 are formed.

Figure 33-6. The first step in tying a bow of ribbon.

Figure 33-7. The second step in tying a bow of ribbon.

Figure 33-8. Forming the first loop in the bow.

Figure 33-9. Forming additional loops in the bow.

Figure 33-10. A completed bow of ribbon.

5. Three or four more loops are made in each direction until the bow reaches the proper size (Figure 33-10). Each set of loops should be slightly larger than the previous set, so the bow will have more character to it.

6. While holding all the loops in the left hand, take a piece of thin florists' wire, chenille stem, piece of curly-Q, or a piece of ribbon and insert it over your left thumb. Pull it down tightly around all the crushed ribbon pieces and twist firmly in the rear. This will hold it tightly together, and it can be attached to the floral design piece.

7. The ribbon bow must be fastened securely right up under the bottom flower and as close to it as possible. A gap between flowers and ribbon is poor design. The excess wire that remains after securing it to the corsage or funeral piece is either cut off or else pushed into the flower stems so that no one will run the wires into their fingers.

Wrapping Wire Stems

The artificial wire stems on flowers for corsages and wedding bouquets are not attractive so they must be covered. The two most common materials on the market for this are Floratape and Para-film. These come in many different colors, but most florists use green, white, orchid, and brown. White flowers should have their stems wrapped with white material, while the orchid is used on regular cattleya orchids and the brown on cymbidium orchids. Green is used for most other stems and is used in larger amounts by the florist than any other color. They come in rolls of 1/2 inch and inch widths. The method of wrapping the tape is to place the material behind the stem as close to the flower head as possible. The flower is held in the left hand and the tape in the right. As the left hand slowly turns the flower, the right hand guides the tape around the wire and stretches it tight. In a few seconds the wire stem is as attractive as the natural one.

Corsages

In making corsages, the flower heads are removed from their stems and an artificial wire stem is attached as discussed previously under "Wiring." We wire flowers with artificial stems for several reasons: to reduce bulk by removing the natural stem, to reduce the weight of the corsage, for ease in making the flowers face the right way, and to keep them in place even if they start to wilt a little.

The flowers should be properly hardened before being used in corsages. After this the stem is removed from the flower, leaving about a quarter of an inch of stem. The flowers are then ready for wiring, and the number of wire to use will depend on the size and weight of the flower head. Usually the florist uses #20 or 22 on roses because the head is heavy. The method of wiring will depend on the type of flower in the corsage as shown in the previous sketches. The piercing method is usually used on roses and carnations; the clutchwire on gladiolus florets; the hairpin on stephanotis, individual hyacinth florets, and day lilies; and the hookwire method on daisy-type flowers. The main factor is to provide a good artificial stem to the flower without adding to the weight.

The wire is next wrapped with floratape or parafilm of the appropriate color.

The retail florist should find out from the customer just where the flowers are to be worn, and the color of the dress if possible. There are usually four places where corsages are worn and each

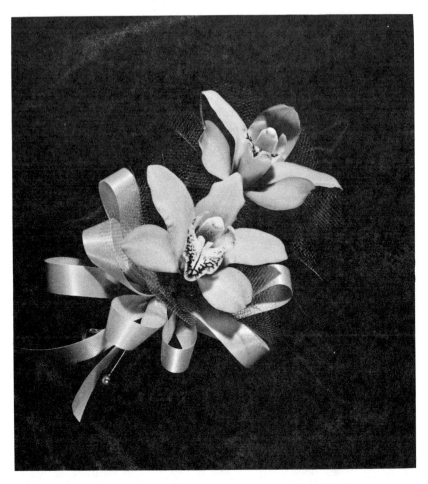

Figure 33-11. A corsage of two cymbidium orchids.

requires a special type. A shoulder corsage is normally triangular or
shield-shaped with the ribbon at the bottom (Figure 33-11). Sometimes
a double corsage is made for the shoulder with the ribbon approximately in the center of the corsage. The waist and wrist corsages are
double corsages made by constructing two small triangular corsages
and tying them together with the bow of ribbon in the center. A
wrist corsage is fastened to a frame (several are on the market)
that will easily fit onto the girl's wrist. A hair corsage is made
without the use of greens or a ribbon and may be made in one
of several shapes. In any corsage the buds and small flowers are

used at the top or outer edges with the larger open flowers at the base, just as in flower arrangements.

Constructing the corsage consists in putting the buds, flowers, foliage, and bow of ribbon together in a pleasing design. Start with a leaf and bud out at the tip, followed by two small flowers as shown in Figure 33-12. Foliage is added at each step in the construction, and not at the end. Tie the first three flowers together firmly by using thread, wire, chenille stem, or curly-Q, or by twisting one of the wire stems around the others. Any method is satisfactory and each florist uses his own. Many of them tie the flowers together with regular corsage thread. The flowers should be turned to the front or to the side to fit into the design. Foliage and one flower at a time are added, making sure to tie or wire them firmly to the others. Cut off all long stems and add a bow of ribbon at the base. The completed shoulder corsage should resemble that shown in Figure 33-13. Always tell customers to wear the corsage with the flowers upright—the way they grow in nature.

Florists use either fresh foliage or artificial leaves in corsages. Rose foliage should not be used as it will not hold up. Many florists use Baker fern, asparagus plumosus (called grass), ever-

Figure 33-12. The first three flowers put together one at a time in a corsage.

Figure 33-13. A shoulder corsage complete with ribbon.

green foliage, huckleberry, magnolia, laurel, or salal. Greens belonging to the flower may also be used such as gladioli, iris, camellia, gardenia, or fancy foliage like croton.

Mossing

Mossing is a procedure considered old-fashioned by some florists, but still used by many others in certain areas of the country. The material used is sphagnum moss which has been well soaked overnight in plenty of water. Moss is used in wreath frames, emblem frames, and sometimes as a base for funeral sprays. The frame is lined with foil to hold in the moss and improve its appearance. The moss is squeezed so that all excess water is removed from it. Then it is packed tightly into the frame and tied with spool wire or wreath thread. It is then ready for the insertion of flowers. They may be wired with a short heavy wire to hold into the moss, while others are attached to a metal pick with a Pix machine and then stuck in the moss. The moss helps to make the flowers last longer. Some florists are using one of the various foam materials or strips of styrofoam in place of the moss. It depends on the florist, and the customs of the locality.

Sprays

There are many ways to make funeral sprays. Some are tied loosely while others are inserted into a foundation base. The primary foundations on the market that can be used are Oasis, Hydrofoam, Jiffy, Quicky, Snopak, Aquatainer, styrofoam, moss, and

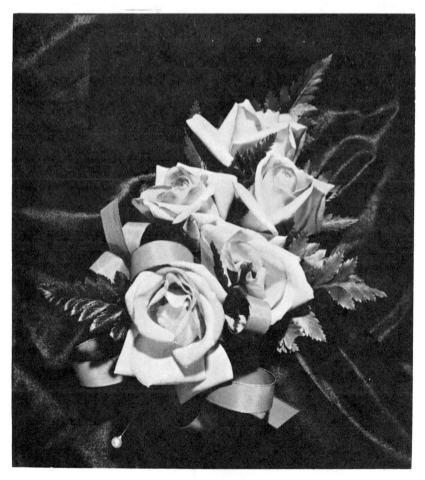

Figure 33-14. A rose corsage with Baker fern backing.

Wet-a-pack. The flowers are wired in different lengths and inserted into the base to form the desired shape of the spray. Foliage is used as a background, edging, and filler for the sprays. Sprays are usually triangular, oval, round, or crescent in shape. They must be made so that they can be easily hung on an easel. If styrofoam

Figure 33-15. A styrofoam bar for making a funeral spray.

Figure 33-16. Salal foliage inserted into a styrofoam bar for a background.

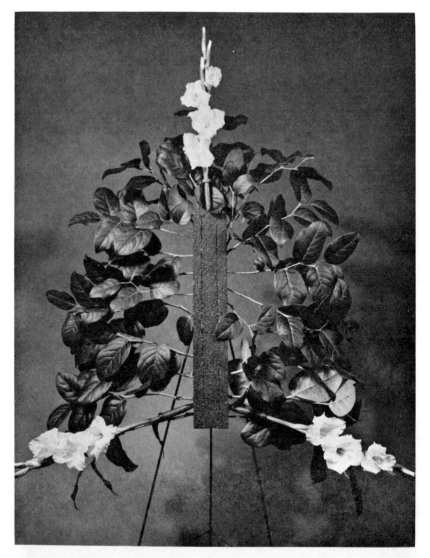

Figure 33-17. The first three flowers are placed to outline the triangular design of the funeral spray.

is used as a base, the flowers are wired and then inserted into a water pick before being inserted into the styrofoam. This is not necessary with the other foundation materials, all of which retain moisture in the media. There are many different sizes of styrofoam spray bars for the base of various sized sprays. Each retail florist has his own way of making sprays and wreaths. Many are pictured in several good funeral design books. The steps in making a funeral spray on a styrofoam spray bar are shown in Figures 33-15 through 33-20.

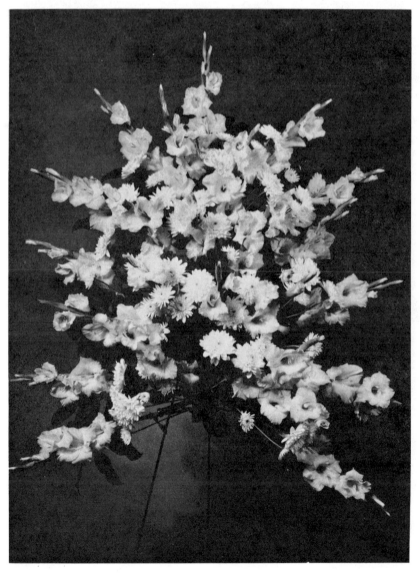

Figure 33-18. Funeral spray is filled in with flowers and greens.

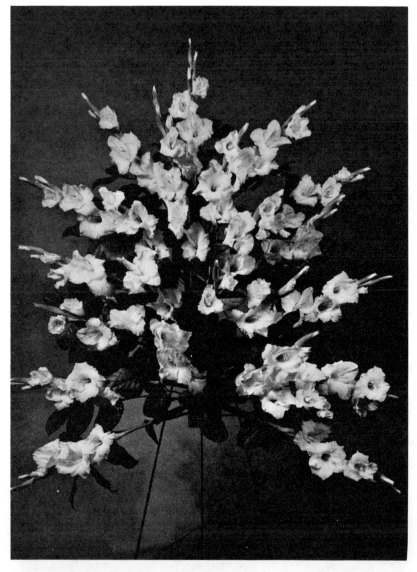

Figure 33-19. Small flowers (pompons) used as a filler to give a full effect to the spray.

Figure 33-20. A completed funeral spray with bow of ribbon.

Baskets

Many materials are used in baskets to make the flowers stay in place. Some florists use greens such as cedar or hemlock, chicken wire, shredded styrofoam, vermiculite, or one of the foam materials. Other florists use a combination of two or more. If the basket has a handle, the florist often wires the first (tallest) flower to the handle and may do the same with several others to keep them in place during delivery and handling. Bows of ribbon are often used in baskets; sometimes on the handle, down front, or attached to a bamboo stake in the middle of the arrangement. Although many florists don't use any bow of ribbon at all, or just one, some will use two small ones and fasten them together with a piece of ribbon. Often this adds color and interest to the arrangement. A bow will also fill in a hole, and may be cheaper than adding two more flowers. Steps in making a basket in a papier-mâché container are shown in Figures 33-21 through 33-26.

Figure 33-21. Papier-mâché container with chicken wire.

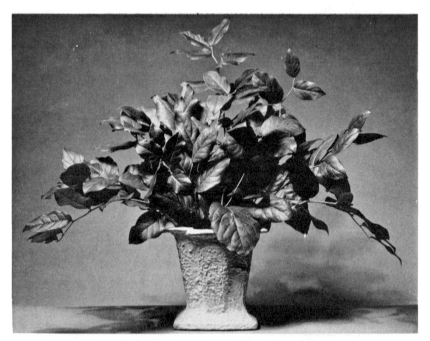

Figure 33-22. Salal as a background for a funeral arrangement.

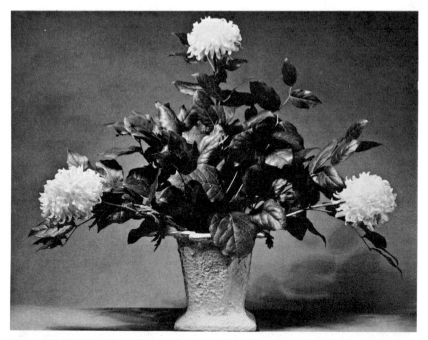

Figure 33-23. First three flowers form the triangular design for this funeral basket.

Figure 33-24. More flowers added to the arrangement.

Figure 33-25. Pompons added as a filler flower to the funeral arrangement.

Figure 33-26. A funeral basket (vase) complete with a bow of ribbon for a focal point.

Foams

The use of the various foam materials has been a boon to the retail florist. They make designing much easier and more varied. They have many uses, and the details of their uses and directions for handling are discussed in Chapter 37.

Styrofoam

The use of styrofoam has increased the artistry and attractiveness of many designs. Florists with imagination and originality have been able to upsell their merchandise, and make a good reputation for themselves. Most florists have a styrofoam cutter to use for small designs, and a regular saw for larger pieces. Novelty items of any size and shape can be cut out, painted, and used in a number of designs. For a musician, a design can include a styrofoam sheet of music, musical note, or some appropriate instrument. For any special occasion an article appropriate to the theme can be cut out of styrofoam: cake, parasol, shoe, Santa Claus, reindeer, tree, flower, instrument, figurines, numbers, etc. There is no limit to the articles that can be shaped out of styrofoam. Styrofoam items are often used in window displays from a small cone up to an organ entirely made out of styrofoam. Many bases for arrangements are made out of styrofoam. One word of caution on using a hot wire styrofoam cutter is not to inhale the fumes. Cut the styrofoam in a well-ventilated room.

Paint

Spray paint in every color imaginable is available to the florist. These paints spray on very easily and can be used on flowers, foliage, styrofoam, pottery, and other items like pine cones. There are advantages to spray painting a design for an occasion like a silver or golden anniversary, particularly where the florist does not have the correct colors of flowers and accessories. They can be used so the arrangement will fit the décor in the customer's home. Foliages are often spray painted at Christmas for more festive effects. A word of caution is not to use spray paint on every arrangement which leaves the shop. It can be overdone. Used correctly and in moderation, spray paint can be a great help in making designs and arrangements more interesting and pleasing to the eye.

Wedding designs and techniques are discussed in Chapter 34.

Other ideas for designing are found in Chapter 19 under "Tricks of the Trade."

There are many more design techniques employed by various retail florists than can be discussed here. The best way to learn is at a design school or college, by observing other florists and designers at work, and from plenty of practice.

There are several excellent retail floral design books on the market today.

Keep in mind that "time is money" and in any design or arrangement that takes time, the retail florist must make the customer pay for it.

Chapter 34

WEDDINGS: DESIGNS, SERVICE, BACKGROUNDS

Weddings represent anywhere from 5 to 20 per cent of a florist's business. According to *Brides* magazine, there were more than 2 million weddings in 1971, and the number will increase to 2.3 million by 1975. The tradition of the June wedding is declining in popularity. The National Office of Vital Statistics reveals that only 12.5 per cent of marriages take place in June. August accounts for 10.9 per cent, September for 9.4 per cent, December for 9.1 per cent, and July for 9.0 per cent. January has the lowest figure—only 5.8 per cent.

Weddings are a time for flowers, and a good part of the total business of many retail florists. The attitude of florists on weddings varies all over the country. Many florists handle hundreds of weddings in a year, while others only have one or two or none at all. Some florists say they don't want weddings and can't make any money from them, while others really cultivate the wedding business like Frances Jones Poetker who has handled over 6,500 weddings. Weddings can run from $10 to $10,000. Wedding bouquets usually cost from $10 up. Selling wedding flowers can often be a tedious and frustrating task, but also a very rewarding one.

Florists in general have the job of introducing the soon-to-be-married customer to the beauties of a wedding that is properly planned with flowers, while the individual florist has the task of selling the potential customer on his particular shop. The extent to which a florist wishes to compete for his share of this profitable business is his own choice. Florists who are really trying for this market will set up special wedding window displays in the spring of the year, and use direct mail advertising to bring this business into their shop. Many florists provide the flowers for fashion shows or bridal shows put on in department stores. A tie-in with a wedding fashion show is invaluable from the advertising standpoint of an individual florist.

Today's bride seems to prefer the natural look in her wedding flowers, with lots of color. A trend also is toward more simple church decorations and more lavish flowers and decorations for the reception.

Bridal Consultation

When a prospective bride comes into the florist shop to discuss her flowers, the florist should have a special place for the discussion. Many florists have a separate bridal consultation corner while others use the office. A separate room is not necessary, but some special spot should be used even in a small shop. A bridal consultation corner should do two things: make the bride comfortable and give her a sense of privacy. Some retail florists simply stand behind the counter and describe the wedding flowers. This is a poor way to conduct wedding business. The minimum

Figure 34-1. A bridal bouquet of gardenias, stephanotis, and ribbon.

requirements for comfort are two chairs (with a third available nearby, to be pulled up when the bride's mother sits in on the consultation), plus a desk or table on which to spread pictures, fabric samples, writing materials, order blanks, and a book of wedding pictures. Some florists have a small projector or viewer set up so the bride can see colored slides of bouquets designed by their shop.

A sense of privacy is important during the bridal consultation. It makes the bride feel that she has your undivided attention, and that she is free to discuss costs without being overheard by others. She feels you are really interested in her and her wedding.

Even in a tiny shop, the illusion of privacy can be given by the use of a temporary screen or some tall foliage plants that help to screen off one corner of the shop. Larger shops may have a special consultation room containing a sofa, coffee table, chairs, and lamps to provide the best comfort possible. Some florists who service large expensive weddings may need room to show the water color paintings that are made to show the bride exactly how the wedding and decorations will look. It all depends on the space available in the shop, and the number and size of weddings anticipated.

A good consultation corner is worth the effort it takes to achieve. Many florists have found that their average wedding order increased by several dollars after they provided a place where the florist and the bride could confer in privacy and comfort.

Costs

A problem which often confronts a florist is when a mother and daughter come into the shop and the mother says, "My daughter is getting married next month, and I would like some flowers for her—something very nice and very pretty, but I don't want it to cost too much." Both the florist and the customer will have prices and costs in mind, but it is a fatal mistake to get caught in the problem of price discussion without adequate information.

The florist should assume the lead by asking questions such as: Where will the ceremony be held? What time of day is it to take place? How many bridesmaids and ushers are in the party? Is it to be formal or informal? What is the name and address of the groom? It is advantageous to get this information in writing. This gives the florist some idea of the size and cost of the wedding itself. Certainly $50 for the flowers will not suffice for a church wedding with a reception afterwards which in itself may run into thousands of dollars. The flowers must be appropriate and adequate for what the customer has in mind.

Some florists express the opinion that the flowers used in a wedding must carry at least a 5 to 1 markup in order to compensate them for the time involved. "It is impossible to say that this markup is correct for every shop," says Herb Mitchell. He believes a florist should make it his business to know exactly what it costs to do a wedding. Find out how much time is spent by each employee involved, and the cost of the materials. From these costs the florist should be able to determine the margin of profit he will make. Time is the most expensive item in the retail flower shop and must be considered. Not only the time to make the bouquets, but also consultation time, time to set up the decorations, and time to take down the decorations and return the props and materials to the shop must be considered. Many florists, unfortunately, forget to figure in time to remove the decorations after the wedding is over. A florist cannot afford to give away his time.

Be sure to price the wedding for profit. A florist in Wauwatosa, Wisconsin, Alan Preuss, uses a formula to estimate the correct price for bouquets. He has worked out a chart for the exact retail price of each flower that he needs to make a profit. Representative 1970 prices would be: roses, $1 each; carnations, $1 each; pompons, 50¢ each; stephanotis, 50¢ to 75¢ each; etc. These prices hold true except for the three major holidays. Another florist in Tampa, Florida, J. W. Wilson, charges the basic retail price times 20 per cent for design materials times 20 per cent of that figure for labor as his formula.

Types of Service

Many florists are offering successfully two types of bridal services. There are some brides who are interested in the absolute minimum flower requirements and want no service whatsoever. There are many weddings in this category. It is important to realize this, for the florist might price himself out of the market if he thinks that every bride is interested in his complete service.

Florists who offer complete bridal service often class their services as *package service* and *custom service*. Flower shops that successfully and profitably promote a complete wedding service, handle the smallest as well as the largest weddings, and have their services well defined. The package service is the least expensive and usually only two or three styles of bouquets are offered with definite prices suggested. Simple bouquets are planned and sold. The bride pays for the wedding before the ceremony and the flowers are delivered to the church without service.

Most florists require a down payment from the bride's family at the time the wedding is booked. The remainder will be paid before the wedding ceremony in the case of a package deal or to a stranger, or else the family will be billed later if they are one of the florist's regular good customers.

The custom wedding service permits the florist to become an important part of the wedding. Some florists will arrange everything including invitations, complete reception including the catering of food and drink, and all details of the wedding. There are many weddings that offer the florist the opportunity to sell his complete service. This will be determined at the first interview. There are two definite opinions about selling this service. Some florists feel that the markup they use for wedding flowers should be great enough to hide all the costs and labor involved in completely servicing any wedding. Other florists feel that they should itemize the service and the extra labor items. Either method is satisfactory, as long as the florist makes sure he is getting a profit for each operation.

Interview

One of the most important responsibilities of the retail florist in developing wedding business is conducting the wedding interview. It is here that the bride will make her decision concerning the type and amount of wedding flowers she will use, and whether or not the interviewing florist will get the business. It is preferable to handle the wedding interview on an appointment basis. This conveys the impression that weddings are important.

Frequently the customer (bride or mother) will have preconceived ideas which are not practical. They should be dealt with tactfully and firmly. A florist should not leave the customer with the impression that he will try to get certain flowers when he knows it is impossible at that season of the year. Or, if they just want a background of greens, it is up to the florist to point out the beauty of the pageant, and that the decorations should be a complete design as well as serving as an appropriate background for the wedding party. Flowers should enhance the natural look

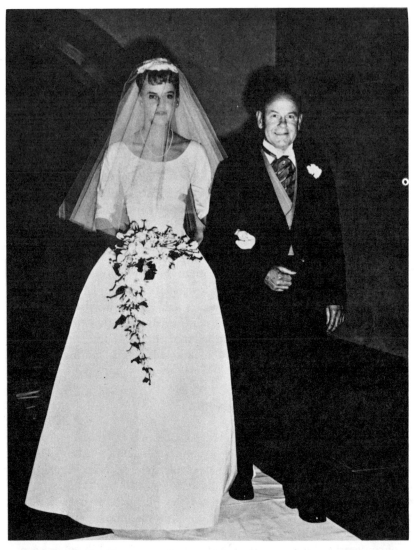

Figure 34-2. A bridal bouquet. (Designed by Albrecht's Flowers, Narberth, Pa.)

of the bride. Colors of bridal flowers, gowns, and decoration must all blend together in perfect harmony. There is no one best design for a bouquet, but loose round bouquets and cascades are particularly popular now. Also, the carrying of one rose with greens is gaining in popularity.

Plus Service

A retail florist who wants wedding business must be able to give plus service. He should be aware that foresight, careful planning, patience, tact, and sound business practices are required if the florist is to enhance his reputation in this field and realize a respectable profit for his efforts. The following steps are used by Frances Jones Poetker in her shop which has serviced over 6,500 weddings:

1. During the first appointment with the bride, adopt a reporter's tactics and get answers to the ancient questions: who, what, when, where, why, and how, as they apply to the decorations. Determine whether the bride and her mother like things to be frilly or tailored, exotic or traditional, stark or sentimental. Ask where the gowns are being bought, what refreshments will be served, how many guests will be invited, and other questions. Costs should not be discussed at the first meeting but get some idea of what the family is planning to spend.

2. The second step is often overlooked by the florist. He should check the credit rating of the customer.

3. Next discuss costs and availability of anticipated merchandise requirements with the wholesaler.

4. If the size of the job warrants it, look at models of dresses chosen. Go and see the church, club, or home, particularly if unknown to the florist before committing himself to the specific price and ideas.

5. Send the customer a detailed estimate with a break-down of costs involved. Indicate how much is allowed for each item. Each item includes a price range of about 30 per cent from maximum and minimum figures. Always include an "if available" clause in the estimate. Be as specific as possible about flowers and colors. *Be sure to include a price for your own time.*

6. Schedule a second appointment to get a firm committment.

7. When all arrangements have been concluded with the mother, try to leave open the bride's bouquet to be decided upon by her alone, or by the bride and bridegroom.

8. Talk to the bridegroom's mother concerning her corsage.

9. Several days before the wedding, check all details with the bride and her mother.

10. Have a final consultation with a representative of the church, club, or hotel to see that no other activity is scheduled just preceding or immediately following the wedding. This could present a problem in setting up and removing the decorations.

Figure 34-3. Attendants' bouquets. (Designed by Albrecht's Flowers, Narberth, Pa.)

11. The precise place and time of delivery of bouquets, corsages, boutonnieres, headbands, etc., must be ascertained.

12. The decorating crew is briefed on any expected trouble or problems, and given a diagram for decorations, and an exact schedule for each activity. A florist needs experienced help to set up and take down the wedding decorations quickly. Just before the wedding, check to be sure the place is clean. Lastly, be certain the candles are straight. No smudges or finger marks must be on the candles. These things are vital to future relationships with everyone concerned.

The preceding steps are excellent for the florist who specializes in custom service for his customers.

Religious Aspects

It is important to know the customs of the various religions and also the specific rules and regulations of the churches or synagogues. Many priests, ministers, and rabbis have definite regulations as to the placement of flowers and decorations in their places of worship. A wise florist will consult these individuals prior to the wedding. The following suggestions are given as general ideas to help the florist, but he must keep in mind that individual churches will have more specific regulations:

1. It is not considered good taste to plan a large wedding during Lent or Holy Week in Protestant churches.

2. Some ministers prefer that weddings not be held on Sundays.

3. The use of altar flowers and other decorations is customary in Protestant churches.

4. The Episcopal wedding ceremony is taken from the Church of England ceremony and often has a nuptial mass for the bride and groom immediately following the wedding ceremony.

5. The use of flowers on the altar and as decorations is customary in the Roman Catholic church. In cases of a mixed marriage, the couple will sometimes stand outside the altar rail which may affect the floral decorations. Each diocese has its own wedding regulations.

6. Jewish tradition undoubtedly calls for a more extensive use of flowers than any other religious faith. The wedding ceremony is considered the most important point in a person's life and is extremely sacred as a family occasion. The ceremony is different because of the requirements of the canopy or chuppah. The two prime musts for the Jewish wedding are the canopy and the table or stand that holds the goblet of sacramental wine. In present times the canopy is stationary and stretches approximately 7 feet by 7 feet. It can be made of silk, satin, plastic, greens, or canvas. The supporting posts can be of wood, wrought iron, steel, aluminum, plastic, or styrofoam. Often the canopy and the background trellis of greens must be supplied and designed by the florist. Normally the canopy is decorated with flowers and garlands which are more popularly used because of their clear and ethereal lines. It is impossible to describe all the ways to decorate the canopy. Other decorations are necessary depending upon where the wedding is to be held.

Extra Flowers

The flowers normally used are in the bride's bouquet, attendants' bouquets, corsages, boutonnieres, and floral decorations in the church and for the reception. There may be several large vases or baskets of flowers on the altar or in the nave of the church as well as small clusters of flowers on the pews, bride's table, wedding cake table, around the cake, etc. There is no limit to the places where flowers can be used. Palms, ferns, cibotiums, and foliage plants can be used by the florist for further decoration and background. Ribbon bows are often placed on the ends of the pews, and candles in candlelabras are used in most weddings.

The average bride and her family are none too familiar with the responsibilities for a wedding and the florist should be prepared to answer their questions. It helps to know the full list of responsibilities for a bride and her family in connection with the wedding, including opinions about the bride's gown and trousseau, wedding announcements and invitations, music for the wedding and the reception, flowers for the wedding and reception, bouquets and gifts for the bridal attendants, reception expenses, wedding cake, wedding photographs, and transportation. In other words, a retail florist should be a professional authority on weddings.

The florist should include in his service such items as the aisle runner, candlelabra, candles, standards, and baskets for rental. Var-

Figure 34-4. A bridal bouquet of gardenias, stephanotis, and ivy.

Figure 34-5. The wedding cake and knife decorated with flowers.

ious florists have found the rental of other items like cake knife, tea service, and punch bowl and cups to be very popular.

Besides the regular flowers for the wedding, the following are items which should be suggested to the bride: (1) flowers surrounding the cake and perhaps a few for the top of the cake, (2) a ribbon bow with a few stems of lilies-of-the-valley tied to the handle of the serving knife, (3) aisle or pew decorations, (4) an arrangement atop the piano or in some other strategic place, (5) flowers for the table at the wedding rehearsal dinner, (6) flowers for the wedding reception dinner table, (7) corsages for the grandmothers, (8) corsages for those who gave special assistance during the reception, and (9) the going-away corsage for the bride, which the groom may forget.

Figure 34-6. Wedding consultation room with fabric on the walls. (Courtesy, Frederick's Flowers, Souderton, Pa.)

Who Pays?

The costs of the wedding flowers and decorations are borne by the bride's parents and the bridegroom according to set standards and protocol in our society. The bride's parents will pay for all the bouquets of the bridesmaids, matron of honor, and attendants. They usually do not pay for the bride's bouquet. They will pay for all the flowers and decorations in the church, home, club, or wherever the service and the reception are held. The groom will pay for the bride's bouquet, bride's going-away corsage, corsages for the two mothers, and all boutonnieres for himself, best man, ushers, and the fathers. It is optional if he wishes to pay for the bouquets for the bridesmaids. The cost of the rehearsal dinner and its decorations are also the responsibility of the groom or his parents.

If the florist is servicing the complete wedding, he should provide the aisle cloth and see that it is placed at the correct time. He should provide the ushers with the bolts of ribbon or cording to be strung across the backs of the pews to prevent guests from leaving the church before the wedding party has left. He should see that the groom has his boutonniere, and that the attendants are carrying their bouquets properly. Often the florist will supervise the wedding party and start each one properly down the aisle.

Wedding Decorations

Wedding decorations can be very simple or very elaborate. They can range from one vase of flowers up to floral displays which cost thousands of dollars. It is impossible in this book to attempt to discuss all of the floral decorations which a florist might use for a wedding. There are many factors involved as well as unlimited possibilities of what a florist can do to decorate for a wedding. Several design books are available with excellent pictures of the decorations for all types and sizes of weddings.

[Author's note: The following wedding decorations were planned and executed by a student who has worked only part-time in two retail flower shops during the past year.]

Two 18-foot blue spruce were sprayed white and placed on either side of the altar. Next came two Hogarth arrangements of chartreuse spider mums, green gladoli, light green scotch broom, and 4 pounds of green grapes in each one. They stood 8 feet high on mahogany pedestals, with smilax around the base. Farther down were two smaller trees (6-foot) also sprayed white. On the altar rail and on every third pew were white vases with two dozen Seventeen roses and a cross of scotch broom sprayed white. White satin bows marked the remaining pews. The aisle was draped with 115 feet of rope made from trailing pine and covered with white cloth.

The bridal bouquet was four dozen white roses and three dozen stephanotis accented by pearl hearts and green velvet leaves. The matron of honor carried green cymbidiums and the two attendants carried white roses in silver bowls. The flower girl carried a basket of white roses and daisies.

For the reception, the tables were draped with white linen. The bridal table was on a 24-foot stage which was draped with white and hung with smilax. Natural blue spruce trees lined the stage. In the center of the bridal table was an arrangement of pink roses, white snapdragons, and two large pink satin hearts joined to two doves with ribbons to their beaks. On each end of the table were fancy cupid candelabra which were 5½ feet high and 4 feet wide which contained two dozen white snapdragons, three dozen pink Sensation roses, and white scotch broom. The cake table was draped in white and hung with smilax. At each peak of the smilax (25 peaks) were clusters of pink roses and bows. The tops of the bridal and cake tables were decorated with emerald foliage and pink roses.

Backgrounds

Backgrounds are very important to weddings and for any kind of decorations. Sometimes the florist uses the church background itself. Often, however, he will provide a background of greens, candles, and flowers. If the wedding is held elsewhere he may provide a trellis or lattice of greens, garlands, and flowers. Or he may decorate one end of the living room for the wedding. Whatever is used must enhance the flowers and the wedding party, but should not dominate the service. Greens and green plants are often used and may be fresh or permanent. They will help to make the flowers stand out. The flowers, greenery, and candles in the background should not be so high that they seem detached from, nor so low that they are obscured by, the wedding party. If the bride is wearing a colored gown, the flowers in the decoration should be in a similar color so that there will be a continuity of feeling. If she is in white, the central flowers in the background should be in white. The flanking flowers may be white or they may pick up the colors worn by the attendants.

At the reception, a background must also be provided for the flowers and the wedding party. Again greens are often used. If there is a special arrangement in the home or club, it might have a black background to make the flowers stand out to their fullest. Never put flowers in front of a window, tapestry, or flowered wallpaper. These are very poor backgrounds. A bold silhouette arrangement is the only exception to putting flowers in front of a window. Not only for weddings, but wherever flowers are displayed they should have the proper background to enhance their beauty rather than detract from it.

The handling and servicing of weddings can be profitable for retail florists if they plan them well and charge enough for each item to make a profit.

References

1. Anonymous. "Be a Bridal Specialist," *FTD News* (May 1966), pp. 25-26.
2. Anonymous. "Bridal Consultation Corners," *Teleflora Spirit* (May 1966), pp. 18-20.
3. Poetker, F. J. "Wedding Service Plus," *Florists' Review,* Vol. 130, No. 3314 (May 17, 1962), pp. 29-30, 66-67.

SPECIAL USES

Chapter 35

FOLIAGE PLANTS; PLANT ARRANGEMENTS

The sale and use of foliage plants has been increasing each year, and is now accounting for a good percentage of the retail florist business.

Consumer preference studies have definitely shown that consumers do want, and will use, foliage plants rather extensively if they can secure high quality plants, properly identified; with accurate information on their habit of growth, care, and use in the home. Much of this will be demanded by consumers to satisfy the increasing collector desires for various groups of plants. The main concern of a consumer is how long the plants will stay in good condition in his home, and how to take care of them.

The broad field of the use of decorative foliage plants has perhaps presented to every florist the greatest challenge in the entire history of the florist industry. The group of plants included in the classification "foliage plants" is made up, for the most part, from ornamental herbaceous perennials that are characteristic of the tropics. The majority of these plants are grown for their ornamental foliage, but some bear attractive flowers as well, according to Professor DeWerth.

The development of modern day architectural styles, along with the tendency of architects to show foliage plants in their sketches and plans of modern buildings to enhance and give life to the severe lines and cold, austere appearance of the rooms, has led to a revived interest in foliage plants. As a result, these plants are now featured more frequently than ever before by the architects and decorators in their plans for homes, offices, hotel lobbies, and public buildings. These developments have created a golden opportunity for the retail florist.

The increase in the apartment dwelling in urban areas has

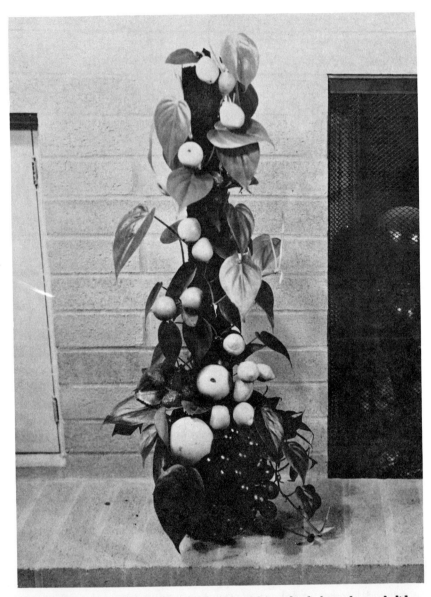

Figure 35-1. Pole philodendron decorated with artificial fruit for a holiday.

increased the demand for durable, less spectacular, small planters, and potted foliage plants.

One new concept of florist marketing—plants for every home—finds its most fertile field with foliage plants. Proper handling of this group of plants by the florist industry can continue to produce and develop a market of using a tremendous volume of plants.

When a florist does not have the necessary facilities or personnel to do more than small dish gardens in his own shop, it should be considered good business to refer customers to someone who is equipped to do this type of work, so that the popularity of these plants does not wane in the public eye. The use of several good large specimens for display can serve as samples, and plants can then be ordered from a grower for later delivery to the customer. The sale of plants by any florist carries with it definite obligations. This is especially true of the foliage plants. The florist should know the names and varieties and how to care for them, and be able to tell his customers how to handle them.

Care of Plants

Pot plants of all kinds provide lasting satisfaction to the customer, and they would receive a much more prominent place in the florist business if the average florist knew more about them and their proper care.

In general, the atmosphere of the average florist shop is too dry and too warm. This is especially true in the winter months in shops where artificial heat is used. Always keep the plants in the coolest, most humid part of the shop. When humidifiers are not used, the plants can be placed on gravel in pans, and the gravel is kept moist, without water standing in the pans. Syringing the plants twice a day is advantageous in freshening the foliage. A small conservatory or greenhouse is of tremendous help to the florist in keeping his foliage plants in good condition.

Improper watering causes a greater loss of foliage plants than any other factor, both in the shop and in the home. Customers frequently ask, "How much water does this plant need and how often should I water it?" There is no set rule that can be given, because humidity and temperature vary in each home. Never water by a rule of thumb, such as one cupful every day or every two days. *The best advice is to water the plant when necessary.*

Overwatering is as detrimental as underwatering. When the lowest leaves on the plant turn yellow and fall off, the plant has probably been overwatered. Never allow a plant to stand in water, and never water foliage plants with water colder than room temperature, if it can be avoided. In pots, containers, or plant beds that do not have drainage openings and are more or less waterproof, place a liberal layer of broken pots or gravel in the bottom for drainage.

The average florist should have a knowledge of soil and fertilizer requirements of foliage plants, because, he is more and more being called upon to replace the plants in interior plantings, and because customers who have had foliage plants for several months, usually seek the florists' advice on repotting and fertilizing. In most cases these plants would not benefit from either process. Plants in most interior plantings are ruined by the use of too much fertilizer. When the majority of the foliage plants used by florists today are not in good healthy condition, they usually need a more healthy growing environment and not fertilizer. When fertilizer is necessary, be certain it is never applied when the soil is dry or the leaves will be burned. A 2-1-2 ratio is most satisfactory, and a soluble fertilizer (liquid) has been found to be the best to apply. Foliage plants do not require frequent soil changes and repotting. They present their best appearance in containers which hold a limited amount of soil.

Every customer should be intelligently informed as to how to take care of the plants he selects and told truthfully what he may reasonably expect from them. Today, with the increased interest in foliage plants, because of the lack of plant knowledge on the part of architects and decorators, and a lack of know-how on the part of some retail florists, the customer is often oversold on the possibilities of these plants. This practice leads to dissatisfied customers and complaints rather than continued interest in these plants and repeated sales. Replanting or replacing every six months to a year is often recommended, depending on the species of plant.

Planters

One of the greatest difficulties for the retail florist is with the use of plants in large interior planting beds or boxes; yet this is a very lucrative field. These boxes or beds should never be filled with soil and then planted by knocking the plants out of the pots and planting them in these areas. By this method, they are always overwatered and roots fail to develop, because good drainage is impossible to obtain, and every person has a tendency to overwater rather than underwater. The best procedure to follow is to place a layer of gravel on the bottom of the bed or planter and then place the plants in on top of this layer, in the pots, and water them well. Fill the entire bed or box with a coarse grade vermiculite or peat moss, covering the pots about one inch above the rim. The material can be watered at regular intervals and the plants will remain in good condition for three or four times as long as when planted in soil. Individual plants are easily removed and re-

Figure 35-2. An artistically designed dish garden with a flower focal point.

placed without disturbing the other plants in the planter. This makes replacement easy, clean, and much less costly. It also provides for ready sales of blooming plants for special displays in these areas. Planters should be designed just as carefully as a flower arrangement. Planter arrangements can be sold only if florists make customers want them, by proper advertising and display.

There is no limit to the number of foliage plants that can be sold if the sale of this group of plants is undertaken as a business opportunity by the retail florist today. In addition to large interior planters and decorative specimens, almost all apartment dwellers have small foliage plants as part of their interior decorations. They will often bring them in to the florist every three or four months for replacement. Frequent replacements are often necessary because the plants are used in positions where proper light and temperature do not prevail.

Specific Plants

There are many plants which can be grown in our homes under various conditions. A partial list of the more common ones is shown in Table 35-1.

Many varieties of philodendrons, peperomias, dieffenbachias, dracaenas, crotons, caladiums, episcias, and bromeliads afford a fascinating range of plants that are easy to grow, and that are available to any indoor gardener who has a desire for improving home conditions by the use of living plants.

The leading colorful foliage plant today is the croton. It requires a warm temperature (60° F.), plenty of light, and moisture. At temperatures below 50° F., or in a dry atmosphere they will drop their lower leaves. They require light to retain their high color. A location in a bright east or south window is ideal. New leaves are usually green, but will color up as they reach maturity.

Another highly colored plant that lends itself well to interior decorations is the fancy-leaved caladium. It requires the same conditions necessary for crotons to keep its high color.

The episcias form a group of small plants that provide colorful effects for use on coffee tables, or in small areas that are in shady locations in the room. They do well in the same locations that are suitable for African Violets and are often misnamed the "red African Violet." They need filtered light and constant moisture. They should be fed with a liquid fertilizer once a month. They are trailing in nature, and must be kept warm like the crotons and

Table 35-1. A Selected List of Various Common House Plants Grown Mainly for Their Foliage.[1]

I. PLANTS THAT WILL GROW IN WATER AND SOIL

Scientific Names	Common Names
Aglaonema modestum	Chinese Evergreen
Coleus Blumei	Coleus
Crassula arborescens	Jade Plant
Dieffenbachia (all varieties)	Dumbcane
Hedera helix (all varieties)	English Ivy
Hemigraphis colorata	Hemigraphis
Nephthytis afzeli	Arrowhead
Philodendron cordatum	Philodendron
Sansevieria zeylanica	Sansevieria
Scindapsus aureus	Devil's Ivy
Tradescantia (all varieties)	Wandering Jew

II. PLANTS THAT WILL WITHSTAND MOST ADVERSE HOUSE CONDITIONS AND ABUSE

Aglaonema modestum	Chinese Evergreen
Aspidistra elatior	Iron Plant
Cissus rhombifolia	Grape Ivy
Crassula arborescens	Jade Plant
Dieffenbachia amoena	Dumbcane
Dracaena fragrans massangeana	Dracaena
Euphorbia mili	Crown of Thorns
Ficus elastica	Indian Rubber
Ficus pandurata	Fiddleleaf Fig
Hemigraphis colorata	Hemigraphis
Howea belmoreana	Kentia Palm
Nephthytis afzeli	Arrowhead
Pandanus veitchi	Screwpine
Paradises liliastrum	Paradise Lily
Peperomia obtusifolium	Peperomia
Philodendron cordatum	Philodendron
Sansevieria trifasciata laurenti	Golden Stripe Sansevieria
Sansevieria zeylanica	Snakeplant
Scindapsus aureus	Devil's Ivy

III. PLANTS THAT DO WELL UNDER AVERAGE HOME CONDITIONS

Acanthus montanus	Mountain Acanthus
Aechmea orlandiana	Aechmea
Araucaria excelsa	Norfolk Island Pine
Asparagus sprengeri	Sprenger Asparagus
Begonia semperflorens	Everblooming Begonia
Begonia ulmifolia	Elm-leaved Begonia
Beloperone guttata	Shrimp Plant
Caladium bicolor	Fancy-leaved Caladium
Cissus rhombifolia	Grape Ivy
Codiaeum variegatum	Croton
Cryptanthus acaulis	Cryptanthus
Cyrtomium falcatum	Holly Fern
Dieffenbachia bausei	Dumbcane

(continued)

Table 35-1, Cont.

Scientific Names	Common Names
Dieffenbachia picta	Dumbcane
Dieffenbachia picta Rudolph Roehrs	Dumbcane
Fatsia japonica	Japanese Fatsia
Fatshedera lizei	Botanical Wonder
Hedera helix (and varieties)	English Ivy
Nephthytis Emerald Gem	Arrowhead
Peperomia crassifolia	Leatherleaf Peperomia
Peperomia obtusifolia variegata	Variegated Peperomia
Peperomia sandersi	Watermelon Peperomia
Philodendron cordatum	Heartleaf Philodendron
Philodendron dubia	Splitleaf Philodendron
Philodendron giganteum	Giant Philodendron
Philodendron scandens	Redleaf Philodendron
Philodendron selloum	Philodendron
Philodendron tripartitum	Trileaf Philodendron
Philodendron wendlandi	Philodendron
Pilea involucrata	Artillery Plant
Piper nigrum	Black Pepper
Piper ornatum	Celebes Pepper
Polyscias filicifolia	Fernleaf Aralia
Polyscias paniculata	Jagged-leaf Aralia
Rhoeo discolor	Three Men in a Boat
Saxifraga sarmentosa	Strawberry Geranium
Schizmatoglottis picta	Painted Tongue
Spathyphllum clevelandi	White Anthurium
Vanilla Planifolium	Vanilla

IV. PLANTS WELL SUITED FOR LARGE TUBBED DECORATIVE SPECIMENS

Acanthus mollis	Artists Acanthus
Acanthus montanus	Mountain Acanthus
Alsophila australis	Australian Tree Fern
Codiaeum variegatum	Croton
Dieffenbachia amoena	Spotted Dumbcane
Fatshedera Japonica	Botanical Wonder
Ficus elastica variegata	Variegated India Rubber
Ficus pandurata	Fiddleleaf Fig
Monstera deliciosa	Cutleaf Philodendron
Pandanus veitchi	Screwpine
Philodendron dubia	Splitleaf Philodendron
Philodendron giganteum	Giant Philodendron
Philodendron selloum	Philodendron
Polyscias paniculata	Jagged-leaf Aralia
Schefflera actinophylla	Schefflera
Strelitzia reginae	Bird-of-Paradise

V. VINES AND TRAILING PLANTS FOR TOTEM POLES AND TRAINED PLANTS

Cissus antarctica	Kangaroo Vine
Cissus rhombifolia	Grape Ivy

(continued)

Table 35-1, Cont.

Scientific Names	Common Names
Ficus pumila	Creeping Fig
Hemigraphis colorata	Hemigraphis
Hoya carnosa	Wax Plant
Monstera deliciosa	Cutleaf Philodendron
Nephthytis afzeli	Arrowhead
Philodendrons (all climbing types)	Philodendron
Piper nigrum	Black Pepper
Piper ornatum	Celebes Pepper
Scindapsus aureus	Devil's Ivy
Scindapsus pictus	Painted Devil's Ivy
Stephanotis floribunda	Stephanotis

VI. LOW CREEPING PLANTS FOR GROUND COVERS IN INTERIOR PLANTING BOXES

Episcia cupreata	Episcia
Ficus pumila	Creeping Fig
Ficus radicans	Climbing Fig
Fittonia vershafelti Silvernerve	Silver Fittonia
Hedera helix Hahn's Star	Hahn's Star English Ivy
Helzine soleroi	Baby's Tears
Hemigraphis colorata	Hemigraphis
Pellionia daveauana	Pellionia
Philodendron cordatum	Heartleaf Philodendron
Pilea nummulariaefolia	Creeping Artillery Plant
Saxifraga sarmentosa	Strawberry Geranium
Scindapsus aureus	Devil's Ivy
Tradescantia	Wandering Jew

[1] Compiled from material by Professor DeWerth, Texas A. & M. University.

caladiums. The leaves will quickly discolor at temperatures of 50° F. or lower.

The most versatile foliage plants for use in interior decoration today are the many types of philodendron. The large leaved types are ideal for totem poles and trained specimens, such as hastatum, dubia, pertusum, and mandianum. The most trustworthy vine for interior decoration in any situation is the common Philodendron oxycardium (cordatum). Many philodendrons have interesting patterns such as lacineatum, panduraeforme, and pertusum.

Bromeliads are especially well adapted to present-day interior decoration. They have foliage of tough leathery nature and grow so that the leaves can hold water in their centers, and thus do not dry out readily, or are not as susceptible to low humidity as other foliage plants. The plants grow in light or shade, but the colors are more intense in sunny locations. There is a wide variation of color patterns in the foliage of the various species of Bromeliads including stripes, blotches, or patches. They actually present a sculptured appearance and are ideally suited to interior decoration where conditions are especially trying, or where the interior decoration is in the contemporary manner.

Foliage plants offer a diversion for even the most conservative person. Plants are important to everyday living, and perform a real function in modern interior decoration, and their care is so simple and easy, that no home, room, or building should be without one.

Specific suggestions for consumers are as follows: (1) air conditioning is not detrimental to foliage plants; (2) plants should not be placed in direct sunlight except for crotons and caladiums; (3) plants should be grown in an average temperature of 60° F. or above; (4) plants should be fertilized only lightly and infrequently; (5) trained plants such as totem poles and baskets should have the tips pinched occasionally if the proper shape is to be maintained; (6) when and if spindly weak growth occurs, it should be removed; and (7) overwatering is the greatest fault of most customers in taking care of foliage plants. They should only be watered when necessary.

Table 35-2 shows a list of cultural recommendations for florists and their customers so that they may combine plants in planters that have similar light and water requirements.

Table 35-2. A Selected List of Exotic Plants and Their Adaptability to Building Interiors.[1]

Key to Maintenance Requirements

Light Requirements:
   High—Bright Light or Full Sun:

Preference:	5000 to 8000 foot candles for average length of day.
Tolerance:	1000 to 2000 foot candles with 12 hour illumination.

   Medium—Diffused or Filtered Light:

Preference:	1000 to 5000 foot candles for average length of day.
Tolerance:	500 to 1000 foot candles with 12 hour illumination.
Simple Test:	When hand is passed over plants between them and light source, shadow cast by hand should be barely visible.

   Low—No Direct Light:

Preference:	100 to 500 foot candles for average length of day.
Tolerance:	50 to 100 foot candles with 12 hour illumination.

Soil Moisture Requirements:

Dry:	Soil should be dry for best growth; only occasional light waterings should be given to moisten soil thoroughly at three or four week intervals. Dry, sandy, well-drained soil should

(continued)

Table 35-2, Cont.

Key to Maintenance Requirements

	be used. Examples: Cacti and other succulents, peperomias, and sansevierias.
Moist:	Soil should be kept uniformly moist but never wet. Allow soil to become moderately dry before watering and then water thoroughly. Plants have delicate fine roots which will rot when soil is wet.
Wet:	Soil should never be allowed to become dry. Excellent drainage should be provided in containers so that air is available in soil. Water should never be allowed to stand in saucers under containers.

Plant Use Requirements:

Tub Plants:	Plants which develop into large specimens suitable for lobby decorations in public buildings or to be placed on floor in homes for interior decoration.
Vines:	Plants that require support such as trellises or totem poles or that can be used for ground covers in interior planter boxes or as trailing plants on ledges or over the edges of interior planter boxes.

MAINTENANCE REQUIREMENTS

NAME OF PLANT	Light			Soil Moisture			Uses		
	High	Med	Low	Dry	Moist	Wet	Tub	Vine	Small Planters
Aglaonema commutatum			x		x		x		x
Aglaonema modestum			x		x		x		x
Aloe variegata	x			x			x		x
Asplenium nidis			x			x	x		x
Begonia rex		x			x				x
Caladium, fancy-leaved		x			x		x		x
Cissus rhombifolia		x			x			x	
Codiaeum elegantissima	x				x		x		
Costus speciosa		x			x		x		
Crassula arborescens	x			x					x
Dieffenbachia amoena		x			x		x		
Dieffenbachia picta		x			x		x		
Dracaena warnecki		x			x		x		
Dracaena godseffiana		x			x				x
Dracaena marginata		x			x		x		x
Dracaena sanderiana		x			x				x
Euphorbia mili	x			x			x		x
Fatshedera lizei	x				x		x		x
Ficus benghalensis		x			x		x		
Ficus elastica		x			x		x		
Ficus elastica decora		x			x		x		
Ficus elastica variegata		x			x		x		
Ficus pandurata		x			x		x		

(*continued*)

Table 35-2, Cont.

NAME OF PLANT	Light			Soil Moisture			Uses		
	High	Med	Low	Dry	Moist	Wet	Tub	Vine	Small Planters
Hedera helix	x				x			x	x
Hedera helix Hahn's Self Branching	x				x			x	x
Hibiscus rosa-sinensis cooperi	x				x		x		x
Hoya carnosa	x			x			x	x	x
Hoya carnosa variegata	x			x			x	x	x
Kalanchoe tomentosa	x			x					x
Pandanus veitchii		x		x			x		
Peperomia obtusifolia		x		x					x
Peperomia obtusifolia variegata		x		x					x
Peperomia sandersi		x		x					x
Philodendron cordatum		x			x		x	x	
Philodendron dubia		x			x		x	x	
Philodendron erubescens		x			x		x	x	
Philodendron hastatum		x			x		x	x	
Philodendron panduriforme		x			x		x	x	
Piper ornatum		x			x		x	x	x
Polyscias paniculata		x			x		x		
Rhoeo Discolor	x			x			x		x
Sansevieria trifaciata Hahni	x			x					x
Sansevieria trifaciata laurenti	x			x			x		x
Schefflera actinophylla		x		x			x		-
Scindapsus aureus		x		x			x	x	x
Syngonium albo-lineata		x			x		x	x	x
Syngonium Green Gold		x			x		x	x	x
Syngonium wendlandi		x			x		x	x	x
Syngonium White Gold		x			x			x	x

[1] Professor A. F. DeWerth, Texas A. & M. University.

Water Gardens

Planter arrangements are at home anywhere; in private homes, public rooms, lobbies, and hospitals, and always provide an interesting decorative accent. Planter arrangements are interesting only in proportion to the care taken by the designer. Too often a dish garden may be dull and lifeless without any real design to it. A water garden is a dish garden in which the plants are growing in water, not soil. They are designed and not just planted. The same principles of design apply in designing a water garden as apply in flower arranging. An attractive water garden arrangement is a classical symmetrical or asymmetrical triangle styled out of plant materials in water. It is done in a shallow container which would not hold enough soil for growing the plants, but is perfect when the plants are attached to a pin holder set in water. By using a pin holder and just enough water to cover the root system of the foliage plants used, a graceful, stately design can be achieved. Plants should be selected in proportion to the size and shape of the container, and for a variety of shades of greens.

Figure 35-3. A water garden designed by Gil Whitten, Montclair, N. J.

Water gardens have the advantage of needing very little care, less light than is required for the same plants if planted in soil, and the possibility of combining plants that like different types of soil and environment, but will thrive together in water.

Bamboo placemats make an interesting background for either dish gardens or water gardens which can be augmented by a Chinese figurine to carry out an Oriental motif.

Planter Arrangements

Incorporation of fresh flowers into a planter arrangement adds continuing interest as well as color. When the flowers in water tubes of a dish garden or water garden have passed their prime, the design may look unfinished until the owner replaces the flowers with fresh blooms. This fact can be pointed out to the customer when the arrangement is sold, with the suggestion that the customer may wish to arrange for replacements on a definite basis with the florist. This is an excellent way to get repeat business, or see that the customer will come into the shop each week.

Seventy-five million dollars is the average amount spent each year on plants to decorate the homes of America according to 1960 figures. This is not a small amount of money to add to the gross income for flowers, and most of it can go to retail florists if they will promote these sales and compete favorably with variety and five-and-ten cent stores. The majority of florists who handle foliage plants must make them appealing to the customer. The display of foliage plants in florist shops must be attractive. Displaying pot plants that look as good or better than those of a competitor is not enough if the florist is to get a fair share of the $75 million mentioned previously. Customers should be shown all the places in the home where foliage plants, planters, and water gardens can be used. These include the coffee table, mantel, centerpieces, bookcase, television, side tables, and even on the floor or hearth. The modern home provides countless places where planter arrangements, styled specifically for a known location, can serve a long-lived purpose in the decorative scheme.

A planter arrangement should be planned as carefully as a cut flower arrangement. It needs line, rhythm, color, and mass. Texture makes a contribution to one or more of these design elements. Shape and texture of foliages is the first consideration in planning an arrangement for a given planter. The angularity of a rectangular planter suggests that the major elements in the plant groupings should be somewhat curved for contrast.

Designed for specific locations, planters take on a look of individual personality and become a contributing factor in home décor. Two different types of philodendron might be accented with pine cone roses—made simply by slicing pine cones and giving them wire stems. This design would complement a den, especially if its walls are pine-paneled and the room needs a touch of green.

A small flowering plant for a lamp table will leave the table surface uncrowded, free for its purpose of holding accessories and whatever falls onto it. A kitchen arrangement can be backed with a metal tray and accented with a gay reclining pixie. For a child's room a pedestal bowl planted with a philodendron on a totem pole, accented with fresh or permanent flowers and gay little elves will amuse the small fry.

Plants have become an integral part of the decorator's plan. They can no longer be assembled without thought, either for the design picture they create, nor for the contribution they make to home décor. Both plants and containers should be chosen to complement their ultimate home location.

Bonsai trees are a real money-maker for many retail florists. Also many retail florists feel that the real profit in this field is in selling accessories such as jardenieres, tubs, plant stands, bark, totem poles, fertilizers, and other materials.

The guarantee policy must be made clear so that the customer will understand it.

Another area where the retail florist can make a profit is in the servicing of foliage plants in the home and places of business. He must figure his costs on this and charge enough to make a profit.

Foliage Cleaners

Foliage plant cleaners are used by all retail florists to shine the leaves of foliage plants before they are sent out to the customer or used for decorations. There are many commercial plant cleaning compounds on the market today which are used by the retail florists and housewives to give a shine and gloss to the leaves of foliage plants. Many of the retail florists are aware of the aesthetic value of these materials, but few know of their effect on plant growth.

Experiments were conducted at The Pennsylvania State University during 1962 and 1964 on philodendron cordatum and philodendron pertusum plants using six different commercial plant cleaning compounds on the plants. Some plants were left uncleaned for the period of the test and others were cleaned with plain water. The materials were used on the plants at two week and four week intervals. Data taken at the start of the experiment included the weight of the pot and plant, number of leaves, number of growing tips, total length of growing shoots on cordatum, and height of plant on pertusum. The plants were double potted in a second pot of peat moss and watered as needed. They were fertilized every six weeks with a 20-20-20 liquid fertilizer applied at the rate of one tablespoon per gallon of water. Applications of the materials were made for nine months, and then further data taken on each plant at the end of the experiment. Seven different commercial products were used. Some of the materials were in liquid form, some in a spray, and some in an aerosol form. Several caused quite a bit of burning at the margins of the leaves. Most

Figure 35-4. Gallery display of 37 different foliage plants for home use. (Courtesy, "EXOTICA, Pictorial Cyclopedia of Exotic Plants," Roehrs Co., Rutherford, N. J.)

of the materials reduced the growth of the plants. *For best growth, it is still best to use water,* although they will not have the attractive shine as with a commercial material. One material gave a good shine without any reduction in growth, and several gave a good shine but with a slight burning of the leaves. It is best for florists to try the various materials themselves to find which are best for their plants. Applications every two weeks are too often and not recommended. Aerosols and sprays as a general rule result in more injury than materials put on by hand.

Conclusion

Since the sale of foliage plants is increasing each year, every florist must handle them. It is more important than ever before for florists to learn how to use them and take care of them properly so that they can pass the information on to their customers. Foliage plants play a large part in the commercial account business discussed in Chapter 36.

References

1. DeWerth, A. F. "Trends in Foliage Plant Production and Marketing," *Southern Florist and Nurseryman* (March 27, 1964), p. 22.
2. Pfahl, P. B., J. W. Mastalerz, and E. McGary. "Plant Cleaning Compounds Affect Growth of Foliage Plants," Pennsylvania Retail Florists Bulletin No. 67 (October-November 1963), pp. 7-8.

Chapter 36

COMMERCIAL ACCOUNTS

One of the greatest single potential areas for increasing the florist's business lies in the commercial field. Commercial accounts form a good year-round backbone for the retail florist business. The potential is great, since orders can be expected continuously. The orders are usually large, payments are assured, and employees of the firm may become customers too.

Commercial accounts can be handled on a contract basis, whereby the florist will supply flowers for offices, reception rooms, and customers of the firm on a weekly or monthly basis. Also important with commercial accounts is the fact that these accounts come to the florist for anniversary, gifts, openings, and other special occasions. Often the best way to approach this type of business is through the secretaries who do the ordering for their bosses. Commercial accounts do not develop without initiative on the part of the florist.

Types of Accounts

In interviewing florists across the nation who have had success with business accounts, certain businesses and professions have proved especially profitable according to an FTD survey, shown in Table 36-1.

Development

To develop commercial accounts, the florist must build up a wide circle of acquaintances. This refers to the owner of the firm plus his associates. It will help if the florist becomes an active member in various clubs such as Lions, Elks, Optomist, Kiwanis, Toastmasters, and the Chamber of Commerce. He should attend the meetings, participate, and wear a boutonniere. Participation in

Table 36-1. FTD Survey of Commercial Accounts.

BUSINESS	PRIMARY USE	OTHER USES
Banks	Display	Gifts to patrons, employee relations, and bank functions
Insurance companies	Gifts to customers	Hospital arrangements and office display
Savings & loan companies	Display	Employee relations
Department stores	Holiday display	Employee relations
Stock brokerages	Lobby arrangement	Gifts to clients
Specialty retailers	Gifts to customers	Holiday display
Oil companies	Gifts to customers	Employee relations and office functions
Real estate brokers	Gifts to customers	Local display
Automobile dealers	Showroom display	Special promotion gifts
Photo studios	Photo backgrounds	Studio decorations
Dairies	Personnel remembrances	Employee functions
Accounting firms	Gifts to clients	Office decorations

various community fund-raising drives is also a good way to become acquainted with future business prospects. The more people a florist knows, the more opportunity he will have to add business firms to his list of customers.

There are some fairly substantial advantages to doing business at a commercial level. For example, in most companies people who make the flower purchases or specify who gets the order, always are willing to spend the company's money more freely than they are their own money. The commercial accounts tend to be for large-sized orders as a general rule. Where a buying habit has been established there seems to be a greater freedom in the use of flowers, and a higher frequency of purchase. Another advantage of the commercial account is that there are many more occasions in business, with its many relationships, for dignifying a remembrance or business sympathy with a bouquet, than the average person finds in his own life.

There are drawbacks too in developing commercial accounts. One of these is that selling one of these accounts can be somewhat difficult. In a large company there may be anywhere from 30 to 600 executives or secretaries who must be sifted through to find out who has the authority to purchase flowers. Second, the tendency to regard floral purchases as something that someone has to take care of and is just a chore, makes it difficult. Third, since business relations are ephemeral and memories short, the florist has to keep after the contact on a fairly regular basis to be sure he does not lose the contact. Finally, the average sale requires repeated contact if the sale is to be consummated. It is often not signed on the first attempt.

Most florists have the opinion that commercial accounts will make them rich overnight and solve most of their financial worries. Commercial flower business has exciting possibilities but is in itself not the answer to business success according to Herb Mitchell. In many cities, there is not enough commercial flower business to support a profitable flower shop without proper emphasis in other fields of business. Not all retailers are capable of handling commercial accounts.

Florists should realize that commercial buyers are hammered at day and night by members of other industries which compete with flower sales. *Sales Management Magazine* surveyed 33,000 of its subscribers to find out their gift preferences for Christmas, 1965. Flowers were not even listed in the 20 items which businessmen spend money on for their gifts. To give an idea of the size

of this business, this particular survey indicated that more than
378,000 turkeys were given to customers and employees. One company gave away 8,100 transistor radios, another 3,900 pen and
pencil sets, and still a third gave 3,200 blankets. (How much sentiment is attached to a radio or blanket?)

A good commercial account is a steady month-in and month-
out buyer. In addition, commercial accounts tend to generate other
consumer business, as many employees buy flowers at the same
place as the company does.

Basically there are four important points in developing commercial accounts according to Herb Mitchell: finding accounts,
catching accounts, selling accounts, and keeping accounts.

Finding Accounts

A florist must determine where accounts can be found. He
should develop a mailing list of commercial flower buyers using
the following four steps: (1) secure a list of manufacturers in the
area from the Chamber of Commerce, (2) add to the list all the
professional people in the area from the yellow pages of the phone
book, (3) add all the retailers in the area, and (4) check the city
directory, and select other firms which offer a sales potential. This
list will be much too big to use, so a system of selection must
be set up by the florist so that his final mailing list is one which
he can use to get the desired return on his advertising and promotion budget for these accounts.

After the firms have been selected, it is important to find the
proper name to whom the contact is sent. The best method is
by asking. A phone call will give you the name of the person
who makes the final decision on flower purchases. Often the head
man does not do this, but he influences the purchases. So, he should
be cultivated along with the other purchaser. Often a flower sent
to the secretary will pave the way for an interview. Thus, the
first step in developing profitable commercial business is finding
the market, and then isolating the potential buyers by a realistic
mailing list.

Catching Accounts

The second step is catching the account, and this can be done
only when advertising really catches their attention and precipi-
tates a positive, remembered reaction. It must be repeated many

times. The advertisement must have a sharp impact on the potential customer. It must have a quality of drama and stand out in any crowd. The reader must remember the product being advertised and the florist advertising it. Color is one of the best attention-getters a florist has at his fingertips to use. Size and shape of the direct mail advertising is also important. The ad must be intriguing so that it will successfully compete with the some 560 advertisements which the average American sees in one day. He may notice 76, out of which 12 will make an impression, and only 9 will make a positive impression. Consistent repetition is necessary before the contract will be signed for the commercial account. Personal contact is needed as a follow-up to the advertising campaign.

Selling Accounts

There isn't as much difference in selling commercial accounts by advertising as by person-to-person as some people think. However, one variance is extremely important and never should be overlooked. That is, that selling by advertising must be accomplished fast and with more accuracy. A person-to-person salesman has the advantage of watching the person to whom he is talking. Advertising which convinces, is that which gives assurance with persuasiveness. Any commercial buyer who would purchase a food item, gadget, or liquor for a gift is a likely prospect for a flower gift. To reach this market, a florist must compete advertisingwise and must present his merchandise with more conviction than the others, and also must compete pricewise. Many commercial buyers will spend money but they are not extravagant. Of the dollars spent for business gifts at Christmas one year (over 1.5 billion), about 70 per cent of these dollars were spent on gifts with a price tag of $5 or under. To perk up commercial accounts try including the firm's product or a replica of it in the floral design.

Keeping Accounts

The most important part of any advertising program is the function of keeping accounts sold. The major reason customers change florists is not dissatisfaction in service or price, but because they feel *neglected*. If a florist fails to let his customers know they are needed and appreciated, he is omitting one of the most important aspects of the advertising cycle. Buyers will spread their business to many florists, unless there is contact constantly from one particular florist who gives good service. Many firms buy from more than one florist and spread their business around simply because they said they never heard from their florist except when they were sent a bill at the first of the month. Keeping in constant contact through advertising is more important in commercial accounts than with any other type of customer.

There are several important steps to consider in planning an advertising program which will keep commercial accounts sold: (1) Plan a consistent advertising campaign with at least four exposures during a 12-month period which ask for the business. (2) Acknowledge all new accounts promptly and preferably in person either by a visit or by phone. (3) Keep in periodic touch with a buyer customer. (4) Once a year, send a personal thank-you letter to every commercial account who has made a purchase during the year. (5) Watch the accounts which fall into inactivity and find out why. (6) Become known, by joining and participating in civic organizations, clubs, and drives.

Harry Lazier has presented to florists who have never tried commercial accounts, a set of eight simple steps to follow to set up a procedure for getting started in developing commercial accounts. "Start small, and grow: (1) Advertise in the yellow pages of the phone book for business accounts, because many buyers of flowers for a business have never ordered them before. (2) Make up a list of the most desirable commercial accounts which are within walking distance from the shop. Get the name of the president of each firm. (3) Go to the business address and ask for the president's secretary. (4) Explain your florist business to the secretary and ask her for the name of the person who was specifically entrusted with the responsibility for commercial flower orders. (5) Ask to see the person who buys flowers for these orders if it is not the secretary. Explain your business to that person, and tell him how you are especially equipped to handle the orders from his firm. Tell the person that you would like to have his business, and hope he will call on you for the next order of flowers. (6) Make sure that the purchasers of flowers in this firm will remember you as the florist. Send a small bouquet and a thank-you note for the time given, to the person who does the buying. Also send the president's secretary a few flowers. (7) If the florist does not get the order, then he should call back within a month and do this for six months before giving up and turning his attention to another account. (8) The final point is that after the florist has a commercial account set up on the books, set up a specific date at least once a year to call back personally on the commercial account to check on the fact that the same person was still placing the orders, that everybody was happy, and to mention any new services which the florist has to offer."

It is important to remember that a retail florist should go after commercial accounts only if he has the ambition, energy, and facilities to do a good job. Perseverance is a must when it comes to cultivating commercial accounts, but they can be very rewarding. When a florist serves commercial accounts he must provide service and lots of it.

If a florist has a contract for supplying foliage plants to offices, for bank and hotel lobbies, and for restaurants, it is to the florist's advantage that the plants be in good condition all the time. They need professional care and the retail florist is just the one to give them that care. The florist does not just deliver an order to a commercial account and forget about it. Many florists have set up contracts with banks, hotels, businessmen, and others to install, replace, and maintain decorations on a yearly basis. It is good business and brings in a steady revenue all year. Some decorations, such as for Christmas, may be on a bid basis. A florist should not be reluctant to bid on a decorating job and include a fair profit. He should prepare a bid to give several alternatives, and tell the customer exactly what he will get for his money. It may not be the lowest bid that gets the job. The important factor in bidding on these jobs is not price, but what will be done and how well it will look. Be sure to include the time involved in selling, creating, and installing the job as well as the cost of materials.

Many florists that have had good commercial accounts have lost them because they have taken them for granted and not given the account top quality and good design.

Here is a new angle to the working of commercial accounts— one florist reports that two of his accounts are local banks and they have asked him to notify them when there is a store or business opening. The local medical society also has the florist call the secretary when he learns of a member's illness, or a death in a member's family.

Commercial accounts generally fall into three categories: office and lobby decorations, employee's gifts, and customer's gifts. One or all of them can be cultivated by the florist who has the initiative, ambition, energy, and the facilities to handle these accounts properly.

Office Landscaping

A new concept in commercial accounts using foliage plants is office landscaping. Traffic flow and privacy are achieved by means of plants and planters as screens. Mr. Everett Conklin has divided large spaces into small offices through the use of foliage plants alone in some new and large New York buildings. The potential in this area is tremendous.

Reference

1. Mitchell, H. "Commercial Accounts," *Florists' Review*, Vol. 138, No. 3572 (May 12, 1966), pp. 17, 43-46.
2. Conklin, Everett. *A Guide to Interior Planting*, Everett Conklin and Co., Inc. (1970), 25 pp.

Chapter 37

CARE OF CUT FLOWERS; KEEPING QUALITY; FOAMS

The life of a cut flower is extremely important to the retail florist, and to the customer. Flowers are a luxury item with a relatively short life, and are considered carefully before being purchased. All of our customers are aware of the fact that flowers will only last a relatively short time, and most of them do not know how to make them last longer. Many customers do not know how to properly care for their cut flowers, and it is up to the retail florist to educate them.

The short vase life of cut flowers could be one of the most important reasons for the florists' seeming inability to develop an appreciable home use market in the United States. Consumer surveys have often reported that one reason people do not buy fresh flowers for home decorations more frequently is "they last such a short time." Many people are buying the permanent flowers for the home, not because they are cheap, because any florist knows that the cost of a good polyethylene flower is not low, but because they last longer.

Keeping Quality

The keeping quality of cut flowers is affected by the proper handling of the product from the grower to the customer. The way the cut flowers are grown in the greenhouse, along with various environmental and cultural conditions, will affect the life of the cut flower. The treatment and time involved in getting the cut flower to the consumer will affect its life. It must be moved quickly, and handled properly. There are many factors which affect the keeping quality of cut flowers, but we are going to discuss mainly the ones concerning the retail florist and the customer.

The most important factor determining cut flower life in the home is the ability of the flower to maintain its turgidity, and so it must be put in water as soon as possible.

The quality of the flower is important to the retail florist as well as to the consumer. There are various factors which the florist looks for in flower quality such as: (1) freshness or keeping life of the flower; (2) flower color, intensity, fragrance, shape of the bud, petals, size, and individual flower area; (3) number of florets, spacing, and floret drop in the flower spike; (4) stem length, stiffness, brittleness, and straightness; and (5) perfection and glossiness of the foliage.

There are certain practices which should be followed by all florists and all segments of the industry if the florist is to sell flowers that will last, according to Dr. Marlin Rogers.

General Practices for All Florists

1. Move flowers as quickly as possible from the greenhouse to the living room.

2. Use lower refrigerator temperatures. Most cut flowers should be stored at temperatures between 35° and 40° F. Orchids and gladioli, however, should not be stored below 40° F. There is a lot of deterioration of flowers in storage and this can be kept to a minimum if they are stored as close to 35° F. as possible. Deterioration consists in the following: opening of the flower which reduces its quality, loss of food during respiration which reduces the keeping life of the flower, development of mold which clogs the water-conducting cells, ethylene injury to certain flowers, and fading of the color of certain flowers.

3. Floral preservatives should be used universally by the grower, wholesaler, retailer, and consumer. There are several commercial preparations on the market today including Floralife, Petalife, Morlife, Roselife, Burpees Everbloom, Oasis preservative, and others. Dr. John Mastalerz, The Pennsylvania State University, has shown that the life of some cut flowers can be increased up to 200 per cent by the continuous use of preservatives in the water from the cutting bench to the consumer. Research at Ohio State University has shown that cut carnations will last up to 18 days in a certain preservative solution as compared to 6 or 7 days in plain water. This was accomplished by using the preservative constantly from the time the flower was cut until it died. Chemicals such as QC, CCC, B-Nine, ethylene oxide, nitrogen, sugar plus hydrazene sul-

fate, benzidine, and maleic acid have been studied for their effects on the keeping life of cut flowers. Not all of these materials are effective on all flowers. Some of these are still in the experimental stage. Controlled atmospheres for storing flowers have also been conducted with decreased oxygen and increased carbon dioxide to make cut flowers last longer, but the dosages are so critical that no practical application can be given at this time.

4. Flower vases should be washed after each use. Careful cleaning of the vases gets rid of the micro-organisms that plug the ends of flower stems, and result in premature wilting and collapse of the cut flower.

5. Handle flowers carefully to avoid bruising. Flowers should not be jammed into storage vases or shipping boxes.

6. Watch for ethylene injury from gas leaks, fruits (apples, bananas, avocados, lemons) stored in the refrigerator, or close packing with flowers like callas and peonies which emit ethylene. Roses will turn blue and lose their petals, carnations go to sleep, snapdragons lose their florets, and tulips lose their petals if too much ethylene is present.

7. Throw out diseased material quickly, and keep the refrigerator clean. Botrytis fungus (gray mold) on carnation and rose petals can spread rapidly at low storage temperatures and high humidity.

8. Use hot water or a hot floral preservative solution to revive badly wilted flowers. Water at 100° to 110° F. is best.

Practices for Retailers

1. In the final step before selling flowers, the retailer should take a good look at the way he and his employees handle flowers. Every time someone handles flowers roughly, and bruises them, he reduces their potential keeping quality.

2. Cut the stem end of all flowers as they arrive in the shop and place immediately in hot water to which has been added a preservative.

3. It is the obligation of the retail florist to instruct his customers in the best ways to care for their flowers to give long-lasting satisfaction. The following steps are recommended to the customer to make cut flowers last as long as possible: (a) Cut one-half inch from the bottom end of the stem. Make a slanting cut with a sharp knife. This will avoid crushing the water-conducting cells and will quicken the intake of water. (b) Remove all leaves and thorns

which will be under water in the container. (c) Use a clean vase or container. (d) Harden the flowers by placing the cut stems in hot water (100° to 110° F.) and placing the container of flowers in a cool place for two hours. (e) Use a chemical preservative in the water which may be obtained from a local florist. (f) Add water daily to the arrangement. (g) Do not place the flowers in the direct sunlight, in a draft, or near a radiator. (h) Put the vase of flowers in a cool place overnight. Even down on the floor will help. (i) Consult a local retail florist for information on the best way to make cut flowers last longer.

4. Be careful in the use of foam products for flower support. Be sure there is room in the container to add water after the flower arrangement arrives at the consumer's home. Include with each foam arrangement an "Add Water Daily" tag.

5. Use floral preservatives for all flowers sent out of the shop. The material should be in all vases, baskets, papier-mâché, and foams in containers. Even loose cut flowers in a box should have a small package of preservative included.

6. Use flower wax on those flowers most subject to early wilting, particularly those flowers in make-up work which are not in water.

7. Sear or singe the stem end of latex-exuding flowers before arranging them.

8. Move the flowers as rapidly as possible from the florist shop into the hands of the customer.

Rose Research

Research at Michigan State University has indicated that rose vase-life can be considerably extended, and that virtually all premature wilting of cut roses can be eliminated according to Professor Paul Krone.

Best results are dependent on proper care and handling from the time the rose is cut until it dies of old age in the customer's home. Professor Krone offers the following specific recommendations for handling roses at the retail store: "(1) Upon receipt of the roses, cut the stems with a sharp knife. (2) Remove the lower leaves and place roses in warm water (100° F.) to which a good preservative has been added. (3) Condition all roses in the refrigerator for 4 to 6 hours at 35° to 45° F. (4) Do not cut through the bark when removing thorns or leaves. A quick, safe, and easy way of removing leaves and thorns is to use a glove or cloth on the hand for protection and simply pull it down over the stem. (5) Do not scrape the bark. This procedure will not increase the water up-take and may cause damage by cutting through the water-conducting cells. (6) Do not crush the ends of the stems. This practice can reduce the vase life of the flowers in water by as much as 2.9 days. (7) Use a good preservative in the water both in the refrigerator cans and particularly in vases in which roses are arranged. (8) If foam materials are used be sure the foam is thoroughly soaked, has a preservative, and be sure there is room for the customer to add water every day to the arrangement."

Air Purifiers

There are several air purifiers and ozone machines on the market today for retail florists to use in their storage and display refrigerators. These help to keep down the fungus growth and gray mold in the refrigerator cans. It keeps these cans cleaner much longer than would otherwise occur and some florists have reported a longer life to their flowers. Some damage has occurred, especially to carnations, so the retail florist must experiment with the proper amount of material to be injected into his size refrigerator. Some wholesalers are also using these machines and reporting the air is fresher and the flowers seem to stay fresher, last longer, and look brighter.

Foam Materials

There are many foam materials on the market today being used by retail florists to make designing easier and faster. Some of these materials seem to reduce the keeping life of some of the cut flowers. Improvements have been made in the past few years so that this condition has changed for the better. Foams with preservatives added will now increase the keeping life of cut flowers over foams without a preservative. Recent research at The Pennsylvania State University and Michigan State University has shown that cut flowers last almost as long in *certain* foams with preservatives as in water. However, flowers still last the longest in water plus a preservative. Some of the newer foams have a preservative in them and are very good. Tests have been conducted on materials such as Oasis, Hydrofoam, Jiffy, Quickee, Fill Fast Foam, Camelet, Niagara, and Sno-Pak.

In general, the following recommendations can be made when cut flowers are used in the foam materials according to Professor Krone:

1. Be sure that the block of foam is thoroughly saturated.

2. Change the water frequently in the container in which the foam is soaked.

3. Submerge the block in water containing a preservative or be sure there is a reservoir of preservative water in the container.

4. Keep the cut ends of the flower stems below the water level.

5. Provide a reservoir of water in the container.

6. Insert the foam so that water can be easily added to the reservoir. Do not completely fill the container nor jam it in tightly, unless you provide a V-notch along the side where water can be added.

7. Do not push the cut ends of the stems through the block of foam.

8. Do not move the stems after inserting. If the stems are pulled back an inch, the cut end of the stem is not in contact with the water that is necessary for the survival of the flower.

9. Soak the block of foam in a preservative before using.

10. Instruct all customers to keep the reservoir filled with water at all times.

Packaging

The proper packaging, wrapping, and delivery of plants and flowers are closely related to the keeping quality of cut flowers and pot plants. The retail florist must make sure that the flowers are wrapped and packaged so that bruising does not occur. Cut flowers, floral designs, and plants should all be wrapped properly so that damage from temperature and handling is kept to a minimum. They should be delivered in the same excellent condition as when they left the shop. All of these things will insure the keeping quality of the flowers and result in greater customer satisfaction.

The repeat business in the florist industry is based on quality flowers and materials. The real criterion for quality is how the flowers look to the customers, and how well they last in the hands of the customer. There are other qualities that are important to the retailer such as color, flower spacing, number of florets, length and strength of stem, and other factors, but freshness and the ability to last as long as possible are the main items. It is up to everyone in the florist industry to handle the flowers properly and quickly from the greenhouse to the home. It is the obligation of the retail florist to use only fresh flowers and to tell his customers how to take care of them to make them last longer. This is essential if we are to develop the home market for flowers as mentioned in Chapter 20 to help offset the drop in funeral flower orders.

References

1. Asen, A., C. S. Parsons, and N. W. Stuart. "Controlled Atmosphere for Storing Flowers," *The Exchange,* Vol. 141, No. 24 (June 13, 1964), pp. 30, 45, 54.
2. Halvey, A. H. and S. H. Wittwer. "CCC, B-Nine," *Florists' and Nursery Exchange,* Vol. 143, No. 17 (April 24, 1965), pp. 28-29.
3. Krone, P. R. "Research Leads to Improved Vase Life of Roses," *FTD News* (June 1966), pp. 25-27.
4. Larsen, F. E. and J. Scholes. "Vase Life and Flower Size of Cut Carnations Improved with Chemicals," *Florists' Review,* Vol. 137, No. 3559 (February 10, 1966), pp. 29-30.
5. Sager, W., C. Schroeder, and P. Krone. "Proper Use of Foam Materials Extends Life," Michigan State Florists Association Bulletin No. 405 (November 1964), p. 12.
6. Tayama, H. K. "Keeping Quality of Carnations," Ohio Florists Association Bulletin No. 431 (September 1965), p. 3.

Chapter 38

HOLIDAY PREPARATIONS

There are seven major florists' holidays in the retail industry that are important. These are not holidays from work, but holidays when the retail florist works harder than ever. It is the time when he does the largest volume of business in the shortest possible time. For this reason, the florist must plan and manage carefully so that a large profit can be realized from these holidays. This is where many florists make up for the slack summer months which for many florists are red months on the books. The large volume of business at a holiday is where the best profit can be realized in the retail florist shop. The holidays may be just one day of sales, or extend for a week or more. The seven major holidays are: Christmas, Easter, Memorial Day, Mother's Day, New Years, St. Valentine's Day, and Thanksgiving.

Lesser holidays which are more important for some florists than others are: St. Patrick's Day, Halloween, patriotic holidays, Washington's Birthday, Lincoln's Birthday, Secretary's Day, and Sweetest Day.

Whether the holiday be for 1 day or for 10 days it must be planned in advance. The florist should get his staff together and prepare a work schedule showing specific operations and activities for which each person is responsible. This should be posted on the wall ahead of time with the expected hours of work, so that employees can make their plans accordingly.

Specific Holidays

Let's take a look at each of the seven major holidays to become familiar with the length of the holiday and some of the materials to be sold.

1. **Christmas.** Planning for this holiday, which is the biggest of the year, begins in the summer when novelty items are ordered

and permanent Christmas arrangements can be made up during the employees' spare time, wrapped in plastic, and stored away for the holiday. The rush of Christmas business lasts for about two weeks from the 10th to the 24th of December when orders are taken; and plants, flowers, greens, wreaths, and door swags are sold. The business consists of gifts and home decorations. Many greens are sold and used in designs including holly, pine, spruce, hemlock, cedar, juniper, boxwood, mistletoe, fir, and others. Wreaths, both fresh and permanent, are in demand as well as all types of fresh and permanent door swags. Cut flowers and pot plants are sold in the proportion of about 50-50. Pot plants sold at Christmas will be poinsettias, cyclamen, gloxinia, begonia, azaleas, Christmas cherries, kalanchoe, Christmas peppers, and pot mums. Cut flowers which are most popular are roses, carnations, gladioli, and snap-dragons. Other plants and flowers are sold in lesser amounts. Many styrofoam and other novelties are sold along with permanent arrangements. Ribbons and bows are sold in large quantities, and the retail florist should add an extra charge of 50¢ to $1.00 for tying

Figure 38-1. An attractive display of Christmas arrangements. (Courtesy, Buning The Florist, Fort Lauderdale, Fla.)

the bow for the customer. All work should be finished and delivered by the evening of the 24th. Pot plants are usually delivered on the 22nd and 23rd. Cemetery wreaths are placed early.

2. **Easter.** Easter is usually the second biggest florist holiday although in some areas of the country it has been replaced in volume by Memorial Day. Easter is a rush during the week from

Figure 38-2. Preparing a large display area for Easter. (Courtesy, King Floral Co., Forty Fort, Pa.)

Palm Sunday until Easter Sunday with the biggest day on Easter Saturday. Florists must remain open on Easter Sunday for last minute corsages and will-call orders. The weather on Easter Saturday and Sunday will affect the volume of sales. Easter business is mostly corsages and pot plants with some orders for cut flowers. Corsages will be orchids, cymbidiums, roses, carnations, gardenias, and camellias. Cut flowers include roses, carnations, and snapdragons. Most of the pot plants sold will be Easter lilies, azaleas, hyacinths, tulips, daffodils, cinerarias, calceolarias, pot mums, hydrangeas, and gardenias. This depends a lot on the part of the country where the shop is located.

3. **Memorial Day.** This is a bigger holiday than Easter in some sections of the country, but a minor holiday for other florists. The community and its customers will help to determine the volume of business. It is usually a one-day holiday with many orders ahead of time. The holiday is mainly one of cut flowers, pot plants, bedding plants, and cemetery wreaths. Many wreaths are sold including both fresh and permanent. Cut flowers, arranged in cemetery vases, include gladioli and peonies, with some snapdragons and chrysanthemums. Pot plants include geraniums and pot mums. Bedding plants and combination boxes are also popular for this holiday.

4. **Mother's Day.** Mother's Day is a one-day holiday with most of the orders being delivered on Saturday. The florist, however, will have to remain open on Mother's Day morning for late order corsages. The business for Mother's Day will be mostly corsages, pot plants, and cut flowers along with boutonnieres and some centerpieces. Corsages and boutonnieres are the most important, so a florist must have plenty of orchids, cymbidiums, gardenias, roses, camellias, violets, and carnations on hand. The florist needs white carnations for boutonnieres for men whose mothers are deceased, and colored ones for men whose mothers are alive. Many times women will wear corsages in either a color or white to indicate their own mother as being alive or deceased. Centerpieces are very popular as a gift to mother as well as such pot plants as pot mums, azaleas, hydrangeas, gardenias, hyacinths, tulips, and daffodils.

5. **New Years.** Decorations and corsages for New Year's Eve and centerpieces for New Year's Day make up the work for this holiday. It is a one-day holiday with most of the business on the day before New Years. Many novelty items and novelty arrangements and decorations can be sold. It will only be a good florist holiday for those florists who advertise to get the business. Most people have to be reminded that it is a holiday for flowers.

Figure 38-3. An appropriate arrangement of larkspur, roses, and carnations for Mother's Day.

6. **St. Valentine's Day.** This is a one-day holiday which formerly was a big florist holiday that slipped for several years. For awhile it became more of a candy and jewelry day. However, many progressive florists have been able to revive it recently by advertising, promotion, and display. It is a sentimental holiday in which cut flowers, corsages, and pot plants are sold. Many red roses will be in demand because they indicate "love" to people. White roses, red and white carnations, and snapdragons will be sold along with a limited number of violets. Pot plants in demand will be hyacinths, tulips, hydrangeas, daffodils, and azaleas. Novelty hearts, lovebirds, and other items will be sold singly or in arrangements. Novelty containers will be used for some of the flower arrangements.

7. **Thanksgiving.** This is the first holiday of the fall season and includes cut flowers, pot plants, and table centerpieces. The table decorations will be centerpieces of chrysanthemums, leaves, gourds, corn, and dried material, or else a horn-of-plenty with flowers and fruit. The most popular pot plant is the pot chrysanthemum. Cut flowers preferred are chrysanthemums, although snapdragons, gladioli, majestic daisies, and others are sold. Gourds, Indian corn, strawflowers, and other materials will be available for people who want to do their own decorating.

There are also many Jewish holidays in which flowers play an important part. The most joyous of all Jewish festivals is Hanukkah, a holiday marked by the use of blue and white flowers.

The preceding gives a very brief look at each of the major holidays without going into detail.

Training Tips

The personnel of a florist's shop, including extra help, should be the first thing to consider in planning for the holidays. Extra help can come from middle-aged women, retired persons, high school students, and college students home for the holidays. Forget about good friends and relatives unless they can do a good job for the florist. Do not hire too much extra help but be sure to have enough so the florist won't have to turn down orders and can maintain an efficient organization.

One of the most important points is to have extra help come in a few days early for training and instruction which should include the following: (1) Spend enough time and have a 30-minute class of instruction every day. Three half-hour sessions are better than one session of 90 minutes. (2) First things first. Tell the extra help the hours of work, wages, length of lunch hour, coffee breaks, and the accepted dress. (3) Keep the training simple with as few facts as possible. (4) Go over the stock and get the employees familiar with names of materials that will be sold at that holiday. (5) Call attention to the posted price lists, and go over every item on the price list and ask for questions. (6) Give every person a price list for his or her pocket whether they work in sales, on the phone, or in designing. (7) Give specific instructions for the shop, including the following: write or print plainly, get complete address, initial all orders, do not promise "special time," suggest early delivery, encourage "will calls," do not suggest anything on display unless the manager is consulted, and do not take any order which may give trouble.

Extra sales help should be given the following tips: (1) Smile and be pleasant. (2) Know the prices. (3) Know the system used for sales: charge or cash. (4) Show the more expensive items first as it is more flattering. (5) Use different approaches, since customers are not alike. (6) Do not judge by what *you* can afford to pay. (7) Ask the customer to pay for it and only charge upon request. (8) Be sure the customer has a charge account with this store. (9) Show interest in both the customer and the merchandise. (10) Always thank the customer.

Store Arrangement

Arrange the store for action and for efficiency.

1. Decorate the window with a good window display which will really attract attention and bring people into the shop. Decorate the whole store so that people coming in will feel the festive atmosphere and get in the mood to spend money for flowers. Put your customers in a holiday mood.

2. Group the merchandise. Always display one price and variety of plants together. Group all novelty items together so that the customer can make his or her choice in one spot. Have permanent arrangements priced and displayed where they are easy to sell. Standardize the pot wraps and decorations to save time.

3. The display refrigerator is most important and should always be kept clean and attractive. Use a special holiday background if possible. Show samples of corsages and arrangements, and be sure every item is priced. Do not display "hard to get" items. Check the display refrigerator often and keep it looking in top condition.

4. Make the operation easy for the sales people. If the shop is

Figure 38-4. A timely window display to attract attention. (Courtesy, Miller Florist, Warren, Ohio.)

large enough, have just one person responsible for the cash register. If order books are used, have plenty of them in convenient spots with room to write. Have plenty of table or counter space for sales people to place merchandise during the sale. Have plenty of cards available for the customer, and separated according to the occasion. Have a price tag in every pot plant.

5. Telephones are important and should be away from the noise of the store whenever possible. Phone booths are excellent for taking orders all year around. Select salespeople for the phones carefully and from regular employees if possible. They must know stock and prices, and should have a pleasant voice. A price list should be posted in front of each phone.

6. The workroom should be arranged as efficiently as possible. Be sure to have ample supplies of wire, ribbon, floratape, net, pins, etc. There should be plenty of table space for the designers so they are not crowded. Foam rubber mats should be provided because of the long hours they will be on their feet. One person should be in charge of the workroom. The room should preferably

be away from the salesroom so there will not be so many interruptions from customers and salespeople.

7. The delivery department is just as important as any other department, particularly at holiday time. Make sure the delivery equipment and driver properly represent the business. They both should be presentable and this is one of the toughest jobs at any holiday. The delivery man is often the store's only contact with the public. The delivery department should be a separate department and off by itself. The order tag must be clearly written or typed. One person should be in charge of all deliveries and set up the routes and schedules and see that this is run smoothly and on time. C.O.D. orders should be discouraged at a holiday. An order slip should accompany each item to the delivery department so that the order can be double checked. Each driver should keep a record and initial each delivery.

General Suggestions

There are many suggestions for retail florists to follow when planning and executing holiday orders, such as the following: (1) Keep a diary of important facts for each particular holiday. (2) Pool deliveries with other florists when feasible. (3) Prepare bows, net, and artificial foliages in advance of the holiday. (4) Prepare all permanent arrangements during the dull or slack periods. (5) Make up corsages in advance, pack in cellophane or plastic, and refrigerate. Research has shown that cymbidiums and orchids can be made up four days prior to the holiday, carnation corsages three days ahead, and roses just one day ahead. (6) Separate all orders. (7) Keep an accurate record of all cut flowers sold. (8) Keep a record of returns and complaints. (9) Number all "will call" orders. (10) Be sure to have ample stock on hand. (11) Plan to finish up and close on time the day before the holiday. (12) Have pot plants on display at least five to seven days before the holiday. (13) Try not to book any weddings at a holiday time. (14) Put a sign over each phone reading "For Business Only—Be Brief." (15) Make sure *every* order goes through the cash register.

Phoebe Floral in Allentown, Pennsylvania, has the following set of rules that are followed every Easter and can be adopted for other holidays: "(1) Wear name badge at all times. (2) Remember that the showroom cash registers are for cash-and-carry transactions only. (3) Try to get the customers to take their merchandise with them. (4) The days for plant deliveries are Wednesday, Thursday,

and Friday. Saturday is the delivery day for cut flowers and corsages. (5) There are no special deliveries. (6) Get in the habit of
saying: "Will you pay for this now?" (7) All cemetery orders must
go through the hands of the manager. (8) The only corsages we
make are on the list of nine standard corsages. (9) All gardenia
and violet plants must be wrapped in polyethylene. (10) After
Thursday P.M., we will not take any new special make-up orders.
(11) Do not take any out-of-town phone orders (FTD, TELEFLORA,
etc.) for less than $5.00. (12) Your meal orders will be given to
you by your respective department heads. (13) On every order
that you write you must put the price of the order, and there are
no exceptions. (14) If a customer has a complaint, immediately
turn him over to the owner or the manager. (15) The following
are the department heads and they are responsible for the smooth
operation of their respective departments: (list the names and departments)."

Pot Plant Care

Retail florists can often assure future sales to the same customer
by simply pointing out to him or her some of the characteristics of
the plant just sold. When such information is not available on printed tags, sales personnel can be encouraged to mention a few tips re-
garding the plant's minimum needs. Here are some examples:

1. Poinsettias are sensitive plants but will last for many weeks
if properly cared for. Place the poinsettia in bright light (but not
direct sunlight), where the air is not too dry, and in a temperature
of 60° to 75° F. Reduce the thermostat at night. They should be
kept out of all drafts and particularly away from the front door.
They should be watered when needed (almost every day) and not
allowed to dry out, nor to sit in water constantly.

2. Azaleas should be kept in a sunny location and in a cool
spot while in flower. They should be watered daily and old flowers
should be removed when they have faded and died. Some varieties
can be planted outdoors and will thrive in certain climates.

3. The cyclamen has attractive flowers and is one of the most
beautiful plants for Christmas. It must be grown in the sunlight
during the day and placed in a cool temperature (50° to 55° F.) at
night. If grown properly, the 40 to 60 flower buds should open
over a six-week period.

4. Pot chrysanthemums are now sold all year around in retail
florist shops. It is a very popular pot plant and will thrive in any
home if it is kept in the sunlight and watered every day.

5. The Easter lily prefers partial sunlight and warmer temperatures than some of the other plants to keep the buds opening. It should be watered daily.

6. Hydrangeas will last for several weeks if properly cared for. They should be grown in sunlight, in a warm temperature, and be watered at least once a day and sometimes twice. If the house is hot and dry they will require more water. If the flower head droops before the flowers are dead, plunge the whole pot in a sink full of water for several hours and it will revive and live another five to seven days.

Holiday Records

Retail florists have many different systems for keeping holiday records, from writing on a calendar, to the use of a separate file drawer for each holiday. Many have a separate folder for each one, while others mainly depend on their growers to tell them what they ordered last year. This last system is all right if augmented with reports on what was sold, prices charged, material not sold, and other information.

One of the biggest headaches for the retail florist is what to order, and trying to remember whether or not the items purchased were what were profitably sold to the customer. Another big problem is trying to remember from the previous year exactly how much of the merchandise bought was for holiday business and how much was for normal business.

It is foolish and expensive to waste time compiling information that a retail florist is not able to use. Basically, any holiday report should give 10 things according to Herb Mitchell. These are: "(1) Total sales, cash and charge. (2) A breakdown of this business into holiday and normal business, and how much in special parties or weddings. (3) A net holiday business sales figure. (4) A list of merchandise ordered. (5) A list of merchandise received. (6) A list of merchandise left over after the holiday. (7) Notes about items requested that you did not have that caused you to lose sales. (8) Comparison to last year's business. (9) Information about help as to how much and when used. (10) Accurate delivery information."

It is also advisable to keep a record of the weather on the various holiday reports. Of course, this does not give the information for planning next year except for keeping in mind the change of Easter in terms of expected weather. However, it does help in understanding the present holiday sales. Weather is often a determining factor in cash sales for certain holidays and may affect the total volume.

Records can be as simple or as complex as any florist wishes to make them as long as they give him all the basic information that he will need for planning next year.

The following sheets can be mimeographed and used for Christmas, and adopted for other holidays to fit each florist's business.

Date Written: (12/28/72)   For CHRISTMAS (1973)

1972 SUMMARY

Total Sales (Dec. 18 to Dec. 25)................._____
Inbound FTD Orders, Teleflora, Florafax............_____
Outbound FTD Orders, Teleflora, Florafax..........._____
       Net Sales ...._____

GENERAL INFORMATION

Date	# Cash Customers	Amt. Funeral	Amt. Wedding	# of Deliveries	Weather
12/18					
12/19					
12/20					
12/21					
12/22					
12/23					
12/24					

CHURCHES

Name	Address	# of Plants

POT PLANTS

Poinsettias:

Size	Color	# Bought	# Sold	Retail Price	Supply Source	# for Next Year
____						
____						
____						

Other Pot Plants:

Name	# Bought	# Sold	Supply Source	# for Next Year
Pot Mums				
Begonias				
Cyclamen				
Xmas Cherries				
Xmas Peppers				
Kalanchoe				
Gardens				

WREATHS

Size	Price	# Holly	# Evergreen	# Permanent

GREENS

Material	# Sold This Yr.	# Needed Next Yr.	Material	# Sold This Yr.	# Needed Next Yr.
Boxwood			Magnolia		
Mistletoe			Plumosus		
Ore. Holly			Huckleberry		
Var. Holly			Eucalyptus		
Laurel Roping			Spiral Eucaly		
Pine Roping			Podocarpus		
Sm. Bundle Pine			Broom		
Lg. Bundle Pine			Balsam		
Juniper			Rhododendron		
Ore. Cedar			Laurel		
Fir			Blankets		
Spruce			Other_____		

CUT FLOWERS

Roses Purchased: # Doz. Roses Sold:

	Small	Med.	Large	$5.00	$6.00	$7.50	$10.00	$12.00	$15.00
Red									
Pink									
White									
Yellow									
Total									

Cut Flowers, Cont.

Carnations Purchased:		# Doz. Carnations Sold:				
	Number	$6.00	$7.50	$10.00	$12.00	$15.00
Red						
White						
Pink						
Other						
Total						

OTHER CUT FLOWERS

Name	# Bought	# Sold	Supplier
Gladioli			
Snapdragon			
Pompons			
Chrysanthemums			
Heather			

CORSAGES

Name	# Ordered	# Sold
W. Orchids		
L. Orchids		
Cymbidium		
Gardenia		
Camellia		
Rose		
Carnation		
Other		

SUPPLIES

Name	Number
Corsage boxes	
Rose boxes	
Cut Flower boxes	
Plant wraps	
Cellophane bags	
	Color
1″ Styrofoam	
2″ Styrofoam	

RIBBON

Size	Red	Green	Plastic	Gold
3				
5				
9				
40				
120				

DEER (or other novelty)

Size	Gold	Plastic	Flocked
Small			
Medium			
Large			
Giant			

CANDLES

Size	Red	White	Others
9"			
12"			
15"			
18"			
21"			

CHRISTMAS BALLS AND BELLS

Size	Type	Number
Small		
Medium		
Large		

NUMBER OF PERMANENT MATERIALS

	CENTERPIECE	VASE ARRANGEMENT		MANTEL ARR.	DOOR TRIM
Price	Xmas	Pastels	Xmas	Pastels	
3.00					
4.00					
5.00					
6.00					
7.50					
10.00					
12.50					
15.00					
20.00					

TOTAL NUMBER EMPLOYEES (Regular and Part-Time)

	12/18	12/19	12/20	12/21	12/22	12/23	12/24
Sales:							
Design:							
Office:							
Delivery:							

EMPLOYEES DATES AND HOURS (fill in and stagger hours)

Name	12/18	12/19	12/20	12/21	12/22	12/23	12/24
J. Doakes	(8-5)	(8-5)	(12-9)	(12-9)	(12-9)	(8-5)	(8-5)

NOTES FOR CHRISTMAS_____

Plants:
Cut flowers:
Greens:
Corsages:
Permanent items:
Wreaths:
Delivery:
Extra help:
Office records:
General remarks:

_____

References

1. Curtis, W. D. "You Need Help," *Florists' Exchange*, Vol. 136, No. 19 (May 13, 1961), pp. 15, 65-66.
2. Johnston, J. M., Jr. *Holiday Record Sheets*. Personal interview (1963).

Chapter 39

PERMANENT FLOWERS

Permanent flowers are called "artificial" by some people and "plastic" or "polyethylene" by others. Most retail florists prefer to use the term "permanent" which seems to describe them a little bit better for the general public. These include not only cut flowers but also various foliages and foliage plants which are used for permanent decorations. Some of the permanent trees reach up to 20 feet or more in height.

Up until 10 years ago, most retail florists did not handle the permanent material, and left it in the hands of five-and-ten cent stores, department stores, and variety stores. There was some feeling that the sale of these materials would cut down on the sale of fresh flowers. The past five years have shown this to be untrue. Today, we find permanent flowers and materials in every retail florist shop in the country. Permanent flowers and plants represent about 7 per cent of florists' sales in the United States, according to a U.S. Marketing Research Report. They are especially popular for holidays when incorporated with fresh flowers in the arrangements.

The original quality of the materials was mediocre. However, as the demand for these flowers increased, the manufacturers made terrific strides in improving the quality of their products. The flowers looked more real, and almost life-like, had truer colors, could be manipulated, and most polyethylene flowers and foliage can be washed easily under the water faucet.

Retail florists are mainly handling the better quality material and letting the other stores have the less expensive products.

Permanent flowers of good quality are not inexpensive. The florist should handle this material both as loose flowers and made-up arrangements or designs. Many customers prefer to come into the shop just to purchase a few flowers. A retailer can sell any number, and is not forced by convention and wholesale prices to stick to a dozen, as he is with cut flowers because of the fear of dumping the few that are left once he has broken a dozen.

Permanent arrangements bring in a high price which adds to the volume of the store and the net profit. They make attractive displays in the shop and the window. One of the greatest advantages is that they can be made up months ahead of time during the slow periods. Many florists make up their fall and Christmas permanent arrangements in July and August, price them, cover them with polyethylene bags, and store them away until needed.

Figure 39-1. Permanent materials stored in polyethylene bags to keep them clean. (Courtesy, Bonnie Brae Flowers, Denver, Colo.)

The cut flowers themselves appeal to customers for everyday use in the home. Many people like to have flowers in their homes most of the time and yet they feel they cannot afford to purchase fresh flowers every week. Thus, with a permanent arrangement they can have flowers every day. As for special occasions, the past five years have shown an increase in cut flower sales for the home, and surveys have shown that these same people with permanent flowers will still purchase fresh cut flowers for special occasions. It has not affected the retail florists' sale of fresh flowers except to increase it by making more people aware of flowers for their homes, according to several leading retail florists in the United States.

The sale of the permanent flowers and plants is increasing every year. There are so many countries, so many local manufacturers, and so many retail outlets that it is virtually impossible to tabulate them. However, estimates have been made showing it to be about $59 million in 1959, with approximately $180 million in 1965. Although these are just estimates, they show that the sale of these materials tripled from 1959 to 1965.

The future looks good for the florist who knows how to merchandise this material, and has an appreciation of quality and a recognition of the fact that permanent flowers are going to provide a part of his income as long as he is a florist.

Some florists use poor quality permanent flowers simply because they do not really know good from mediocre quality. Good quality is what the retail florist should handle, because it is what his customers want.

Permanent materials are used very effectively in places other than the home. They are a natural for offices, lobbies, hotels, hospitals, apartment houses, banks, and churches. There are many places with conditions so poor that the proper growing of live plants is quite difficult, or where there is no one available to take the responsibility to care for them. These are the places where permanent materials can be used. It is up to the retail florist to provide these, and receive the profit from them that would otherwise go to someone else.

Permanent planters can be used in several ways, such as the following: strictly for decoration; to hide or screen radiators, equipment, or architectural defects; to highlight a particular feature in the office; to control walking areas; and to define the sides of stairways in the event that there is no railing.

Permanent foliages and planters can be used in dozens of places including the following list: airports, auto showrooms, balconies, banks, Chambers of Commerce, convention halls, country clubs, drive-ins, executive offices, exhibition halls, foyers, funeral chapels, hotels, libraries, motels, museums, patios, reception rooms, restaurants, schools, service stations, shopping centers, swimming pools, and theaters.

The retail florist also can take advantage of national advertising that he does not have to pay for. Plastics in all forms have been widely advertised by almost every major department store and many manufacturers. Selling them is not much different from selling any other gift item.

Permanent flowers and plants are a natural sideline in the retail florist shop (Chapter 21). They can be used very profitably on a contract basis as in commercial accounts (Chapter 36).

Florists who go into the business of renting out permanent foliages on a large scale must have a big storage area and an attractive prop room. The permanents should be set up to show the effect they will create in the desired setting. The rental and maintenance of permanents is time-consuming but financially profitable.

Permanent flowers are here to stay in our retail florist shops. This is not just a temporary fancy of the general public as once believed by many people.

There is a nice profit to be made by the sale of both individual cut flowers and foliages, and made-up arrangements and planters. The retail florist is the logical one to receive this profit. And, remember, it will not hurt the sale of fresh cut flowers and pot plants in the retail florist shop.

References

1. denBrok, S. E. "Are You Afraid of Permanents?" *Florist and Nursery Exchange,* Vol. 147, No. 22 (June 3, 1967), pp. 11-13.
2. Havas, N. *Profile of the Retail Florist Industry.* U. S. Department of Agriculture Marketing Research Report #741 (1964), 27 pp.
3. Thompson, J. "Permanent Flower Future," *Florist and Nursery Exchange,* Vol. 147, No. 22 (June 3, 1967), p. 14.

MARKETING

Chapter 40

MARKETING CHANNELS; WHOLESALING FLOWERS

There are four groups of people involved in the marketing of cut flowers, greens, and pot plants. The growers produce the merchandise for the market. They may sell directly to consumers from their greenhouses, sell directly to retailers, or may sell through wholesale commission houses. The latter is the way that most of the producers' merchandise is handled.

The second group are called brokers. These people sell to growers and retailers and often sell between one producer and another. They handle such merchandise as cuttings, bulbs, seeds, fertilizers, and other materials needed for the greenhouse production of flowers. Usually they do not handle the merchandise itself except to transfer it from one producer to another. They hire salesmen to take the orders for material which is then shipped to the grower. They operate on a low commission and make their money on volume business.

The third group concerned with the marketing of floral products is the retail florists who buy from growers or wholesalers and sell to the consumer: the general public.

The fourth group concerned with marketing cut flowers, greens, pot plants, and supplies is the wholesale florists. Their operation will be discussed in this chapter.

Marketing

What is marketing? Marketing is a series of services or functions performed efficiently and in an orderly sequence so as to convey the product from the producer to the consumer, where, when, and in the form wanted. The product will have particular value for the consumer, will induce him or her to devote a justifiable share of his income to the purchase of the product, and will return an equitable share of the consumer's dollar to the producer and the marketing agencies. Also, the marketing system should relay the desires of the consumer to the producer. The key to selling is to please the consumer or convince her she "needs" the product.

Marketing Channels

There are three primary marketing channels in the transfer of the merchandise from the grower to the consumer: (1) the grower may be what is called a retail-grower and sell directly to the consumer, (2) the grower may sell directly to the retailer who sells to the consumer, and (3) the grower may sell to the wholesale commission merchant who sells to the retail florist who in turn sells to the consumer. Figure 40-1 shows the percentage of florist crops handled by the various channels according to the 1950 census.

In Figure 40-1, farm value represents wholesale value to the grower. Information is not available to show the proportions of each of the two kinds of wholesale sales that are made to each of the three kinds of retailing. Variation in the amount of service associated with the retail selling of the crops by the three kinds of retail trade causes the percentage of retail trade done by retail-growers to be disproportionate to the percentage of the farm value of the crops that enter into their retail sales.

Wholesale Florist

The wholesale florist is one of the mainstays of the whole florist industry. He is the middleman between the retailer and the grower. He is the storehouse for the retailer. He operates on a commission basis for most of his materials. He may buy some local material or unusual material outright in order to be sure of a supply of that item, but 75 to 85 per cent of his material is on consignment. The amount of material purchased outright from growers is increasing each year.

A wholesaler's primary stock in trade is service, which allows the modern flower shop to offer the buying public a wide range of perishables and non-perishables. He helps prevent the retailer from having to maintain excessive amounts of working capital in either freight or inventory.

The wholesaler tries to get the highest price possible for his growers and yet give the retailer a fair price, without pricing himself out of the market. Much of the price for the merchandise is based on supply and demand. With the large demand for flowers at holiday times, the prices

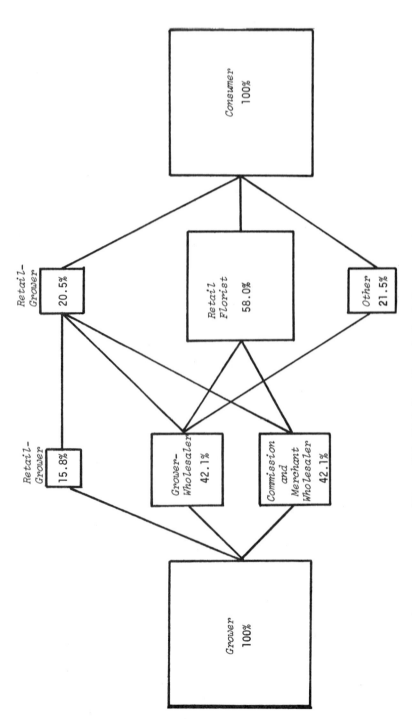

Figure 40-1. Marketing channels for florist products.

on flowers go considerably higher than during normal times. Prices will fluctuate day-to-day and even during the day. Some of the more perishable items like roses, which cannot be kept by the wholesaler more than one day, will change during the day: going lower and lower as the day progresses. Some of the flowers are quite stable and change little from week to week. Most greens will remain the same all year. Weather conditions in certain areas of the country will also affect prices. This is particularly true of a freeze in Florida which greatly affects the price of gladioli and chrysanthemums.

Each grower has a number which is used for bookkeeping purposes. This aspect of the wholesale florist business is most important. Accurate records must be kept on all merchandise sold, as well as that dumped. The sale price for each bunch of flowers for each grower must be recorded, and each grower must be credited with the proper amount of the sale. The wholesale florists at present charge a commission which varies in different wholesale houses and on different materials from 15 to 30 per cent. Greens are normally handled at about a 100 per cent markup.

An accurate bookkeeping system that is also speedy must be set up. Some of the larger wholesale florists have set up a complete system using data processing cards and IBM machines.

Figure 40-2. Data processing of accounts for a wholesale florist. (Courtesy, Denver Wholesale Florist Co., Denver, Colo.)

Figure 40-3. The centralized grading of over 300,000 carnation blooms a day. (Courtesy, Denver Wholesale Florist Co., Denver, Colo.)

Figure 40-4. Wholesale refrigerated storage of 500,000 flowers. (Courtesy, Denver Wholesale Florist Co., Denver, Colo.)

Each wholesale florist employs many salesmen to work in the shop. Each salesman tries to build up a list of his own customers who are retail florists. The salesman develops the confidence of his customers by honesty and integrity, and learning what flowers, quality, and price will appeal to each customer. If he has a "good buy" on 1,000 roses the wholesale salesman must know which retail florist will be interested. Often the salesman will have the power to lower the price on certain merchandise during the day in order to make a sale.

Wholesalers have many excellent chances in the course of the daily business to build sales. Handling the phone, taking care of mail orders, and in-person sales could be used to boost sales.

The flowers should be handled very carefully by the wholesale florist. They should be put in water with a preservative and refrigerated as much as possible. Many of the larger wholesale florist establishments are air-conditioned to help prolong the life of the flowers.

The flowers may be displayed on tables and benches either in cans of water, or laid out in the open. Both methods are used and will depend on the type of flower and the desires of the manager.

The growers are paid either weekly or monthly by the wholesaler (less his commission), and he in turn is paid monthly by the retailers. One of the burdens to the business is the fact that some retail florists are slow in paying their bills, so the wholesaler must have capital on hand to pay the growers regularly. Another burden is the air freight and trucking charges which must be paid within a week according to law. This is often a large sum of money, particularly in the winter when up to 50 per cent of the cut flowers come in to the North and East from Florida, Colorado, and California.

The wholesale florist carries many supplies for retail florists other than cut flowers, greens, and pot plants. Most wholesalers will handle a limited supply of ribbon, wire, tape, candles, foams, styrofoam materials, pottery, and many other items.

There are many things that wholesale florists must do to stay in business. Right at the top of the list is having a good collection program. The object is both to hold a customer's good will and to get the money.

Co-ops and Auctions

Cut flowers are also marketed through co-ops and auctions, although in very limited quantity in this country.

In certain areas like Boston and San Francisco, the flower growers go together and rent a building with booths or stalls for each grower.

Figure 40-5. The cut flower department in a wholesale florist business. (Courtesy, S. S. Pennock Co., Philadelphia, Pa.)

Figure 40-6. The rose department in a wholesale market. (Courtesy, S. S. Pennock Co., Philadelphia, Pa.)

Figure 40-7. The ribbon and supply department in a wholesale florist business. (Courtesy, S. S. Pennock Co., Philadelphia, Pa.)

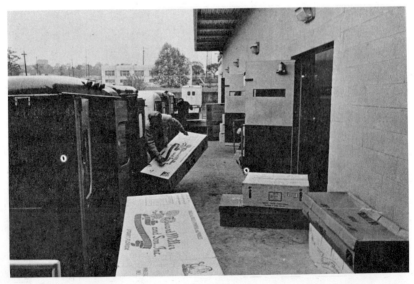

Figure 40-8. Loading boxes of cut flowers from the loading platform of a wholesale florist. (Courtesy, S. S. Pennock Co., Philadelphia, Pa.)

There is a manager to the co-op and also several salesmen to take care of the retail florists as they come to the co-op. Some growers have their own salesmen, while others will go together and hire one salesman to represent several growers. Some co-op's require identification to get into the building, whereas others will let in anyone who wishes to buy wholesale.

Flowers sold at auction go to the highest bidder and are sold in large quantities; often the whole lot from one grower at a time. Prices fluctuate during the day and material not sold to an exporter, wholesaler, or retailer is usually dumped.

The largest auction is at Aalsmeer, Holland, where all cut flowers are by law sold by auction. The flowers are brought by cart into the auditorium and discussed as to the grower, and the quality of the merchandise. The auctioneer sets the hands on the dial of a large clock to a high price and as the hand turns it passes, for example, from 30¢ to 29¢, etc. When it reaches the price that a buyer likes he pushes an electronic button which stops the clock and records his purchase. Buyers are wholesalers, retailers, and exporters from other European countries. Flowers not sold that day are dumped.

The wholesale commission florist is a vital link in the marketing of cut flowers and greens. He must try to keep both the growers and the retailers happy and this is one tremendous job. He also serves as a disseminator of information to the two other segments of the florist industry.

Pot plants are seldom handled by wholesale florists because of their weight and bulk unless the wholesaler happens also to be a pot plant grower.

Reference

1. Turp, John. *The Wholesale Flower Business.* Personal interview (April 1967).

Chapter 41

FUTURE OF THE INDUSTRY

Most of the floricultural and economic experts are agreed that the future looks bright for the florist industry of the '70's and '80's but will include some significant changes.

Florists will have to prepare for changes, and many predict that florists will have to start operating larger shops or get out of business. Expected are mergers of a number of businesses, with the big shops getting bigger and the little ones going out of business. If he wishes to stay in business, a florist must provide good services and quality merchandise.

Another change is in the growth of non-florist outlets for floricultural products. It is predicted by M. Truman Fossum that during the 1970's more than half of the number of flowering and foliage pot plants purchased by consumers will be sold by non-florist outlets. He says that inter-city florist trade will continue to expand and reflect trends in total consumer expenditures for the goods and services of floriculture in all outlets.

During the past 30 years the American economy has expanded at an unprecedented rate, and the social environment has undergone radical change. The florist industry, however, showed little change from 1939 to 1969, according to Max E. Brunk. He has taken a critical look at the industry in light of changes for the 1980's and offers the following guidelines to florists who want to get ahead:

"1. Learn to work together as an industry and learn to have confidence in, and listen to the ideas and opinions of growers, wholesalers, retailers and suppliers.

"2. Identify your competitor not in terms of product handled or service rendered but in terms of consumer values offered.

"3. Within your own industry, seek out ways to become distinctive, to become identified with a specific value, to serve a definite and distinguishable market segment.

"4. A reasonable amount of company growth and industry growth should be planned and realized from the efforts of the firm or industry itself.

"5. Evaluation of a competitor is a poor substitute for thinking and initiative.

"6. Pricing is to marketing what labor efficiency is to production.

"7. Recognize, analyze and capitalize on the nature of demand for your product and service.

"8. The markets of the future will show several changes that will affect florists: (1) Inflation will continue at an accelerated rate. (2) Family life will be materially altered. (3) Attitudes towards females, around whom so much of the florist business is centered, are undergoing enormous changes. (4) As society becomes more affluent, man's traits, fads and customs change. (5) Quality displaces quantity and choice of variety becomes more important. (6) Long established social customs are being overturned. We are increasingly being married and buried on the run."

L. M. Berninger also predicts a new era for the florists of the 1970's. Particularly in the retailing of floriculture crops he sees chain operations coming into existence with many of our retail shops expanding in several directions. He sees the supermarkets expanding the sale of potted plants. A new concept of merchandising may arise in some of the major metropolitan areas of the country. He also predicts that the number of wholesale florists will drop.

Thus, the prospects for the future seem bright for those retail florists who are willing to change and able to plan for the future.

References

1. Andrews, J. "Florists Must Prepare for Industry Changes," *Southern Florist and Nurseryman* (October 3, 1969), pp. 10, 21.
2. Berninger, L. M. "What's in Store for the '70's?" *Florists' Review* (December 11, 1969), pp. 23, 52-53.
3. Brunk, M. E. "Take a Critical Look at the Industry," *Florists' Review* (December 4, 1969), pp. 27, 28, 46-51.
4. Fossum, M. T. "What's Ahead for 1970?" *Florist* (January 1970), pp. 57-59.

GLOSSARY

Accessories—Supplementary items and objects sold in conjunction with flowers.

Accounts payable—A liability to the business, carried on open accounts, usually for purchase of goods and services.

Accounts receivable—Accounts of customers who owe for merchandise or services.

Adjunct—One thing added to another, such as a different type of store or merchandise.

Advertising—Supplying information to the public to induce people to buy a product.

Aesthetic—Pertaining to a sense of beauty.

Allied—A group of growers, wholesalers, and retailers in an area, contributing a percentage of their gross for the advertising and promotion of flowers.

Assets—Items of ownership belonging to the business.

Asymmetrical—A flower arrangement with the two sides of the center line different in appearance but equal in visual weight to give it stability.

Auction—Flowers sold to the highest bidder.

Backboard—A plaque designed on a piece of styrofoam to use as a background for a floral design.

Bad debts—Uncollectable accounts now and they seem so in the future.

Balance sheet—A tabular statement of both sides of an account in which the debit and credit balance are equal. The financial position of a business on a specified date.

Bedding plant—Any annual flower or vegetable plant grown for resale for a home garden.

Bonsai—A tree or shrub that has been dwarfed by certain methods and grown in a pot or container.

Book value—The value of a business or property as stated in a book of accounts.

Botany—The study of the classification and processes of plants.

Boutonniere—One flower worn in a man's lapel.

Browse—To look leisurely at goods displayed for sale.

Cash-and-carry—Merchandise paid for in cash and taken by the customer. No design, delivery, package, or bookkeeping involved.

Cattleya—The most popular hybrid orchid; white or lavender in color.

Centerpiece—A flower arrangement for the center of the table.

Chenille stems—A straight wire with a fuzzy stem.

Chuppah—A 7 by 7 foot canopy under which a Jewish couple are married.

Cibotium—A type of large tree fern used for decoration.

Circulation—Open areas to provide freedom of movement for people in the shop.

Consignment—Merchandise sent to a wholesaler for sale to a retailer on a percentage basis.

Container—A receptacle to hold flowers and greens.

Control center—Office or manager's desk from which all orders and deliveries are processed.

Co-op—Several growers offer merchandise for sale to retailers under one roof.

Curly-Q—A spool of thin wire coated with plastic or enamel.

Custom service—Wedding bouquets and decorations designed specifically for the customer.

Cut flower—A flower that is cut from the plant and sold.

Cut-off time—A certain hour of the day after which no orders will be taken for delivery that day.

Cyclic billing—Sending statements over a 30-day period by alphabetical order.

Cymbidium—A type of orchid growing 30 to 50 flowers on a stem. Smaller than most cattleyas.

Data processing—The handling of accounts by machine.

Depreciation—A decrease in value due to wear and tear, and allowed on the account of the business in computing the value of property for tax purposes.

Designing—The art of arranging flowers and plant material in an artistic manner.

Direct mail—Sending advertising and promotional materials by mail to a select list of customers.

Discounts—Material offered at a reduced price.

Dish garden—A container in which several different low growing foliage plants are grown in soil.

Display—To visibly show merchandise to the public.

Display refrigerator—A refrigerator in the sales area with an all glass front.

Display window—Any window in the florist shop which has merchandise on view to the public.

Double spray—A funeral spray, twice the size of a normal spray with the bow of ribbon in the center. Used as a casket cover.

Dowel rod—A round piece of wood similar to a peg or table leg.

Driftwood—Old wood seasoned by water and weather for use in interior decorating.

Drive-in—Designed so the customer can transact business without leaving his car.

Drop-in—Deciding suddenly to stop.

Dumpage—Material thrown out each day because it wasn't sold or is too old for sale.

Efficiency—Accomplishing a job with a minimum amount (expenditure) of time and effort.

Elemental operation time—The amount of time for an operator to complete each element of the operation.

Elemental transportation time—The amount of time for an operator to travel for each element of the operation.

Emblems—A funeral design symbolizing the loss of a loved one.

Ephemeral—Lasting a very short time.

Facets—Different aspects or phases of the business.

Far corner—The opposite corner from the main stream of traffic.

Filler—A flower or green used to fill in spaces in an arrangement. A material used in a container to hold the flowers in place in a design.

Fleurin—An international unit for medium of exchange between florists of different countries.

Flocked wire—A florist wire with a white coating of flocked material.

Florafax—Florafax International, Inc.

Floratape—A tape used by florists to cover wire stems.

Floriculture—The producing, marketing, using, and sale of florist crops.

Flow diagram—Pictorial representation of the layout of the process and the paths of travel during the process.

Flow process chart—A graphic representation of all operations, transportations, and delays during a process or procedure.

Flower cart—An ornamental cart used to display merchandise.

Flowers-by-wire—Transmitting orders from one city to another by phone, mail, or telegraph.

Fluctuate—To continually change from one thing to another as in the price of flowers.

Foam—A plastic compound which absorbs water used to hold flowers in place in a design.

Foil—Rolls of colored aluminum foil used to wrap pots. Also a roll of tin foil for putting around the back of wreath frames.

Foliage plants—Any pot plant grown for its foliage effect.

Foot traffic—Amount of pedestrian traffic passing the store.

FTDA—Florists' Transworld Delivery Association.

Garden center—An area devoted to the sale of outdoor garden merchandise.

Garland—A wreath or festoon of flowers, foliage, or other plant material used as a decoration.

Gift line—A series of various colors, sizes, and shapes of the same type of an item.

Glut—An oversupply of a product on the market.

Greenhouse—A structure covered with glass used to produce cut flowers and pot plants.

Gross—The total amount without deductions.

Hard foliages—A group of foliages used by florists which will hold up out of water for several days if stored in a refrigerator.

Hardgoods—Same as staples or inventory items.

Headhouse—An enclosed structure connected to a greenhouse for potting, transplanting, and doing other jobs required in the growing of plants.

Horticulture—The science, art, and business of improving, producing, storing, and processing fruits, vegetables, flowers, and ornamental plants.

Image—The picture or idea represented in the customer's mind of a particular person or business.

Impulse sales—The purchase of an item other than that which the customer entered the store to buy.

Inventory—Staple items on hand for resale and use by the designers.

Jardiniere—An ornamental receptacle or stand for holding plants or flowers.

Keeping quality—The ability of a cut flower to last as long as is normally expected of the flower.

Kimpack—An insulation material used in packing cut flowers for shipment.

Layout—The arrangement or plan of a certain area such as the design and sales areas in a retail flower shop.

Leasing—A contract for renting a piece of property for a certain period of time at a specified price.

Liabilities—Obligations owed by the business.

Make-up work—Any arrangement of flowers that must be designed.

Manzanita—Dried branches, bleached by the sun, used in decorations.

Markup—A system for determining the sale price of an item based on the cost of merchandise.

Mass display—Display of an item in a large quantity.

Mass market—Any supermarket type of operation.

Mechanical aid—Any material used in a container to make the cut flowers and greens stay in place.

Media—A means of offering merchandise for sale to the consumer.

Merchandise—Material offered for sale.

Merchandising—Offering the right merchandise, at the right price, to the right people, at the right time, and in the right place. It is volume selling at a lower than normal markup.

Mossing—Placing wet sphagnum moss in a frame for funeral and Christmas wreaths.

Motivation—A state or condition of being persuaded to act. An incentive to do something.

Near corner—The location at the closest corner to the main artery of traffic.

Net worth—The net value of the business.

Non-perishable—Items of merchandise other than flowers, pot plants, or plant material. May be used in design work or for sale.

Novelties—Unusual articles for sale that are chiefly decorative and often used with flowers.

Opaque—Will not allow light to pass through.

Open house—Promotion to get the general public to visit your shop to see the displays, usually prior to a major florist holiday.

Order taker—A poor salesman who simply writes up the orders for the customer without any salesmanship involved.

Overhead—Expenses and the general cost of running a business.

Package service—A set service for weddings with just a few selections of bouquets and decorations from which to choose.

Packaging—Wrapping arrangements and cut flowers for delivery.

P&L—Profit and Loss statement showing the condition of the business at any particular time.

Papier-mâché—Containers made out of paper pulp and glue pressed together, inexpensive.

Parafilm—A roll of plastic material used to cover the wire stem of a flower.

Partnership—Two or more people in business together.

Pegboard—A composition wall board with regular perforations for the insertion of hooks to hold shelves and merchandise on display.

Per capita—So much for each individual person.

Period Arrangement—An arrangement typical of an era in Western history.

Perishable—Subject to decay. Does not last very long.

Permanent materials—The artificial flowers and materials made out of polyethylene.

Personal delay—A percentage of time allotted to accommodate the personal needs of the operator.

Physiology—The study of plants and the functions of their organisms.

Pickled flowers—Flowers which have been held too long in water in a refrigerator and are not salable.

Pinholder—A holder of steel needles used to hold flowers in place in a low container.

Planter—A watertight container for growing plants.

Plastic—Bags and other materials made out of one of the synthetic materials.

Please Omit—The notice in the death notices asking people not to send flowers to a funeral.

Polyethylene—Refers to the flowers and greens constructed out of a type of plastic polymer of ethylene. Also clear plastic bags used in packaging.

Pot plant—A plant grown and sold in a pot. Sometimes called a potted plant.

Preservative—A chemical preparation to make cut flowers last longer.

Promotion—The act of getting public recognition for a business or merchandise through advertising.

Proprietorship—One person as a sole owner of the business.

Prospects—Potential customers or flower buyers.

Protocol—Customs and regulations dealing with etiquette. Acceptable to the majority of people.

Public relations—The act of promoting good will between a business or person and the public.

Publicity—Public notice resulting from mention in the press, radio, or other medium.

Qualifications—Necessary characteristics which fit a person for a particular job.

Quality—Characteristics of a high grade of merchandise.

Random—A process of selection whereby each item has an equal chance of being selected. A selection without a definite aim.

Rapport—A harmonious relationship between individuals.

Receiving florist—Florist who receives a flowers-by-wire order and fills it by sending the flowers to the proper person.

Retail-grower—A retail florist who grows some or most of his merchandise.

Retail-only—A retail florist who does not grow any of his own merchandise.

S. A. F.—Society of American Florists.

Salesmanship—The art of selling.

Salient—Conspicuous feature.

Seasonal variation—Availability of certain cut flowers according to the season of the year.

Sending florist—The florist who takes the order and transmits it to a member florist in another city.

Shadow box—A rectangular frame used to display special floral designs or items of merchandise.

Shatter—A flower is bruised and begins to lose its petals.

Sheaf—A cluster of cut flowers tied together at one end with a bow of ribbon.

Site—The place where the shop is located.

Smilax—A trailing green plant grown on twine, used for decoration, and draped as a garland.

Social-psychological behavior—The explanation of why people act the way they do in society.

Special occasion—A particular time to celebrate such as a birthday or anniversary.

Spray—A flat horizontal arrangement of flowers with the stems in some type of foundation, for a funeral.

Stability—The condition of being stable—not inclined to fall over.

Standard deviation—A measure of variability in terms of the units of measurement, usually of a total population.

Staples—Non-perishable items for use and for sale, such as ribbon, wire, paper, etc.

Stock container—A container used for the cut flowers (stock) to be used by the designers, and kept in the storage refrigerator.

Stock control—Keeping an accurate account of the merchandise in the store.

Storage refrigerator—An enclosed refrigerator in which the bulk of the flowers and greens are stored.

Styrofoam—Plastic material used for novelty cut-outs and bases for dried and permanent arrangements which will not absorb water.

Swag—A sheaf of flowers and/or greens tied together for the door.

Symmetrical—Both sides of the centerline are the same.

TELEFLORA—Teleflora, Inc.

Terralite—A horticultural grade of vermiculite.

Time-motion—The study of time and motions comprising an operation.

Time standard—Computing the time required for an *average* operator, fully qualified and trained and working at a *normal* pace, to perform the operation.

Totem pole—A pole, bark, or frame used to support trailing types of plants.

Trade fair—A group of exhibitors of novelty and staple items from whom florists will order for the store.

Transient—People who are going by in the street; or are temporary, not permanent.

Translucent—Permitting light to pass through but diffusing so objects are not clearly visible.

Tubbed plants—Foliage or flowering pot plants grown in a wooden tub.

Tufflite—Shredded styrofoam used as a mechanical aid to hold flowers in place in a tall container.

Turnover—Number of times items are sold in a given time and re-ordered for sale.

Unencumbered—Not impeded nor hindered.

Upsell—Persuading the customer to spend more money than she had intended for an item.

Values—Ideals or customs of a society towards which people of a society have a high regard.

Vermiculite—A group of platy minerals and silicates used by florists for propagation of plants and as a mechanical aid in containers.

Water garden—An arrangement of foliage plants on a pin holder in a shallow container of water.

Will call—Orders which will be picked up by the customer.

Window box—A wooden box for growing plants outdoors.

Wire orders—Customer's orders which are sent by one florist to another by wire, phone, or mail.

Withdrawal—Taking cash out of the business for purchases or personal needs.

Workroom—The design area in a retail flower shop.

INDEX